COLUMBIA UNIVERSITY STUDIES
IN THE
HISTORY OF AMERICAN AGRICULTURE

EDITED BY

HARRY J. CARMAN
PROFESSOR OF HISTORY IN COLUMBIA UNIVERSITY

AND

REXFORD G. TUGWELL
PROFESSOR OF ECONOMICS IN COLUMBIA UNIVERSITY

ADVISORY BOARD

II

THE AGRICULTURAL FAIR

ELKANAH WATSON

FATHER OF THE AMERICAN AGRICULTURAL FAIR

THE
AGRICULTURAL
FAIR

BY

WAYNE CALDWELL NEELY

ASSISTANT PROFESSOR OF SOCIOLOGY
HOOD COLLEGE

NEW YORK: MORNINGSIDE HEIGHTS

COLUMBIA UNIVERSITY PRESS

1935

PRINTED IN THE UNITED STATES OF AMERICA

EDITORS' FOREWORD

No institution, perhaps, has exerted greater influence upon American rural life than the agricultural fair. Yet the story of its Old-World origin, its transfer to this side of the Atlantic, and its many-sided development in the United States has long awaited the pen of some one who was competent to trace its history and to evaluate its social significance. Fortunately Professor Neely, who essayed this double task, was admirably fitted by temperament and by training to undertake it. Born and reared in a rural neighborhood in the great agricultural state of Iowa, he attended dozens of fairs and stock shows, large and small, in the valley of the Upper Mississippi. As a consequence he acquired at first-hand a wealth of information about almost every aspect of the fair. Even more, he came to understand the social atmosphere of the fair, without which one cannot fully appreciate its significance. To first-hand knowledge has been added the fruit of years of careful research. Hundreds of documents bearing on the problem have been subjected to the scrutiny of the disciplined mind of the historian and sociologist. Finally, the materials thus garnered have been woven into the pages which follow, pages which portray a picturesque and even fascinating institution.

It is frequently asserted that the agricultural fair is out-moded and in process of decay. Professor Neely does not accept this generalization. Rather he views the fair as a changing, differentiating institution. There is, he maintains, no immediate or accurate yardstick by which the fair or, for that matter, any social institution can be measured. The fair, like every institution, irrespective of what social group or groups it may serve, is in his opinion always responsive to forces within itself and to the physical and cultural environment in which it functions.

While the author is particularly interested in the social significance of the fair, he devotes fully two-thirds of this volume to the history of the fair. Any dynamic or changing institution, he rightly holds, cannot be understood except in a setting of time and space. In other words principles of change or social significance cannot be discovered except from historical events. These events are inextricably mingled in the numberless currents and cross currents of life. Social institutions and social relationships are dynamic expressions of a hundred interplaying forces which must always be linked to the historical particulars to which they give rise and from which many of them spring. Any analysis must, therefore, be made in the light of historical events. That Professor Neely fully appreciates this fact is evident throughout the volume.

In the last chapters of the book the author considers the fair functionally in its educational, recreational and social-izational aspects. Here the emphasis is upon the twentieth-century fair. The general reader as well as the student of social history and sociology interested in the story of one of America's leading rural institutions, and the statesman anxious for guidance in formulating agrarian policies will welcome Professor Neely's contribution.

H. J. C.
R. G. T.

Columbia University
January 15, 1935

PREFACE

THE county fair is a significant social tradition in the evolution of American society. The mere mention of the institution elicits in the average American the memory of autumn days spent mingling with a motley crowd from city, town and countryside. Bucolic lowing from the cattle barns and staccato cackles from the poultry house pierce the incessant "tin-panny" drone of the merry-go-round mechanically grinding out last year's musical hit. The muffled blare of the band from the minstrel show helps to temper the seductive lure of that from the oriental dancers' tent. The monotonous pop-pop of a dozen gasoline engines turning some new farm implement or machine is interrupted by the crack of the rifles from the shooting gallery. A variegated assortment of spielers outdo one another with outrageously extravagant claims for the wonders of their shows or the ease with which one can get something for nothing if he will only "try his luck." Shrill crys from the ferris wheel or the giant swing alternate with the clanging of the bell in the starter's tower at the race track, to be followed soon by a clatter of hoofs and excited shouts of "They're off! They're off!" as a horse race gets under way. A half-permanent, half-temporary city has suddenly sprung to life, flags waving from its prominent buildings, bunting decorating its stalls and pens and booths, gaudy banners fronting the tent of snake charmer, palmist or sword swallower giving but "a mere suggestion" of what may be seen within. In the stock-judging ring a bovine drama is under way, in which last year's champion may be compelled to bow before a younger rival, or the horses are submitting to the inspection of a critical judge, at the con-

clusion of which some equine monarch will wear his purple
rosette as proudly as any human monarch wears his crown.
In the agricultural hall long rows of yellow corn and plates
of fragrant apples, glasses of sparkling jelly and exhibits of
hand-painted china draw the visitor's attention to the arts
of farm and home. Small boys contemplate their last nickel
of spending money in a heart-rending decision between an
ice cream cone and a bottle of pop while more adult epicures
make rash guesses as to how many pies might be made from
the giant pumpkin or how many chops cut from the champion porker. All these and countless more images are
recalled as the kaleidoscopic picture of the fair surges to
the memory.

The journalist may say, "There's a story here." The
historian may say, "Here's an unwritten chapter in the
expansion of the American people." The sociologist, agreeing perhaps with both, may say, "Here's a social institution
challenging an analysis of its evolution and changes, its
functions and its social significance." The county fair is but
the most widely experienced, traditional type of a much
broader social phenomenon. How has the agricultural fair
come to be what it is? What forces in society brought about
the establishment of fairs, what motives have led men to
organize and perpetuate them? What changes has the fair
as an institution undergone, how have types evolved within
the agricultural fair as a type, what special interests of
human beings have been served thereby? What is the status
of the fair in the present day American agricultural scene?
What influence does it exert in the community in which it is
held and in the general agricultural, industrial and social
life of the nation? What problems has the fair confronted
at different times and places? What are the sociological
aspects of the fair in actual progress?

The following pages attempt to answer these and other

questions concerning the evolution and function of the agricultural fair in the United States. That these answers may be as complete as possible considerable attention has been given to Old-World background. The fair in one form or another, or in several of its various forms, has had a long and continuous existence. Like the society of which it is a part, the fair is subject to eternal change; we see it at one time or another assuming characteristic forms, now given a new direction, now fulfilling some new interest of society, now dropping some old function as it becomes obsolete or is elsewhere better performed. Something called the fair may be discerned in organized social relationships in primitive times; and from its early beginning we can trace the evolution of the institution, important now in its commercial, now in its educational, always in its social aspects.

This study of the agricultural fair has been approached from the standpoint of the social historian and of the general sociologist interested first of all in the evolutionary and functional aspects of a dynamic American institution. Like every other social institution, the fair is eternally evolving, differentiating. The use of the evolutionary clue, necessitating as it does, constant reference to historical material, outlines for us the process by which the fair functions in its psychosocial environment and by which it comes to assume new forms, to satisfy new interests, to play new rôles in the social drama. We confess to a genuine interest in the agricultural fair, picturesque, colorful and fascinating as it is. The lure of the romantic and spectacular atmosphere which undeniably surrounds, and always has surrounded, the institution may be capitalized admirably by the social scientist in his scientific and artistic quest.

In the preparation of this volume the author has had the good fortune to have the assistance of many friends to whom he has often turned for guidance. He wishes in particular to acknowledge his obligation to Professor R. M. MacIver, with whom he was in consultation during the entire preparation of the volume. To other members of the department of sociology of Columbia University, especially Professors A. A. Tenney, R. S. Lynd and R. E. Chaddock, he is indebted for many suggestive criticisms. The treatment of numerous points in the study has been influenced by conversations with Professors L. H. Gulick, A. P. Evans, Carter Goodrich and J. A. de Haas, all of Columbia University, and with Professor J. H. Kolb, of the University of Wisconsin. Acknowledgement is also due the authorities of the Columbia University Library, the New York Public Library, the Iowa State College Library and the McCormick Historical Association Library, who have placed their facilities at the author's disposal. The officials of numerous fair associations throughout the country not only have been generous with data pertaining to their organizations but have expressed an encouraging interest in the progress of the work.

Finally, to Professor H. J. Carman is due most sincere appreciation, not only for his invitation to include the study in the Columbia University Studies in the History of American Agriculture, but also for his constant aid and stimulation during the later stages of the preparation of the volume and its publication.

W. C. N.

Frederick, Maryland
January 15, 1935

CONTENTS

PART III
THE FUNCTIONAL ASPECTS OF THE
AGRICULTURAL FAIR

PART IV
CONCLUSION

ILLUSTRATIONS

PART I

EARLY HISTORY AND TYPES OF FAIRS

I
THE FAIRS OF EUROPE: A HISTORICAL NOTE

THE evolutionary viewpoint in the study of social institutions precludes the setting of exact limits to the span of their life. Underneath the crystallization or liquefaction of specific forms there runs the current of social life, human needs and desires and their fulfillment, out of which our social organization arises and into which it sometimes sinks again. We cannot, therefore, know precisely the origin of the fair. We can trace certain of its elements back to medieval and certain others back to primitive times, the while regarding its modifications as illustrative of the evolutionary process.

MEDIEVAL MARKET FAIRS

The word "fair" has been used to designate a periodic concourse of people, though the principal purposes for which they came together as well as many of the activities in which they engage may vary widely. Generally speaking, fairs have emphasized one or more of four characteristics; namely, religious, commercial, educational and exhibitive. In fact, we could with a considerable degree of accuracy describe the evolution of the fair in the foregoing sequence. Many of the earliest known fairs were gatherings of religious worshipers who engaged also in various kinds of primitive commerce. Those of the Middle Ages were well established and necessary organs of national and international trade. The last century and a half witnessed the rise of the exposition, the primary purposes of which are education and advertisement. Finally, during the same period, the offering of prizes for competitive displays of products has become an important feature especially characteristic of the agricultural fair. No one of these characteristics has ever completely overshadowed the others; yet these and many more have at certain times and at certain fairs furnished the dominant design into which, from a thousand sources, the fabric of the fair is woven. For example, probably no fair, ancient or modern, is entirely free from some manifestation of the festive spirit, though merrymaking may range from the avowed *raison d'être* of the fair to a very incidental by-product. Or again, every fair has its commercial aspects whether it be a medieval market fair, a modern sample fair or a competitive display that serves to advertise the winning products.

Exactly what kind of gathering was first called a fair we do not know. If we could depend wholly upon etymology, we might be sure that the earliest fairs were primarily of religious significance. The word is derived from the Latin *feria*, holiday, and is related to *festus*, festal.[1] And of course, the word "holiday" is merely the contracted form of "holy day." Likewise the German *messe*, fair, is derived from the Latin *missa*, mass. G. M. Wrigley, writing of the origin of fairs, emphasizes the importance to primitive people of springtime and harvest, these critical seasons calling forth gatherings of the devout for prayer and praise, gatherings that inevitably assumed a mercantile character.[2] P. Huvelin, in his detailed and careful study of markets and fairs, while recognizing that fairs may arise out of any of the assemblages of primitive people, judicial, legislative, military or religious, says that religious fêtes are by far the most general forerunners of fairs,[3] and sums up the matter thus: "There is

[1] According to *Webster's New International Dictionary*, the derivation is from the Latin "*feria* holiday, pl. *feriae*, days of rest, holidays, festivals, akin to *festus* festal."
[2] "Fairs of the Central Andes," *Geographical Review*, Feb., 1919, p. 74.
[3] *Essai historique sur le droit des marchés et des foires*, Paris, 1897, pp. 33 *et seq.*

no great festival without a fair, no fair without a festival. . ."[4] Certain it is, also, that many fairs of the Middle Ages were granted to churches or monasteries as a means of increasing their revenue, and many of them took their names from the feast day of some saint. The fairs of St. Denis, St. Germain and St. Bartholomew evidence the grafting of a commercial institution upon the celebration of certain religious feasts.[5]

It is not difficult to understand how readily gatherings of scattered primitive people came to assume commercial aspects. In the first place, as Huvelin points out, such assemblages were rare. Whenever they did take place commerce was created of itself, and finally supplanted the interests which first drew the people together. Such assemblages resulted in the accumulation of many kinds of goods, and it was inevitable that exchange should arise. To the more shrewd, no doubt, occurred the idea of bringing here the articles which they possessed but did not want, and of supplying their own needs and desires from the stock of others. It was only natural that curiosity should be aroused and appetites whetted by the possessions which these primitive people saw in the hands of others at these early meetings. The worshipers at the religious fêtes were, therefore, no longer worshipers only; they became merchants as well. In these shrewd observers perhaps we have the prototype of the modern business man, keen to take advantage of opportunities to create or enlarge his market, and to anticipate public demand.

As specialization advanced a little, there came upon the scene the vendor, as such—the individual to whom trafficking

[4] *Ibid.*, p. 40.

[5] Cf. Thompson, James Westfall, *An Economic and Social History of the Middle Ages*, New York, c. 1928, *passim*; Lipson, E., *An Introduction to the Economic History of England*, London, 1926, I, 196 *et seq.*; Zetter, C., *Évolution des foires et marchés a travers les siècles*, Paris, 1923, *passim*; Kulischer, Joseph, "Fairs," *Encyclopaedia of the Social Sciences*, New York, 1931, VI, 59.

becomes a primary rather than an incidental occupation. He is the logical adjunct of any great concourse of people. Some of his wares may have been necessities — food and, among the devout, religious emblems; others may have been of more trivial nature — trinkets and toys, ornaments and refreshments. But whatever his wares, here he could appeal to the vanity of the individuals, who, at these festivals, furnished a background upon which that vanity could play; here he could take advantage of certain crowd phenomena, such as imitation and suggestion; and it is safe to assume that the primitive vendor easily learned to seize upon his opportunities. And there were, then as now, vendors of entertainment as well as merchandise. To these festivals came actors and acrobats, clowns and musicians, drawn by the prospect of financial gain. We can only conjecture as to the methods and success of the primitive "ballyhoo artists," but at least the undisciplined and inexperienced primitive mind furnished fertile possibilities for their activity. Crowds away from home are proverbial for their pliability.

The significance of these early assemblages was, however, more than local. The religious fêtes, occurring periodically, became the regular stopping places of caravans of traders and entertainers, who created a sort of primitive commercial route, retraveled year after year and linking the sites of the fêtes by commercial if not by spiritual ties. At the places where these trade routes crossed or at the watering places or camp sites, the caravans were accustomed to stop for a time while the neighboring people assembled to buy their merchandise. Thus the system of periodic commerce was extended gradually beyond strictly religious pilgrimages, and commercial fairs were thereby created.[6]

Periodical gatherings, whatever their primary purpose, came more and more to be centers of commercial activity.

[6] Huvelin, *op. cit.*, pp. 47 *et seq.*

The impetus to the changing complexion of fairs probably did not arise, however, altogether from secular sources. It is quite likely that the religious authorities, at both the primitive and the medieval fairs, took advantage of the commercial and festal aspects of these gatherings in much the same way that merchants took advantage of the religious aspects. In the first place, the times of religious celebration were times of peace, and the religious authorities could extend this peace to all that came, whether for purposes of worship or of trade. They thereby encouraged both buyers and sellers to enjoy the freedom from otherwise perpetual hostility, and threw a cloak of divine sanction about commercial transactions.[7] Again, these gatherings could be made the occasion of religious ministries even though the people may have assembled primarily for another purpose.[8] The more people, the more probability of increasing the number of the penitent. Priests must have flocks; and at these fairs they undoubtedly found sufficient numbers of the unshepherded to enlist their most worthy efforts. Finally, as a source of revenue the fair was of no mean importance. This was particularly the case in the Middle Ages, when the monasteries were heavily obligated by requirements of charity and education, and when they assumed such tasks even as the repair of the roads as an act of mercy. Consequently, fairs were often sought by the monasteries, and merchants and entertainers using them could be charged tolls, customs or stallage fees for the privilege of setting up their booths or plying their trades.[9]

We discover then, as we pass on to a consideration of the medieval fairs, a strange mixture of religion and commerce and entertainment. We see the fair assuming certain

[7] *Ibid.*, pp. 338 *et seq.*
[8] Walford, Cornelius, *Fairs Past and Present*, London, 1883, p. 2.
[9] Morrish, R. W., *A History of Fairs*, Chicago, n.d., p. 10.

characteristic features, molded by the exigencies of the social and economic life of the time. To the end of the Middle Ages, however, it remained dominantly commercial. There were two general types of medieval commercial institutions, markets and fairs, most of them established by royal sanction and subject to elaborate regulations. The markets were daily, semiweekly or weekly events serving a local need and specializing in retail trade. The fairs took place at greater intervals, served a wider area, specialized in wholesale trade and were under a higher feudal jurisdiction than the markets.[10] It is probable, too, that the market was almost wholly a business resort, while the fair, though principally an occasion for commerce, was also partly a religious festival and partly an opportunity for pleasure making.[11] These markets and fairs were indispensable organs of medieval trade, furnishing in fact almost the only opportunity for the buying and selling of foreign products. They flourished at a time when the villages did not afford a market sufficient to justify a permanent town merchant, when goods were not produced in a steady stream to meet a public demand, and when transportation and communication were still on primitive levels. The importance of the fairs to medieval economic life can be understood only when we have some comprehension of the difficulties and dangers of travel. They were inventions of necessity. The old Roman roads had fallen into decay, the countryside was infested by brigands, local proprietors assessed exhorbitant tolls upon all that passed their way; and the government was too unorganized to effect immediate changes. Furthermore, there were no banking or postal facilities. The merchant was compelled to go to the fairs personally in charge of his goods and to sell from

[10] Cf. Kulischer, *Encyclopaedia of the Social Sciences, loc. cit.*; Thompson, *op. cit.*, p. 586; Lipson, *op. cit.*, pp. 220 *et seq.*

[11] Garnier, Russell M., *History of the English Landed Interest*, London, 1892, I, 227.

his present stock; there was no such thing as standardized products, no facilities for filling orders if they could have been taken.

An institution of such importance was naturally the object of a great deal of zealous regulation. We have already seen how it was made to serve religious ends. It was no less sought after by the feudal lords and, since it represented a source of revenue and power, grants were rarely made except by royal prerogative. Elaborate rules for the conduct of the fairs (and also markets) usually accompanied the grants, and these rules along with the commercial practices then in vogue grew finally into a well recognized code of international merchant law. Provision was made for summary judicial proceedings at the fairs. In England the law merchant was administered by the courts of piepowder,[12] in which commercial cases were settled expeditiously without resort to the more complicated procedure of the common-law courts. The law merchant was distinct from common law, and was characterized by the summary nature of its procedure and by the type of case brought to it. The courts of piepowder were competent to hear cases concerning debts, contracts, trespasses, breaches of assizes, etc., and to deal with the collection of tolls and the maintenance of peace and order.[13]

The law merchant was the forerunner of many modern commercial practices. But these are not our only inheritance from the medieval commerce that centered in the fairs and markets. At the present time we use Troy weight, a survival of the set of weights and measures used at the Troyes fair in France. Many present day banking devices also originated in

---

[12] Courts of the dustyfooted, so named from the dusty travelers that resorted to them.
[13] Lipson, *op. cit.*, pp. 196 *et seq.*; Huvelin, *op. cit., passim*. Cf. also Gross, Charles, *Select Cases concerning the Law Merchant, A.D. 1270-1638*, London, 1908, Vol. I, for cases dealt with by the law merchant.

the commerce of these early fairs, especially those of Champagne. Medieval financial systems were crude and undeveloped, but money naturally flowed to the fairs, called out by the necessity of paying tolls, fees and debts, and of effecting the exchange of goods. The *changeur* became, therefore, indispensable. A confusing mass of money of different coinage and value came to the fairs, and the *changeurs* received deposits, changed the money (for which they received a regular rate of exchange), made loans and gave *lettres de foires* or bills of credit; and thus began a number of banking practices and devices that have survived to modern times. The Lombards and Jews were the most noted of the *changeurs*, the enterprising citizens of an Italian town sometimes forming a partnership and sending one of their number to Champagne to turn the subscribed capital to good account.[14]

The growth of medieval economic institutions was, of course, a gradual process. The awakening of commerce and industry crystallized them into more stable and more specific forms, the markets becoming regular and frequent places of local trade, and the fairs periodic events for a wider commerce.

The most important medieval fairs on the Continent were those of Champagne. Well established and flourishing institutions at the beginning of the twelfth century, they were really a series of fairs constituting for the Champagne region an almost continuous market. Though smaller fairs were held locally, the six great fairs, each lasting for a period of more than six weeks without conflicting dates, attained international importance. They were sponsored by the counts of Champagne, who ruled in unbroken line from 1010 to 1284, as a means of increasing their revenue and

[14] Thompson, *op. cit.*, pp. 600 *et seq.*; Schevill, Ferdinand, *Siena*, New York, 1909, pp. 98 *et seq.*

extending their power. A remarkable development took place in local agriculture and industry, stimulated by the commercial activity incident to the fairs.[15]

There were other notable fairs in France, many of which became known for a particular product. Bordeaux, for example, was known for its wines; Caen, in Normandy, for its woolens; Notre Dame, for its onion fair and for its pork or bacon fair.[16] The international Lyons fairs were characterized by their advanced banking facilities, and in the sixteenth century eclipsed all other fairs in France.[17] Beaucaire became the largest and most noted of French fairs at the end of the seventeenth century.[18] St. Denis, which probably was established in the seventh century, enjoyed a varied commerce with the added distinction of being the source of parchment supply for the University of Paris. The rector of the university visited the fair annually, and with considerable ceremony secured his parchment for the following year.[19] Never able to regain its former importance after a lapse during the Hundred Years' War, St. Denis was eclipsed by the St. Germain fair, noted for its sale of luxuries and its amusements.[20] In fact, both the St. Denis and the St. Germain fairs evidenced the trend toward amusements that caused the abolition of many fairs, and marked the changing purposes of the fair as an institution. St. Denis, before it was abolished in 1608, had become a scene of riotous disorder and even bloodshed, and St. Germain, with its taverns and dance halls, its theaters and gambling houses, was a rendezvous for Paris pleasure seekers from the king down.[21]

[15] Thompson, op. cit., pp. 589 et seq. Cf. also Bourquelot, Félix, Études sur les foires de Champagne, Paris, 1865.
[16] Walford, op. cit., passim.
[17] Zetter, op. cit., pp. 131 et seq.   [19] Huvelin, op. cit., pp. 266 et seq.
[18] Huvelin, op. cit., p. 306.   [20] Ibid., p. 268.
[21] Walford, op. cit., passim; Zetter, op. cit., passim. The fair was last held in 1786, though Napoleon, in 1811, opened a regular market on the site of the old fair. Cf. Zetter, op. cit., pp. 113 et seq.

These great periodical fairs abounded in other sections
of Europe — Germany, Russia, the Low Countries and
Spain — and were an indispensable part of the economic
and commercial life of the times. Nowhere else, however,
did they attain the fame that they enjoyed in France and
England. Every medieval English town had its market and
its fixed market days when the handiwork of the town artisans and the products of the surrounding fields were exposed
for sale. Foreign products could be bought only at the great
fairs.[22] Four items of foreign commerce figured prominently
in the needs of the otherwise self-sufficient English village;
namely, salt, to preserve the meat upon which the people
lived for five months of the year; iron for plows and other
farm implements; tar for the treatment of scab in the great
flocks of sheep; and millstones.[23] During the ninth century,
foreign merchants had been permitted by Alfred the Great
to come only to the "four fairs" and to remain in England
no longer than forty days[24] and Domesday Book mentioned
two fairs and forty-two markets in England.[25] The system
expanded rapidly, however, in the next few centuries. Between 1199 and 1483, it is said, over 2,800 grants of
markets and fairs were made, over one-half of them during
the first 74 years of the period.[26] Like the fairs of the
Continent, those of England arose out of the unorganized
state of commerce and communication. A commerce growing
faster than the means of communication demanded fixed
centers of periodic exchange. And we must not forget that
the growth of fairs and markets was abetted by the prospects
of increased royal or ecclesiastical profits and power, and by
a demand for popular amusement.

[22] Ashley, W. J., *An Introduction to English Economic History and Theory*,
London, 1909, I, 98 *et seq.*
[23] *Ibid.*, pp. 35-36.
[24] Walford, *op. cit.*, p. 19.   [25] Lipson, *op. cit.*, p. 198.
[26] Rew, R. H., *An Agricultural Faggot*, Westminster, 1913, p. 46.

The most famous English fairs were Stourbridge fair at Cambridge and St. Bartholomew fair at Smithfield, London. Both were originally granted to religious orders; both ran their course as great commercial institutions that finally came to serve no end except amusement. At its height St. Bartholomew was the chief cloth fair in England, and at Stourbridge iron, cloth, wool, leather and books formed a large part of the trade. To these fairs flocked a medley of people with myriad kinds of goods [27] — Jewish and Lombard money changers, Italian merchants with their luxuries, Flemish weavers, Spanish iron merchants, Norwegian tar merchants, Hanse townsmen with furs and amber, and Englishmen from far and near. Here, too, came a mixed multitude to buy — nobles, their luxuries; franklins, their farm materials; the bailiffs of college and monastery, their cloth. Side by side with commerce were amusements of every sort. And on Sunday a near-by canon came, said mass and preached in a booth assigned for religious worship.[28] Certainly it was a spectacular and cosmopolitan event. Daniel Defoe visited Stourbridge in 1723, and has left an enduring description of what he saw,[29] and St. Bartholomew found a historian in Henry Morley.[30] Both these fairs survived until the nineteenth century, though their later days were marked almost entirely by amusements and debaucheries that drew forth denunciation from the pulpit [31] and repeated attempts on the part of civil authorities to close them.[32]

[27] It is said that the modern "Fair Store" derives its name from the old medieval fairs with their endless variety of wares. Cf. Iowa State Department of Agriculture *Yearbook*, 1918, Des Moines, p. 106.
[28] Rogers, James E. Thorold, *A History of Agriculture and Prices in England*, Oxford, 1866, I, 142 *et seq.*
[29] *A Tour Thro' the Whole Island of Great Britain*, London, 1753, I, 89-95. Quoted also in Walford, *op. cit.*, pp. 133-42.
[30] *Memoirs of Bartholomew Fair*, London, n.d.
[31] Cf. Dillon, R. C., *A Sermon on the Evils of Fairs in General and of Bartholomew Fair in Particular*, London, 1830.
[32] Walford, *op. cit., passim.*

The Modern Sample Fair and the Exposition

In the seventeenth and eighteenth centuries fairs lost much of their commercial importance. Chief among the factors contributing to their decline were, of course, the improvement in the means of communication and in the processes of manufacture. Retail shops became established in the towns and villages, and traveling salesmen carrying samples of standardized goods came to make the contacts between buyer and seller. Commission houses and jobbers frowned upon the direct selling principle of the fair as the basis of too keen a competition. The development in the nineteenth century of telegraph, telephone, postal and railway systems made possible the ordering and delivery of goods. Banking and credit facilities were revolutionized by the establishment of stock exchanges, banks, clearing houses and post offices. Above all, new methods in industry resulted in the standardization of manufactured products.

It is notable that in eastern Europe, where economic and industrial development was slow, fairs retained their primary commercial importance much longer than in western Europe. The great Nizhni Novgorod fair in Russia, the center of internal Russian trade as well as of that between Russia and Asia, was still prosperous at the close of the nineteenth century, though with the coming of the railroad its importance was beginning to dwindle. In Soviet Russia, the fairs, after a three-year cessation from 1919 to 1921, enjoyed a revival, especially the fair of Nizhni Novgorod. But in the present economic system, in which private trade is so overwhelmed by state trade, fairs are of little use, and in 1930 all Russian fairs were abolished.[33] It is also notable that during and after the World War, fairs throughout Europe experienced a remarkable revival. The war recreated in a sense the old conditions under which fairs had

[33] Cf. Kulischer, *Encyclopaedia of the Social Sciences, op. cit.,* p. 63.

flourished, by disrupting the ordinary channels of trade, by causing a shortage of goods and by raising almost insurmountable barriers of communication. The Allied countries attempted to fight Germany economically and to foster new industries for the products of which they had formerly relied on that country. These new fairs were chiefly sample fairs, many of which, energized by this new stimulus, have remained even after postwar trade restrictions have been largely removed.

This revival of commercial fairs constitutes an interesting chapter in economic change. As sample fairs they are, above all, meetings of merchants and manufacturers. Samples of various manufactured products are displayed and the general principle followed is to prohibit retail trade. At most of them there is some attempt to interest the general public, sometimes even by providing a midway, amusement section or athletic contests. But the great object is to provide a place where manufacturers may advertise and sell their products to distributors and retailers, and where buyers may find concentrated side by side samples of the merchandise in which they are interested. To both there accrues the advantage of being able to compare trade data, to receive new ideas and to forecast the trends of popular demand. These fairs may be local or international in scope, and they may include a wide variety of products or be confined largely to the products of one or two industries. The largest of the international commercial fairs are the Leipzig Trade Fairs, held semiannually at Leipzig; and the International Sample Fair at Milan and the Paris International Fair at Paris, each held annually. The Leipzig fairs present an outstanding example of the conversion of the old type of commercial fair into a modern sample fair. They have a history of some seven hundred years, though only in 1894 did they become definitely sample fairs. During the World War they were held chiefly as fairs for substitute articles, but since the War they have grown rapidly and constitute at present the leading sample fairs of the world. Both the spring and the fall fairs are divided into two main sections, the sample fair and the technical and building fair, housed in some seventy permanent halls or "fair palaces." Some of the other European fairs serve more or less specialized purposes. The Bordeaux International Fair, for example, pays particular attention to French colonial trade; and the British Industries Fair, held simultaneously at London and at Birmingham, is confined, as are most of the British commercial fairs, to products of the countries comprising the Kingdom.[34]

It is evident that fairs are the creation of the society underlying them, and that they are established, shaped and sometimes abolished in response to the processes that change that society. In addition to the development of the agricultural fair, which is the main object of our study, three quite distinct trends characterize the fairs of the last two centuries. We have already seen how some of the commercial fairs, no longer finding place as economic institutions, degenerated into amusement centers that public opinion refused to sanction. We have seen, too, how others were made to serve new commercial ends by becoming sample fairs instead of places of exchange. We have still to consider the third trend, the growth of the exposition, with its purposes of education and display.

The first event to which the name "exposition" was given was held in 1756, though the first international exposition or "world's fair" was not held until nearly a century later. The distinctly commercial fair of medieval times became, as we have seen, less and less necessary as a place of

[34] Cf. Kulischer, *Encyclopaedia of the Social Sciences, op. cit.*, pp. 62 *et seq.*; Haas, J. Anton de, *Foreign Trade Organization*, New York, 1923, pp. 137 *et seq.*; Junkin, Kathryne, *International Fairs and Expositions*, United States Department of Commerce Trade Promotion Series, No. 75, Washington, 1929.

exchange; the commercial fairs that survived did so by becoming largely sample fairs. They remain as gatherings of merchants, appealing only incidentally to the general public. The exposition, on the other hand, while it possesses many of the characteristics of a merchants' fair, makes its primary appeal to consumers. Merchants and manufacturers must, of course, furnish a great part of the exhibits, but the capture of public attention and support rather than direct selling, is the essence of the exposition. One of the most important results of the passing of direct selling and the development of modern commercial organizations is the philosophy and technique of advertising. And the exposition, after all, is essentially an organ of advertising. Its importance lies in the fact that it developed in a period in which selling rather than production became the dominant economic problem. In so far as it is a commercial institution, the exposition is, therefore, closely related to the sample fair in its underlying general principle; the distinction lies in the fact that it advertises to the general public, rather than to a specialized group or groups of merchants and distributors.

The first exposition, which was only national in its scope, was held at London in 1756 by the Society for the Encouragement of Arts, Manufactures and Commerce. For nearly a century there followed numerous national expositions in England, France, the Netherlands and other European countries. The possibility of inviting foreign exhibitors to participate was sometimes discussed but never effected until 1851, when the first international exposition was held, also at London, under the patronage of Prince Albert. This first international exposition was remarkably successful: it closed with a surplus of over £200,000; it acquainted both English and foreign visitors with the industrial development of the countries represented; it stimulated British export trade. Within a few years national or international expositions were organized at Dublin, New York City, Munich, Paris, Haarlem and Brussels. In 1862 a second British exposition and in 1867 a second French exposition were held at London and Paris respectively. During the remainder of the century the world was inundated with expositions, engendered by both national and metropolitan rivalries quite as much as by the efforts of industries to secure new markets. Though they have, throughout their history, specialized in the exhibition of industrial products and processes, there has been an ever-increasing emphasis on elaborate outward display and attempts to outdo former events of the same character. From the one building that housed the London exposition in 1851 the typical international exposition has grown into an elaborate city of scores of buildings, courts and plazas, colonnades, fountains and statues; the serious, businesslike atmosphere has changed to one of luxurious and spectacular entertainment.[35]

This change in the character of the exposition is due partly at least to the attempts made to interest the general public. The necessity of reaching the consumer demanded that the exposition become a thing of display, a gorgeous spectacle appealing to his curiosity, his imagination, his vanity and his pride. Soon the strictly commercial purposes were almost, if not completely, lost sight of, while the exhibition of the resources or achievements of particular cities, regions or countries or the celebration of notable events became the function of the exposition. The public, therefore, must be "inspired" and "educated," and above all it must be duly impressed with the "progress" of the arts, sciences and industry. In later years these expositions have been primarily celebrations commemorating some national event or significant achievement. The fourth Paris

[35] Cf. Norton, C. B., *World's Fairs from London, 1851, to Chicago, 1893,* Chicago, 1890.

International Exposition in 1889 celebrated the centenary of the French Revolution; the Turin Exposition in 1911, the fiftieth anniversary of Italy as a kingdom. In the United States the centennial of the Declaration of Independence was celebrated in Philadelphia in 1876, and the sesquicentennial, in 1926. The four-hundredth anniversary of the discovery of America was celebrated by the Chicago Exposition in 1893; the centennial of the Louisiana Purchase, at St. Louis in 1904; the opening of the Panama Canal, at San Francisco in 1915; and the one-hundredth anniversary of the incorporation of Chicago as a village, by the "Century of Progress" in 1933.

These expositions have, however, had a wider significance than their commemorative features might at first indicate. Many of them have marked a new stage in the scientific and technological, and even the cultural, development of the Western World. Often they have exercised a strong influence, especially on architecture, and in some cases they were partly responsible for the projection of ambitious programs of civic improvement. In London the Crystal Palace stands as the legacy of the first international exposition held there in 1851. In Paris the Eiffel Tower was built for the Paris Exposition of 1889. The Chicago Exposition of 1893 not only inaugurated a period in which the designing of exposition buildings became almost a profession, but it set a strong example of classicism in American architecture, which came definitely to be reflected in the new public buildings erected in the United States. In a period when industrial expansion was particularly rapid, the expositions no doubt gave millions of people a new vision of the world, a new concept of beauty and a new appreciation of social achievement, as well as furnished them with some of the most thrilling experiences of their lives.

The utility of expositions, however, has been questioned

more and more in recent decades. The tendency toward lavish expenditure has come to entail almost intolerable financial burdens; the expositions exact a drain on public and private purse that public support often does not repay.[36] Magazines, newspapers, outdoor displays and the radio have become important means of bringing commercial products to the attention of buyers. Above all, world's fairs are faced with the impossibility of bringing together a truly universal exposition and with a keen competition with other means of entertaining the public and enlarging its outlook. Whether or not the day of the world's fair is past is perhaps a moot question, but certain it is that the automobile show, the radio show, the business show and the art exposition, for example, are indicative of a new trend in the matter of industrial and artistic display; indeed for many products they may well be thought of as sample fairs. In them new purposes are served, new adjustments are made; and the fair attains some of its more differentiated forms.[37]

Agricultural Fairs in Other Lands

The agricultural fair, while it cannot be considered a direct lineal descendant of any of the types of fairs discussed above, nevertheless has many characteristics in common with them. It represents the adaptation of the fair idea to the agricultural industry. It is essentially a rural institution, reflecting the interests of rural people, though these interests are often entwined with those emanating from urban centers, and the institution itself is usually dependent upon urban as

[36] The United States Government is said to have taken part in more than forty foreign and national expositions, between 1862 and 1926, at a cost of approximately $30,000,000. Since 1884, when a group of French exhibitors formed a self-protective association, numerous private and governmental agreements have been aimed at correcting some of the abuses of these fairs. Cf. Ford, Guy Stanton, "International Expositions," *Encyclopaedia of the Social Sciences*, New York, 1931, VI, 24, 25.

[37] Cf. Haas, *op. cit.*, pp. 123 *et seq.*; Ford, *Encyclopaedia of the Social Sciences, op. cit.*, pp. 26-27.

well as rural support. The universally avowed purpose of the agricultural fair is the improvement of agriculture. It is invariably described by its supporters as "primarily educational," though sociologically it presents other characteristics quite as interesting and important. Unquestionably it has developed with the so-called educational features constituting a sort of main stem. Its essential element is a competitive display of agricultural products, supplemented usually by exhibits of agricultural colleges, governmental agencies, promotive associations and manufacturers, all designed to stimulate the improvement of farming practices and modes of rural living. These were essentially the means employed by its earliest promoters to bring to the attention of farmers new methods and new ideals of agricultural production. We may be sure, however, that the first agricultural fairs had a significant social aspect, in that always they provided occasions for social mingling, and usually for actual recreational activities. We may be sure, too, that though the agricultural fairs have never been important as places of actual exchange, they have had from the first important commercial aspects. In the course of their development they have come to possess a great variety of features, some of which are wholly extraneous to their avowed primary purpose. In pursuing the evolutionary course of the agricultural fair it is easy to see how it partakes of the nature of the exposition with its ostentatious display, how it resembles in some respects the commercial sample fair, how it still retains a touch of the primitive harvest festival, how amusement and recreation attractions combine survivals of medieval days with the latest devices of thrill and spectacle. And we may see how the use of competition for prizes at agricultural fairs has aided in giving to later-day fairs one of their most distinguishing characteristics. It is our purpose in this volume to trace this development of the agricultural fair as illustrative of the process of social evolution and to analyze it in some of its functional aspects.

Though we shall confine ourselves primarily to the story of the agricultural fair in America and to its immediate English background, we may pause briefly to consider its status in other parts of the world. Today it is held both locally and nationally in practically all civilized countries, particularly in western Europe, North and South America, Australia and South Africa. In western Europe are to be found great numbers of local fairs to which the farmers bring their produce to compete for prizes and to sell, and which provide the occasion, also, for a great deal of social festivity. Germany has its National Agricultural Exhibition, held in a different city each year, which presents displays of live stock, agricultural products and farm machinery. The holding of this national show is the chief work of the German Agricultural Society, a nonpolitical organization of all classes of agriculturists and representatives of industries whose products enter into farm life. France has the Concours Général Agricole de Paris, a national agricultural show, and also numerous horse shows, the latter being exhibits of purebred horses for which France is particularly noted. In Spain there is a national show organized by the General Association of Breeders, and in Italy, Belgium and the Scandinavian countries there are various types of agricultural fairs of lesser scope. Argentina and Uruguay hold the greatest agricultural fairs in South America, both being particularly noted for their fine displays of cattle.

But in England and the United States as nowhere else the agricultural fair developed and became, we might almost say, an essential part of the agricultural system and of rural social organization. English farmers and gentlemen led the agrarian revolution of the eighteenth century, and it was English farming that felt its first and most epoch-making effects. The men who then experimented with new crops and new methods of cultivation and started systematically to improve the breeds of their live stock gave to England, and indirectly to America, world leadership in the matter of agricultural improvement. They were confronted with the problems of stimulating other experiments of the same nature and of disseminating the results of their work. As we shall see, the agricultural societies organized for these purposes eventually fathered the agricultural fair.

PART II

THE EVOLUTION OF THE AGRICULTURAL FAIR IN AMERICA

II

THE LEARNED AGRICULTURAL SOCIETIES IN ENGLAND AND AMERICA

THE development of American agriculture and the institutions associated with it can best be understood by reference to their English antecedents. In this respect, the agricultural features of American civilization do not differ from other phases of our culture. An overwhelmingly large percentage of the colonists were British in origin; naturally they reproduced in large measure their British social heritage. So it was that our agriculture, in respect to population, live stock, crops, methods and machinery, traditions and institutions, came to borrow much from the mother country.

THE AGRICULTURAL REVOLUTION

The agricultural revolution of the eighteenth century provided the general background for the inception of agricultural fairs. Agricultural products figured prominently, of course, in the trade of the medieval commercial fairs, but just as the commodities of the artisan found new channels of commerce in the developing economic and commercial systems, so the commodities of the farmer came to depend less and less upon the old commercial fairs as places of distribution and exchange. At the same time agriculture as an industry was undergoing significant changes — an aspect of the great social and economic transformations through which western Europe was passing. English agriculture especially was steadily, though slowly, unfolding at the hands of an outstanding group of gentlemen farmers. In general terms, farming was developing into a commercial occupation. Instead of providing meager supplies of food and clothing for a self-contained feudal-manorial village it increasingly produced for a commercialized-industrialized nation, a transition that necessitated both increasing the amount and improving the quality of the output to meet the demand of a greatly changed social and economic order.

It was in the eighteenth century also that England underwent that phenomenal social transformation known as the industrial revolution. These two revolutions, the agricultural and the industrial, cannot be divorced from each other. The main threads of each may be unraveled but the events and trends unite to form a single social process. Each had its own outstanding leaders, its own remarkable inventions of machinery and processes. But the two so complemented each other that any consideration of the period must recognize their concomitant development. The peasant society became an industrial society, the local economy, an international economy. The increase of population and its concentration in cities are familiar aspects of this change. From 1700 to 1750 the population of England increased between 17 and 18 percent, and from 1750 to 1800 it increased over 52 percent.[1] Expanding industry and commerce gave rise to an artisan class able to afford more food, and this fact coupled with the frequent wars resulted in rising prices for agricultural products. Increased consumption of fresh meat instead of the salted carcasses of oxen and old cows, and of wheat bread instead of oats, barley and rye, witnessed a rising standard of living and created a period of relative prosperity for agriculture. Industrial expansion concurrently demanded new laborers and resulted in an increase of the necessities upon which they lived. The new demand for food fell upon the rural population, which had probably shared in the numerical growth of the total

[1] Toynbee, Arnold, *Lectures on the Industrial Revolution of the Eighteenth Century in England*, London, 1927, p. 8.

population little or not at all. The agricultural leaders, sensing the improvements that were possible as well as the demand that was arising, attempted to demonstrate to their neighbors the desirability of adopting new methods and new crops. In their activities lay the germ of the agricultural fair, which in the next century was to become a distinctive feature of English and American agriculture.

Though great changes had been taking place, most English peasants farmed in the early eighteenth century as had their medieval ancestors. The manorial village, largely self-sufficient, lived on what it raised and worked under traditional methods of cultivation. The ordinary villager still followed the three-field system of farming, his strips of land scattered here and there, his crops dictated by custom, his methods of cultivation determined by his neighbors. He still turned his live stock to pasture on the common under the supervision of cowherd, shepherd or swineherd. Vast areas of English land still lay idle; even in 1795 the Board of Agriculture estimated that over 22,000,000 acres in Great Britain were uncultivated — in England and Wales alone nearly 8,000,000.[2] Methods of drainage and fertilization were either unknown or practiced in the crudest manner. No improved crops or live stock could be grown under such a system: weeds spread from the plot of the slothful farmer to that of his more industrious neighbor; the promiscuous mating of live stock on the common was "the haphazard union of nobody's son with everybody's daughter";[3] and the diseased easily and quickly contaminated the healthy. Breaking this reign of custom and superstition awaited a change in the basic system of farming.

Such a change came in the process of inclosure. In many of the villages men had built their cottages on the common

[2] Ernle, Lord, *English Farming Past and Present*, London, 1919, p. 152.
[3] *Ibid.*, p. 181.

and surrounded them with inclosed fields, appropriating the common to their own use. The advantages of inclosure soon becoming evident, whole villages had sometimes re-allotted the fields so that each villager now held a block of land instead of his former scattered strips. Though inclosure had been going on for centuries, it did not become a general practice until the eighteenth century. In earlier years the high price of wool had attracted most of the owners of inclosures to turn them into sheep pastures, but in 1660 the exportation of British wool was prohibited and arable farming was newly stimulated. The process of inclosure and the improvement of agricultural practice were reciprocal in their effects; inclosure prepared the way for individual initiative in the introduction of new methods of cultivation and breeding at the same time that advocates of new crops and improved stock pressed their demands for further inclosure. Agricultural improvement was thereby enormously advanced.

The remarkable agricultural progress of the eighteenth century can be traced largely to the gentleman farmer. Men of this class formed the connecting link between scientific agricultural experimentation and practical farming. The meager scientific knowledge of the day was the possession of the very few. Public agencies for experimentation and diffusion of information did not exist. Many of the working farmers were unable to read, and did not possess the leisure, the money or the equipment for carrying on experimentation. They were too busy meeting the immediate problems of everyday life. Hence it was that this era of agricultural experimentation was largely the creation of men of comparative wealth, of wide experience in travel, public life and contemporary learning, and of sufficient vision to grasp clearly the significance of the changing society in which they lived.

The changes constituting the agricultural revolution are identified chiefly with the names of Tull, Townshend, Bakewell, Young and Coke.[4] The principal contribution of Jethro Tull was his theory of cultivation. Tillage, said he, was equally necessary before and after seeding; wheat and turnips should be drilled instead of sown broadcast, so that they might be cultivated. For this purpose he himself invented a drill that planted the seed in rows and covered it exactly. With his "very ordinary" microscope and homemade equipment he conducted experiments to test his theories. He observed and experimented with the selection of seed, the practice of steeping, the depth of planting and the thickness of sowing. And scholar that he was, he published in 1731 a book called *Horse-Hoeing Husbandry* in which he set forth the principles upon which the agricultural revolution in tillage was based.

Charles Townshend's advocacy of turnips in the scheme of agricultural improvement earned for him the sobriquet "Turnip" Townshend. Throughout most of his life he had been active in politics. Twice he had been secretary of state, but following a quarrel with his colleague Walpole, he retired in 1730 to his estate in Norfolk where he developed the Norfolk or four-course system of farming — the alternation of cereals, roots and artificial grasses. The use of turnips made possible the wintering of larger numbers of live stock, and therefore constituted both a direct and an indirect source of fertilizer for the enrichment of the land.

The production of live stock, while not an integral part of Townshend's system, was stimulated by his work. The scientific improvement of the contemporary nondescript and neglected live stock made Robert Bakewell the greatest of the world's pioneer breeders. Before 1750, when Bakewell

[4] Cf. *ibid.*, Chaps. VII-X, for a brief yet complete discussion of the work of these men.

began his work, sheep had been the mainstay of English agriculture, and at times, the basis of the nation's foremost industry. For three centuries English wool had been the chief concern of English agriculturists. A little constructive breeding had been done during that time but it had revolved around the production of wool rather than meat. The fleece, not the carcass, was the source of value. Even so, the points that had been considered in selection and breeding were largely nonessential ones, such as the length or shape of the horn, or the color of the face or legs. Cattle before Bakewell's day were valued for milk or draft power; like sheep, they were generally ignored as sources of meat. They were usually gigantic, ill-shaped beasts, their size and their long legs constituting the points of their supposed superiority; points, however, not to be ridiculed in the light of the miry roads and swampy fields over which they had to travel. Some attention had been given, also, before the eighteenth century, to developing types of horses suitable for racing, fox hunting, war and travel. But the cart, the plow and the packsaddle had still to be provided with equine power.

With such materials Bakewell began his experiments. Lord Ernle calls him "the agricultural opportunist who saw the impending change, and knew how it should be met." [5] Opportunist or not, he centered his attention upon the production of sheep for mutton and cattle for beef, and succeeded in discovering the principles of animal breeding that have guided live-stock breeders ever since. He envisaged the type to which he wished his animals to conform, and then selected as his breeding stock those most likely to perpetuate the chosen qualities. By inbreeding, not only within the same native breed but within families, he was able to establish the qualities he desired. Since mutton and beef were his chief concern, he sought to create types of

[5] *Ibid.*, p. 181.

animals that turned their feed into the choicest cuts of meat in the shortest time and at the least expense — strains of compact, short-legged, symmetrical, small-boned sheep and cattle that quickly put on the most meat in the places most desired by the butchers. Bakewell achieved his most notable success with sheep. His new Leicesters, an early maturing breed adapted to the lowlands of inclosed arable land, proved the soundness of his theories. He was less successful with his cattle breeding, but the principle of live-stock improvement had been found. The rest was comparatively easy. Scores of other breeders imitating his work soon established breeds suitable to various natural environments and possessed of whatever characteristics their creators particularly sought. Lincoln, Southdown and Cheviot sheep were bred for the hill countries and the mountains. In cattle breeding Bakewell's imitators achieved marked success — the Colling brothers with their Shorthorns, and Benjamin Tompkins, "the Younger," with his Herefords. This new interest in live-stock breeding was one of the outstanding phases of the agricultural revolution.

The brilliant successes of Tull, Townshend and Bakewell must not blind us, however, to the fact that their practices in general were but slowly accepted by their neighbors. The improved methods were known as a rule only locally. Bakewell was perhaps the most readily received of the experimenters, because he himself was a tenant farmer and because the results of his work were more easily discerned. But Tull's system of cultivation found no favor generally in England until it had proved its success in Scotland, and Townshend's practices were not universally adopted in his own county until the end of the century.

Again it was a gentleman farmer that came to the rescue. Arthur Young failed thrice as a practical farmer before starting in 1767 on his tours of England, Ireland and

France. But he redeemed his failures by becoming the foremost agricultural writer of his time. To him more than to anyone else belongs the credit for the collection and dissemination of agricultural information and the creation of agencies for bringing the farmers together and stimulating them to agricultural improvement. A literary devotee from his youth, Young found writing a facile means of contributing to the agricultural awakening. In 1784 he began the publication of a monthly magazine, *Annals of Agriculture*, which continued to 1809. In 1793 he was appointed Secretary of the Board of Agriculture, in which capacity he undertook the compilation of agricultural reports in each county. From every corner of the country came substantiation of the benefits of inclosure to general farming practice, and Arthur Young saw to it that this information was incorporated into his reports. Up and down the land he went organizing farmers' clubs and urging the adoption of the new agricultural methods.

The last of this group of agricultural benefactors was Thomas Coke of Holkham, the great champion of large-scale farming. He believed in investing as much money and labor as possible in the land, constructing permanent buildings and building up the fertility of the soil. He encouraged his tenants to improve their live stock and crops, to adopt new machinery and to build up their farms with a view to long-time occupancy. To justify such constructive planning and the necessary outlays of labor and capital, he adopted a system of long-term leases that attracted to his land the best tenants in England. Soon after Coke had retired to his estate, he succeeded in growing good crops of wheat where only a light crop of rye had grown before; in the winter he stall-fed droves of Scottish cattle which he bought on their way to the London market, and thus increased his fertilizer supply; he was the first landlord to select certain varieties

VIEW OF THE CUMBERLAND FAIR GROUNDS
ALLEGANY COUNTY, MARYLAND

of grass for hay and pasture, and in the spring he gave simple botanical lessons to the children of his tenants and dispatched them over the countryside in search of the seed he desired.

THE PUBLIC ACTIVITIES OF THE LANDED GENTRY

The work of these and scores of less influential men suggests the main trend of the agricultural revolution. It soon made of farming a landlord's fad. Many of the great landowners, some of them motivated by an economic desire for higher profits or rents, some by pride in their estates, some by sheer enthusiasm for an engrossing novelty, made of agricultural pursuits their most absorbing avocation. Heirs to landed estates and younger sons both joined in the movement. Many a politician thought as much of the affairs of farming as of the affairs of state. George III himself established a model farm at Windsor, delighted in the title "Farmer George" and wrote articles for Arthur Young's *Annals of Agriculture*.[6] Both psychological and economic in its bases, this enthusiasm emanated primarily from the wealthy landlords. Their chief concern was to win adherents for the new agriculture among working farmers sometimes slow to see its advantages, and more often wary of risking their family's bread upon the adoption of newfangled methods proposed by opulent gentlemen. By investing freely in buildings, machinery and live stock and by imposing certain conditions in their leases, they urged their tenants to adopt the practices they had found successful. By holding farm demonstrations, cattle shows and plowing matches and finally by establishing agricultural societies, they sought to popularize the new breeds of live stock and the new methods of cultivation.

Thomas Coke instituted a series of popular farm demon-

6 *Ibid.*, pp. 207 *et seq.*

strations that foreshadowed to some extent the agricultural fair. Confessing his own ignorance in agricultural matters, when he began to build up his Holkham estate, he invited the suggestions of his neighbors and other agriculturists for the improvement of his lands. Other gentlemen farmers imitated Coke's gatherings both as agencies of agricultural improvement and as occasions for their own social intercourse. These annual sheepshearings, as they were called, became most famous in the hands of Coke and the Duke of Bedford, who attracted to Holkham and Woburn respectively all classes of English farmers and others interested in agriculture as well — dukes and earls and lords, farmers, breeders and graziers, agricultural theorists and working farmers; and mingled with them were interested persons from the Continent and the United States. These meetings usually lasted several days. The forenoons were spent in inspecting the live stock, the farm lands and the crops. The sheepshearers worked in pens where they might easily be watched by the visitors; field trials were made of the plows, drills, harrows, rakes and other farm machinery; in a few cases prizes were awarded to visitors who exhibited specimens of their cattle or sheep or who took part in the plowing matches. Each day the host entertained his guests at dinner — sometimes as many as two or three hundred. They feasted richly on English beef and mutton; they drank the King's health and listened to toasts on subjects such as "The Fleece," "The Plough," "The Memory of Mr. Bakewell" and "Success to Agriculture." They examined cloth made of various kinds of wool, and Mr. Coke "hoped [his] fair countrywomen would prefer such dresses for the winter, and no longer expose themselves in muslins to those accidents from a devouring element, which had proved so fatal to many of them." [7] At the close of the week many a neigh-

---

[7] *Farmer's Magazine*, Aug., 1806, p. 349.

boring farmer left with a pair of Coke's Devon cattle or with a ram or a pen of ewes he had hired for the season, or bought outright, to improve his own flock; and the wool dealers who had attended departed with their purchases of the annual clip.[8]

Another enterprise of these gentlemen farmers was the organization of agricultural societies. This was a natural result of the general agricultural awakening. While the idea of agricultural organization was not altogether new in the last quarter of the eighteenth century, it received then its clearest definition up to that time. Societies for mutual aid and the study of technical problems had existed in both Roman and medieval times. Thanks to physiocratic influence similar organizations appeared in eighteenth century France, for the glorification of agriculture and rural life.[9] In England, too, local societies had existed earlier in the century. As early as 1723 a society was organized in Edinburgh called the Society of Improvers in the Knowledge of Agriculture, and in 1731 a society was established in Dublin for the conduct of an experimental farm.[10] The Society for the Encouragement of Arts, Manufactures and Commerce, established in London in 1754, promoted the improvement of agriculture as one part of a broader program.[11] But the activity of the agricultural revolution soon resulted in a considerable differentiation of

[8] Cf. *ibid.*, pp. 346 *et seq.; Gentleman's Magazine*, Aug., 1799, p. 703; Clarke, Ernest, "Agriculture and the House of Russell," *Journal of the Royal Agricultural Society of England*, London, 1891, 3d Ser., II, 128 *et seq.; Farmer's Magazine*, July, 1800, pp. 328 *et seq.*
[9] Crawford, Nelson Antrim, "Agricultural Societies," *Encyclopaedia of the Social Sciences*, New York, 1930, I, 570.
[10] True, Rodney H., "The Early Development of Agricultural Societies in the United States," American Historical Association, *Annual Report*, 1920, Washington, 1925, p. 295.
[11] This society is said to have been the first in England to offer specific awards for agricultural improvement. Cf. Philp, Robert Kemp, *The History of Progress in Great Britain*, London, 1859, p. 108.

interests. More exclusively agricultural interests began to emerge, followed by more exclusively agricultural societies, the most important of which were the Bath and West of England Society, founded in 1777, and the Smithfield Club, founded in 1798. In all parts of Britain, county societies multiplied rapidly, especially after 1790. Many of them were short-lived; one at least was said to have been unsuccessful because it was "made a party business for electioneering purposes." [12] But their number testifies to the new enthusiasm that had seized agriculture.

The fact that these societies were formed by the landlords and so-called amateur farmers gave them a decidedly learned character. They met several times a year for the discussion of technical agricultural questions, the reading of dignified papers and the enjoyment of social amenities. Though membership seems to have been open to anyone who wished to "subscribe," it is probable that few practical farmers or laborers felt like expending the minimum guinea or two-guinea fee. Some of the larger societies held agricultural shows to which no doubt many of this class came; but usually their premiums were offered for the undertaking of elaborate experiments and projects on the farms of the county and were paid to those who could embody their reports in a learned dissertation quite beyond the comprehension of the ordinary farmer. For example, the Society for the Encouragement of Arts, Manufactures and Commerce offered premiums in 1799 for the best experiments designed to ascertain the component parts of arable land; for discovering an effectual cure for sheep rot, verified by experiments, and reported in an account of its cause and prevention; for ascertaining the best method of training oaks, not fewer than one hundred, into compass forms for

[12] Mavor, William, *General View of the Agriculture of Berkshire*, London, 1809, p. 499 n.

shipbuilding; etc.[13] In 1800 the Board of Agriculture, which had for one of its chief objects the encouragement of these societies and the coördination of their activities, offered among others the following premiums: [14]

To the person who shall draw up and produce to the Board, the best, simplest, and most practicable plan for ameliorating the condition of the labouring poor of this kingdom, by alterations in the poor laws, of easy execution, and without materially increasing poor-rates — *the Gold Medal.*

To the person who shall build on his estate the most cottages for labouring families, and assign to each a proper portion of land, for the support of not less than a cow, a hog, and a sufficient garden — *the Gold Medal.*

To the person who shall lay before the Board the most satisfactory account, verified by chemical experiments, or other sufficient authorities, of the nature of manures, and the principles of vegetation — *the Gold Medal.*

To the person who shall consent to his tenant applying the greatest quantity of old pasture land for the cultivation of early potatoes, (and the land so applied) which shall be brought to market and sold before the end of July, not less than 50 acres — *the Gold Medal.*

It is evident that these premiums were intended for the gentry. Though many of the meetings of the agricultural societies were as much events for the social intercourse of the prosperous landlords as for the encouragement of agriculture, they nevertheless constituted the chief means of stimulating interest and of disseminating agricultural information. Political interest in the agricultural revolution culminated in 1793 in the formation of the Board of Agriculture. Sir John Sinclair, long an ardent advocate of such a body, finally succeeded in enlisting the aid of Pitt in securing an act of Parliament and a charter from the King. Sinclair was made president and Arthur Young secretary of the new

[13] *Gentleman's Magazine,* April, 1799, pp. 330 *et seq.* Each of these particular projects was to be rewarded with the society's gold medal or fifty guineas.
[14] *Communications to the Board of Agriculture,* London, 1800, II, v *et seq.*

board. Its program was an ambitious one. Among other things it proposed to collect information regarding the state of the nation, to stimulate the organization of local agricultural societies and to act as a sort of clearing house for their experimental results, and to make statistical surveys of England for which a yearly grant of £3,000 was made.[15] Thus organized agriculture came under the patronage of the government, the Board forming a connecting link between the government and the private agricultural associations. Unfortunately it failed to survive the economic depression following the Napoleonic Wars, and was abandoned in 1822. It did succeed, however, in 1821 in holding the first national agricultural show in England.

The Smithfield Cattle and Sheep Club deserves a word of special consideration. It represented a further differentiated agricultural interest in that it was chiefly the concern of live-stock breeders influenced by the work of Bakewell. Smithfield was the great live-stock market of England.[16] Rivalries ran high between the advocates of the various breeds of cattle and sheep who gathered here on market days. They often issued challenges to compete against one another; and at the Smithfield market day just before Christmas in 1798, a club was organized, under the presidency of the Duke of Bedford, to encourage the breeders of live stock by holding annual shows and awarding prizes to the best animals exhibited. Not only did the live-stock display come to be one of the principal features of the agricultural fair, but the specialized live-stock show, modeled essentially on the Smithfield plan, has evolved as a differentiated type of the institution.[17]

[15] *Ibid.*, London, 1797, I, iii *et seq.*
[16] It is interesting to note the improvement in live stock evidenced by the fact that in 1710 the average weight of cattle and sheep on the Smithfield market was 370 and 28 pounds respectively, while in 1795 it had increased to 800 and 80 pounds respectively. Cf. Ernle, *op. cit.*, p. 188.
[17] Cf. *infra*, Chap. V.

EARLY AGRICULTURAL ORGANIZATION IN AMERICA

Having noted the conditions under which agricultural organization emerged in England, let us turn our attention to America. Here the nondescript live stock formed a less important source of the colonists' food than did cereal crops, and little provision was made for it in the way of winter shelter or specially grown animal feed. Sheep breeding had received some encouragement from colonial assemblies in an effort to stimulate the home production of wool and woolen cloth, but fleet-footed razorbacked hogs that could be captured only with a gun ran wild in the woods, and cattle were valued chiefly for their hides and fat and a scanty flow of milk.[18] Cultivation, too, was conducted upon most unenlightened lines. The system of fallow fields, left in their unproductive years to grow up to weeds, was still in evidence at the time of the Revolutionary War. The lowlands were generally undrained and the uplands exhausted by extractive farming. A dearth of useful information regarding cultivation, crop rotation, fertilizing and productive machinery was reënforced here as in England by time-honored routine and prejudice.[19]

Support for the American Revolution was recruited largely from the farms; the Tories were concentrated in the cities. Farmer-soldiers returning home after the War met deplorable agricultural conditions. In 1784 there were no specialized agencies of information or improvement, no agricultural journals, no agricultural societies. The farmers faced the task of helping to build the new nation, with ill-constructed buildings, inferior live stock and crude and inadequate machinery. As in England, the movement for agricultural improvement spread downward

---

[18] Gras, Norman Scott Brien, *A History of Agriculture in Europe and America*, New York, 1925, pp. 313 *et seq.*

[19] Poore, Benjamin Perley, "History of the Agriculture of the United States," Commissioner of Agriculture, *Report*, 1866, Washington, pp. 512 *et seq.*

from a group of national leaders — Washington, Jefferson, Randolph, John Adams and others. As the most traveled and best informed men of their times they were cognizant of the revolutionary changes taking place in English agriculture, and as great landowners they were anxious to effect the same improvements in America. Not only has Washington been called the father of his country, but also its first farmer. He corresponded with Arthur Young and Sir John Sinclair; he urged in his last annual message to Congress the establishment of a board of agriculture and the use of public financial aid for its work.[20] Jefferson envisaged an agricultural rather than an industrial nation, the virtues of whose people were to be the foundation of national greatness. Both he and John Adams conducted numerous experiments on their farms, Jefferson inventing a plow that won him a gold medal from the Agricultural Society of Paris.

The working farmers of America, like those of England, were handicapped by lack of equipment and incentive to improve their conditions, but these national leaders sought to transplant the agricultural revolution to the newly born nation. Prior to the Revolution there had been very little organized life among the colonial farmers. Every community, even every farm, was practically self-sufficing. Farmers were busy clearing the land and wringing a livelihood from the soil. With some exceptions there was little market for their produce; farming for profit was a matter of the future. Scattered on their individual homesteads the farmers had few common interests and little need for close association. Leadership for the improvement of American agriculture, therefore, devolved upon the large landholders. And they naturally seized upon much the same methods as were used by the gentlemen farmers of England in spreading the results

[20] Richardson, James D., *A Compilation of the Messages and Papers of the Presidents, 1789-1908*, 1909, I, 202.

of the new agriculture. In other words they resorted to the devices with which they were familiar — the formation of agricultural societies modeled after the British societies of that time.

The first American agricultural societies of any importance were organized at Philadelphia and at Charleston in 1785. The former numbered among its members George Washington, Timothy Pickering, of Massachusetts, who was a temporary resident of the city, Benjamin Franklin and other merchants, professional men and large landowners. The organization of these societies served as a model for others at Kennebec, Maine, at New York City and at Boston, until by 1800 there were perhaps a dozen scattered along the Atlantic seaboard.[21]

These first societies, with the exception perhaps of the Kennebec society, were decidedly learned in character. They were modeled not only after the English agricultural societies but also after the learned and philosophical societies then in existence. The American Philosophical Society had been founded in 1743 at Philadelphia. Franklin was its leading spirit, and it collected all the philosophical information of the Old World and discussed at its sessions all sorts of philosophical problems. Other societies of the same character were patterned after it, notably the American Academy of Arts and Sciences at Boston in 1780 and the Connecticut Academy of Arts and Sciences at New Haven in 1799. Since the agricultural societies depended for their leadership upon men who, through their travels, correspondence and learning, were familiar with the intellectual life of the time, it is not surprising that they should savor strongly of their learned forerunners. Their membership included merchants, lawyers, doctors, ministers and public men of all sorts, whose interest in agriculture was only one of many interests, and often one of minor importance. Not only did the membership fail to

21 Poore, *op. cit.*, pp. 513 *et seq.*

include the working farmers, but the methods employed by the societies to promote agriculture were such that they could rarely participate, if indeed, they had been able always to comprehend. The societies offered premiums for scientific experiments and discoveries, held meetings at which agricultural subjects were discussed and published their scientific transactions or memoirs. But the working farmers could muster scant enthusiasm for such erudite proceedings. The premiums offered were for the solution of general agricultural problems, not for itemized products which the farmers grew. For example, the Philadelphia Society for Promoting Agriculture offered in 1791 such premiums as the following:

> . . . a gold medal for the best essay, the result of experience, on the breeding, feeding, and management of cattle, for the purpose of rendering them most profitable for the dairy, and for beef, and most docile and useful for the draught; and for the next best — a silver medal.
>
> For the best comparative experiments on the culture of wheat, by sowing it in the common broad-cast way, by drilling it, and by setting the grain, with a machine, equi-distant; the quantities of seed and produce proportioned to the ground, being noticed — a gold medal; for the second best — a silver medal.
>
> For the greatest quantity of ground, not less than one acre, well fenced, producing locust trees, growing in 1791, from seed sown after April 5th, 1785; the trees to be of the sort used for posts and trunnels, and not fewer than 1500 per acre — a gold medal; for the second — a silver medal.[22]

The Massachusetts Society for Promoting Agriculture offered, among others, the following premiums in 1807:

> To the person who shall invent a cheap method of raising water, for the purpose of irrigating land from rivers and ponds from ten to twenty feet above the level of the same, and give evidence thereof to the satisfaction of the trustees, on or before January 1, 1808, *one hundred dollars*, or the society's gold medal.

[22] Philadelphia Society for Promoting Agriculture, *Memoirs*, Philadelphia, 1808, I, xxxi *et seq.*

To the person who shall present to this society the most complete (being nearly complete) Hortus Siccus, exhibiting distinct specimens of the greatest variety of grasses, in general use, and specify, to the satisfaction of the trustees, their respective qualities, productiveness and usefulness as food for different kinds of animals, the gold medal, and *fifty dollars*; to be claimed on or before the 1st of October, 1807.[23]

Such premiums were quite beyond the reach of the ordinary farmers, who had neither leisure nor equipment for undertaking the necessary experiments and who were apt to be suspicious of "book farming" anyway. This difficulty was intensified by the fact that there was little market for agricultural produce. The efforts of these learned agricultural societies to enlist interest in their theories and schemes for improvement seem, therefore, to have been largely wasted as far as working farmers were concerned. Their published works, however, preserve for us a body of useful contemporary agricultural literature, and their activities deserve recognition as the first attempts at agricultural experimentation and education in America.[24]

The attempt to popularize agricultural enthusiasm resulted finally in a gradual democratization of the societies and in the establishment of exhibitions in which the farmers could compete. At these exhibitions theoretic principles could be linked to practical exhibits in the hands of the men whom the agricultural leaders were anxious to reach; the exhibition became a nexus between theory and practice. Here the idea of improved products could be seen in the concrete illustrations of the exhibits, and the farmers' interests could be more easily enlisted because the problem was one of

[23] Massachusetts Society for Promoting Agriculture, *Papers*, Boston, 1806, pp. 7 *et seq.*
[24] Cf. Bidwell, Percy Wells, and John I. Falconer, *History of Agriculture in the Northern United States, 1620-1860*, Washington, 1925, pp. 184 *et seq.*; True, Rodney H., American Historical Association, *Annual Report*, 1920, *loc. cit.*

everyday reality. This is in fact the pattern of the agricultural fair as it developed in the nineteenth century, but there are a number of other threads that we must trace as the institution unfolds before us.

THE FAIR IN TRANSITION FROM SALE TO SHOW

Market fairs similar to those of medieval Europe were held in all the American colonies except Connecticut.[25] Considering them essential to the prosperity of towns and cities, early proprietors sometimes instituted these fairs; in 1686, for example, the first colonial assembly in New Jersey established a weekly market day and semiannual fairs.[26] They were gatherings to facilitate commerce where people came to exchange their live stock and other goods, and to indulge in various amusements, of which horse racing, rough "home-made" sports, and the shows of traveling performers and vendors are said to have been the most conspicuous. Courts of piepowder were often established; the colonists took advantage of the periodic gatherings to pay their debts, to obtain bills of exchange, and sometimes to buy land. These fairs seem, however, never to have attained the importance that they attained in Europe; many of them had already been abolished or abandoned by the time of the Revolution. In 1804 Dr. William Thornton, the first Commissioner of Patents, suggested that there be held at Washington a market fair for the sale of live stock and domestic products.[27] Acting upon this suggestion, the municipal authorities passed an act establishing semiannual fairs and three were held — in October, 1804, and in April and November, 1805. At the second fair "premiums to the amount of one hundred dollars were awarded to the best lamb, sheep, steer, milk cow, yoke

[25] Andrews, Charles M., *Colonial Folkways*, New Haven, 1919, pp. 120 *et seq.*
[26] Whitehead, William A., *Contributions to the Early History of Perth Amboy and Adjoining Country*, New York, 1856, p. 305.
[27] Poore, *op. cit.*, p. 516.

of oxen, and horse actually sold."[28] Here we see the competitive and exhibitive features strongly emphasized; the sale is becoming a show. That this feature assumed considerable importance in the eyes of the people may be seen in the fact that municipal authorities and private citizens were willing to contribute to the premium fund.

Just why these events were discontinued we do not know. But agricultural activity around Washington was stirred again in 1809 when a number of residents of Maryland, Virginia and the District of Columbia organized a so-called national society, the Columbian Agricultural Society, for the promotion of rural and domestic economy, and instituted a series of six semiannual fairs.[29] These fairs were again a combination of sale and show, but whereas the Washington fairs of 1804 and 1805 were sales where prizes were given for the live stock sold, the Columbian fairs were shows where the prize-winning live stock and produce might later be sold. Substantial prizes were offered at least at some of the fairs —from $60 for the best bull shown and $40 for the best piece of fulled and dressed woolen cloth to $10 for the best pair of fine woolen knit stockings and $15 for the best pair of stout coarse blankets for laborers. Interestingly enough, $30 was paid for the best pair of fine woolen blankets and the same amount for the best pair of fine cotton blankets. These fairs were visited by President Madison, members of the cabinet and other high government officials, who no doubt lent an air of dignity to the excitement and gaiety of the assembled crowds. The President, on one occasion, wore his homespun inauguration suit, and General John Mason, then United States Indian agent, a suit made from nankeen cotton grown on Analostan Island. The manufactured cloth, "exclusively domestic," emphasized the possibilities of

28 *Ibid.*, p. 517.
29 *Ibid.*, pp. 518 *et seq.*

complete American self-sufficiency in the production of woolen, cotton and linen goods. The sheep on exhibition were highly commended by both the visitors and the judging committee. The man "shearing a sheep in the neatest, safest and most expeditious manner" was awarded a prize. And at the spring fair in 1812 a field trial was held to determine the awards for the best three-horse plow, the best two-horse plow and the best weeding plow. The Columbian Society was submerged and finally dissolved in the confusion of the War of 1812, but the series of fairs which it conducted played an important part in the establishment of the agricultural fair on its modern basis.

Still a third type of event featured this period of transition — namely, sheepshearings. The annual sheepshearings held by Thomas Coke and the Duke of Bedford were the models for many similar gatherings in both England and America. George Washington Parke Custis, the adopted son of George Washington, inaugurated on his estate at Arlington about 1803 the famous Arlington sheepshearings, which became in the first decade of the nineteenth century the most popular rural festival in America. Custis, like many another of his contemporaries, conceived the encouragement of sheep raising as a patriotic duty. The determination to wear goods of domestic manufacture, an aspect of the nationalistic spirit of the time, soon made of sheep breeding a widespread mania. At the Arlington sheepshearings, Mr. Custis provided at his own expense prizes for the best sheep, wool and domestic manufactures exhibited by his neighbors and visitors. During the day the sheep were shorn; both wool and animals were carefully weighed and measured; the breeding of the sheep was discussed to determine what blood had produced the most desirable results. Sheepshearing contests were held, in which the most rapid workman, "a native American," be it noted, was given a prize. At the 1809 meeting, the family that had produced the greatest amount of wearing apparel of domestic manufacture and used the least of foreign importation was awarded the largest prize fleece; and the family proving that, to a given number of female children, the most were good spinners was given the second largest fleece.

Though they were devoted primarily to the promotion of the sheep industry, these events were important as gatherings of socially prominent people. The visitors were generously entertained. Arlington may have drunk no toasts to the King, as did Holkham and Woburn, but the memory of Washington lent color to these festivities held each year in the great war tent he had used on his campaigns in the Revolution. The host "called out" visitors from various parts of the country, and added to their responses anecdotes of Washington as well as reminiscences of his own childhood at Mount Vernon. Above all he never failed to make a speech advocating, among other things, the establishment of a national agricultural organization to be attached to a national university.[30]

Thus we see in the first quarter century following the close of the Revolution several series of steps in the stimulation of American agricultural improvement. First there was the recognition by the national leaders of the need of improving the general agricultural conditions of the country. This was followed by the founding of a number of learned agricultural societies, which because of their type of organization and extension methods were inherently unsuited to make a popular appeal to practical farmers. The awarding of prizes for competitive exhibits at the Washington municipal fairs, the Arlington sheepshearings and the Columbian Society fairs was a step toward the popularization of agri-

[30] Cf. Poore, *op. cit.*, pp. 517-18; Carman, Ezra A., H. A. Heath and John Minto, *Special Report on the History and Present Condition of the Sheep Industry of the United States*, Washington, 1892, pp. 59 *et seq.*

cultural improvement. At the Washington events, however, prizes though important were still incidental; at the Arlington and Columbian events the socially prominent visitors gave unmistakable evidences of their interest in social intercourse; from none had all the vestiges of the commercial market day disappeared. It remained for yet another gentleman farmer to establish an agricultural society that would appeal to the practical farmer, and that would excite him to emulative efforts. This gentleman farmer was none other than Elkanah Watson, and to him we shall now turn.

III

ELKANAH WATSON AND THE PRACTICAL SOCIETIES

THE agricultural fair as a distinctive institution owes its establishment in America to the work of Elkanah Watson more than to that of any other person. His was the perspicacity that evaluated the previous attempts at agricultural organization in terms of the fundamental human desires of his neighbors, as well as of the more general attitudes of the contemporary American population; his was the organizing genius that gave to these units of the social heritage distinctive direction in the social development of his day. Watson was endowed with certain well recognized characteristics of the leader and propagandist: inexhaustible energy, a more than ordinary dash of egotism, unflagging faith in the rightness and benefits of his schemes, a subtle understanding of human nature and an interest in multitudinous affairs that both guided his efforts and wrought for him a large measure of success. Social institutions, of course, are not cut from whole cloth; back of them lie the desires and attitudes and interests of human beings, factors that crystallize into ways of acting and into organized attempts at satisfaction. Furthermore, they are built upon the total experience of the human race and especially in their organized or associational aspects they are partly the result of the social heritage of those who have to do with their formation at any historical moment. The agricultural fair, therefore, as first established in America owed its birth, or rather its crystallization, to three factors: a social heritage consisting of various attempts at agricultural organization and gatherings to promote agricultural activity, a complex of desires, attitudes and interests that we may roughly

designate as the social temper of a historical period, and
finally the leader who, selecting from the total social situation certain factors of the social heritage and the social
temper, was able to give events a distinctive turn.

We have already traced the historical and social evolution
of certain significant factors of the social heritage. We have
seen how in religious festivals, commercial gatherings and
other concourses of human beings, the interest of social
intercourse looms large, though usually incidental to the
main purpose. We have seen how the agricultural revolution
gave rise to a new and widened interest in theoretic as well
as practical agricultural improvement, and how, in their
zeal for advancing this interest, groups of leaders both in
England and America formed associations which they
deemed responsive to their needs. Our task now is briefly
to place in its historical setting the social temper of the
American people at the time Elkanah Watson conceived his
idea, and then at more length to analyze this man's work in
the promotion of a distinctive type of agricultural society.

The Post-Revolutionary Zeal for Domestic Manufactures

In the half century from 1765 to 1815 the American
people, first as English colonists and then as American
citizens, found all their activities colored by their political
relations with England. From the passage of the Stamp Act
to the close of the War of 1812 American society in its
economic, political, literary and social aspects manifested
an accumulation of intense nationalistic sentiment. The
organization of the new American government, though of
course it drew strongly on English heritages, professed
outwardly at least a reaction to British political principles.
Likewise, American society, evolving under the constant
pressure of this spirit of nationalism, demanded the unification of the people and the integration of their social life.

This nationalistic social attitude dictated the acceptance or rejection of every kind of social relationship and activity — not completely of course, as evidenced by the defection of the Federalists before 1800 and of the New Englanders during the War of 1812, but generally, considering the period as a whole.

One of the most important manifestations of this attitude was the agitation for an independent American commerce and industry — an economic life that freed America from reliance upon British products and consequently upon some measure of British authority. This zeal for domestic manufacture was particularly intense in the case of cloth. Undoubtedly the agricultural fair owes more than is outwardly perceptible to this complex of nationalistic and economic factors which led certain men of the time so ardently to promote American cloth manufacture. Several facts give us the clue for verifying this connection. We have already seen that many of the events marking the transition of the means of stimulating agricultural improvement from the essentially philosophical discussions of the learned agricultural societies to the offering of prizes for specific, itemized products which the working farmer might exhibit, made large provision for the recognition of domestic manufactures. The agricultural interest of the Arlington sheepshearings aimed almost wholly at the promotion of the sheep industry and of domestic manufactures, particularly those of woolen goods. Likewise, the fairs of the Columbian Agricultural Society handsomely rewarded the exhibitors of domestic manufactures, and of the animals at these fairs sheep were by far the most prominent. Finally, as we shall see, it was the exhibition of two Merino sheep that apparently first gave Watson the idea of holding an annual agricultural exhibition and of organizing a particular type of society for its promotion. And Watson's interest in Merino sheep was directly due to his desire to insure a wool supply for his New England woolen mills.

Sheep raising in colonial America had been a precarious occupation. The sheep was the most perishable of domesticated animals in the neglected state of colonial agriculture, and the depredations of wild animals were scarcely less to be feared than the jealous machinations of British politicians. Influenced by the mercantilist doctrine, England in 1660 prohibited the export of sheep and wool, and in 1699 forbade the colonies to export wool or woolen goods to one another or to any other country.[1] The colonists at the beginning of the Revolution were still generally dependent on British woolens; they were wholly so in the case of the finer cloths, though the use of a considerable amount of coarse home-grown wool in household industry had helped the status of sheep raising earlier in the century. The hostility engendered by the Stamp Act and other restrictive measures marked, however, the beginning of a multitude of popular demonstrations in favor of domestic manufactures. Merchants agreed not to import British woolens; a few crude manufacturing plants were set up; women's patriotic organizations held all-day sessions in spinning; legislators, clergymen, college presidents and graduating classes made their public appearances proudly clad in homespun; patriotic citizens agreed to eat no lamb. At the outbreak of the Revolution both Continental Congress and colonial Assemblies took measures to increase the amount of manufacturing machinery and raw materials. The United Company for Promoting American Manufactures was organized in Philadelphia, and a butchers' association in the same city signed an agreement to slaughter no sheep.[2] The War tremendously increased the demand for home-grown

[1] Wright, Chester Whitney, *Wool-Growing and the Tariff*, Boston, 1910, p. 5.
[2] Cole, Arthur Harrison, *The American Wool Manufacture*, Cambridge, 1926, I, 61 *et seq.*

wool, the needs of the Continental Army creating a new demand at the same time that the British supply was all but completely cut off.[3]

The War undoubtedly had considerable influence upon domestic manufacture. The increase of manufacture and home industry which it necessitated reënforced the nationalistic spirit that cried so loudly for self-dependence, and this spirit, developed by the various aspects of the struggle, lingered on with the coming of peace, in spite of a number of serious hindrances to the immediate prosperous advance of American woolen manufacturing. In matters of machinery, raw material and labor England had the advantage of the United States, and American goods could, therefore, ill compete with the British product.[4] The inflow of British woolens in the last decade of the century helped to break, though it did not completely crush, the sentimental resistance to foreign goods. Again the American sheep industry languished. A few individuals, however, motivated probably by both patriotic and economic interests continued their efforts to increase the supply of American wool. But in spite of a few economic encouragements between 1784 and 1807, the advancement made in American woolen manufacture during these years was decidedly less the result of tariffs, profits and bounties than of the underlying spirit of nationalism. This sentiment could be given tangible form also; the wearing of homespun, for example, was heralded as a patriotic duty. The government tariff on woolens, starting at 5 percent in 1789, was raised steadily until it stood at 35 percent in 1812. Alexander Hamilton pronounced the home production and improvement of the breed of sheep the most effective aid to the manufacturing

[3] The value of exports of woolen goods from the United Kingdom to the colonies decreased from £925,643 in 1772 to £15,657 in 1776. Wright, *op. cit.*, p. 9.

[4] Cole, *op. cit.*, I, 65 *et seq.*

industry. The South Carolina Agricultural Society and the Massachusetts Agricultural Society had offered, the former in 1785, a premium for the establishment of the first flock of pure-bred Merino sheep in their respective states. The New York Society for the Promotion of Useful Arts had a set of instructions printed and sent to captains of vessels sailing to foreign ports, adjuring them to secure sheep of the Spanish or Barbary strains. Washington, by giving his flock his own personal attention, had made it one of the finest in the country, and it had been carried on by Mr. Custis after the founder's death.[5] Yet the value of fine-wooled sheep was so little realized that in 1793 a pair which had been tendered a Cambridge man as a gift he quite unwittingly slaughtered for mutton.[6]

Merino sheep, originally improved by the Moors during their occupation of Spain, historically have been the source of fine wool used in the manufacture of the finest woolen cloth. Attempting to maintain a practical monopoly over the breed, Spain prohibited the exportation of these sheep in the latter part of the eighteenth century, and the only way of securing specimens was by royal gift or by smuggling them out of the country. Small flocks had been established, however, in other European countries. Just at the turn of the century several small importations came to the United States. Du Pont de Nemours and M. Delessert succeeded in landing one ram lamb at New York in 1801, and in the same year Seth Adams was awarded the premium of the Massachusetts Society for Promoting Agriculture for bringing the first Merinos to that state. In 1802 Robert R. Livingston, United States minister to France, sent two pairs of Merinos to his New York estate. The first extensive introduction of these sheep into America occurred in the same year when

[5] *Ibid.*, pp. 72 *et seq.*; Wright, *op. cit.*, pp. 10 *et seq.*
[6] Carman, Heath and Minto, *op. cit.*, p. 133.

David Humphreys, United States minister to Spain, imported about one hundred head to his Connecticut estate. During his residence at Madrid, Humphreys had become well acquainted with some of the Spanish grandees who owned flocks of Merinos and with their shepherds, and though the Spanish law restricted the exportation of the sheep the American diplomat was given a special dispensation. Unfortunately, American farmers in general were not yet sufficiently interested to engage in the promotion of the Merino type. Consequently these early importations found their way almost entirely to the estates of gentlemen farmers. Both Humphreys and Livingston voiced their disappointment, but did not give up their efforts to improve American sheep. So intense was Livingston's interest that he started out to collect the scattered remnants of the flock bred from the Delessert ram, paying for them prices that probably shocked their owners into some realization of their worth.[7]

The year 1807 saw the reintroduction of an effective economic stimulus into domestic manufacturing in America. The progress made between 1784 and 1807 was the work of a few vitally interested men for whom the nationalistic and economic interests latent in all the population had become more clearly defined. By 1807 western Europe was in the throes of the Napoleonic conflict, and America's world trade, buffeted back and forth among British orders and French decrees and American embargoes, was threatened with total paralysis. Wright estimates that American imports of foreign woolens decreased by one-half.[8] American woolen manufacture, protected by a 17.5 percent tariff and enjoying now the prohibition of both raw materials and manufactured articles, grew by leaps and bounds. Dozens of woolen factories sprang up; men like Humphreys, Livingston and Du Pont, prominent in introducing the fine-

[7] *Ibid., passim.*   [8] *Op. cit.,* p. 17.

wooled sheep, began building woolen mills.[9] Prices of Merino wool soared. Much of the pure-bred product sold for two dollars a pound; some is reported to have sold for as much as $2.75 a pound. The sheep themselves became the object of an insane fad, the "Merino craze." Humphreys is reported to have sold four head for $6,000; many a ram sold at $1,000. Farms for sale were advertised as peculiarly adapted to the raising of Merino sheep; ships, cattle, new varieties of potatoes and even children were named Merino; [10] public opinion forced everyone to wear clothes of American manufacture. Merinos were relatively scarce in America, and under the prevailing economic stimulus the thing to do was to increase the number of these precious animals as rapidly as possible. The opportunity was soon at hand.

The armies of Napoleon Bonaparte were at this time invading Spain, confiscating all property they could lay hold of and living off the land as was their wont. The Spanish nobles and the Junta then in control of the government were willing to disperse their great Merino flocks in order to avoid their destruction by the invaders or to raise money for the prosecution of the war. Taking advantage of the Spanish extremity, the American consul at Lisbon, William Jarvis, landed forty-five head of these sheep at Boston on April 13, 1810. Eleven of them sold for nearly $1,000 a head. In the next few months Jarvis shipped about 4,000 head to America, and between April 1, 1810, and August 31, 1811, it is estimated, nearly 20,000 Merinos were brought to the United States.[11]

These unwarranted values of course could not endure. The tremendous increase in the number of sheep and a new influx of British goods following the War of 1812 with its

9 *Ibid.*, p. 17.   10 Carman, Heath and Minto, *op. cit.*, p. 171.
11 *Ibid., passim.*

consequent collapse of American woolen manufacture, conspired to precipitate an abrupt deflation. Merinos were soon despised as keenly as they had been sought; and many of their bankrupt and disappointed owners slaughtered them or sold them in a disgust quite as unfounded as their earlier adoration.

Incidentally the Merino craze furnishes rich material for an analysis of the herd spirit in human beings, but it is not within our province to discuss it here. It is significant in the present connection as the spectacular culmination of the post-Revolutionary enthusiasm for domestic manufactures. As has already been pointed out, the prizes offered at the sheepshearings and fairs of the time witnessed attempts of public men to promote American industry; and the agricultural fair finally took shape in the hands of Elkanah Watson, who was interested at first in promoting the breeding of fine-wooled sheep. This spirit of nationalism was the outward social attitude of the American people, though it rested upon more deep-seated desires, which the agricultural fair helped to satisfy.

ELKANAH WATSON AND THE BERKSHIRE SOCIETY

Elkanah Watson was, in 1807, a rich Albany business man and banker, who after having apparently exhausted all other prospects for adventure, found himself ready to engage in farming. He had had a wide variety of personal interests and had engaged in an almost unbelievably large number of hobbies, travels, promotion schemes and business enterprises.[12] At the age of twenty, as one of his biographers suggests, he probably had seen as much of America as anyone of his time. That was in 1778. In the following years he traveled and engaged in business in Europe. He became

[12] Cf. Pound, Arthur, *Native Stock*, New York, 1931, Chap. on "Elkanah Watson," pp. 197-267.

a patron of the arts, a philanthropist and a student of foreign languages. Upon his return to America in 1784 he began to rebuild the fortune he had made, and lost in European business ventures, and to promote a number of internal improvements — schools, turnpike roads and especially canals. He had finally settled at Albany to engage in business and banking, but in 1807 his zeal for new enterprises led him to purchase an estate near Pittsfield, Massachusetts.

> ... I was induced, [he says,] at the age of fifty, to hazard my own, and my family's happiness, on the experiment of seeking *"rural felicity,"* — a life I had for twenty years sighed to enjoy; my only mistake was, I commenced too late. In consequence, I soon found my error, — my habits being settled for city life: to retreat was impossible, — to labour in person, *was impossible.* To fill up the void in an active mind, led me first to conceive the idea of an Agricultural Society on a plan different from all others.[13]

By virtue of his numerous travels and his variety of interests, Watson had become acquainted with most of the public men of his day. He had held no public office himself (he was not even a Revolutionary War veteran), but the intense nationalism of the post-Revolutionary period burned in him as fiercely as in any of his contemporaries. No one was more interested than he in seeing his country independent of foreign commercial dominance; no one spoke more loudly in favor of internal improvements and domestic manufacture. Upon his removal to Pittsfield he engaged in woolen manufacture and shrewdly sought to improve the quality of his raw material by extending the production of Merino sheep in the surrounding country. Only a few months after he had taken up farming he secured from Livingston a pair of the prized Merinos, the first to be brought to the Berkshire country. Though Watson was somewhat disappointed in them, he and everyone else who examined their wool "were

[13] Watson, Elkanah, *History of Agricultural Societies on the Modern Berkshire System*, Albany, 1820, p. 115.

delighted with its texture and fineness." [14] Always a shrewd promoter, Watson now sought ways of interesting his neighbors in the extension of Merinos, which he considered invaluable, "especially in the hilly countries of New England." [15] Hence it was that soon after he procured the sheep he exhibited them on the public square in Pittsfield, a display that, to accept his own account, gave him the idea of creating a new kind of agricultural society.

Many farmers, and even women, were excited by curiosity to attend this first novel, and humble exhibition. It was by this lucky accident, I reasoned thus, — If two animals are capable of exciting so much attention, what would be the effect on a larger scale, with larger animals? The farmers present responded to my remarks with approbation. — We became acquainted, by this little incident; and from that moment, to the present, agricultural societies, cattle shows, and all in connexion therewith, have predominated in my mind, greatly to the injury of my private affairs.[16]

The next three years Watson spent in advocating the spread of Merino sheep, stocking his farm with improved cattle and swine (and even his pond with fish) and trying to arouse the farmers' interest in his proposed agricultural society "different from all others." By the fall of 1810 he had succeeded in getting twenty-six of his neighbors to sign an "appeal to the public" announcing the Berkshire Cattle Show. Unfortunately Watson does not enumerate the exhibits; we do not know whether the name "cattle show" is a literal description or not. At any rate the live-stock display was the important feature. There was some hesitation on the part of the farmers. They "held back their animals in the vicinity," wrote Watson later, "for fear of being laughed at, which compelled me to lead the way with several prime animals." [17] After a committee had been appointed to arrange for the next annual show, Watson

14 Ibid., p. 116.   15 Ibid., p. 116.   16 Ibid., p. 116.
17 Ibid., p. 119 n.

headed a procession of farmers who marched around the square. As they separated he "stepped in front, gave three cheers, in which they all united"; and then they parted "well pleased with the day, and with each other." [18]

There is evidence in this event of the molding of an institution by the leadership of an enthusiastic promoter. The interest had been supplied, popular support, though perhaps still weak, had been enlisted and certain distinctive activities had been engaged in. The next step was the formation of an association to give the activities cohesion and to insure their perpetuation and to secure further popular support. This was accomplished in 1811 with the incorporation of the Berkshire Agricultural Society. The second annual cattle show was held under the egis of this organization. The event this time followed much the same pattern as that set by the first, yet the institution of the agricultural fair became considerably clearer and more definite.[19] For the first time prizes were offered — $70 for the best live stock. This cattle show was therefore not only a display, but a competitive display. At this second show, too, we have the introduction of the annual address, a feature that characterized the fair for many years to come. Watson himself made the address, emphasizing the necessity of the patriotic cohesion of the people, comparing the state of agriculture in Berkshire with that in England and other foreign countries and eulogizing the virtues of his society to work good in the land. Finally there was another procession, much enlarged over the previous one and eminently successful. Watson was a good showman. Having prepared two hundred wheat cockades — two heads of wheat tied with a pack thread for members and three heads tied with a green ribbon for officers — he distributed them to the marchers in order that they might decorate their hats. Sixty yoke of oxen drew a plow

18 *Ibid.*, p. 119.   19 *Ibid.*, pp. 120 *et seq.*

held by two of the oldest men in the county. A stage-coach filled with American manufactures, and another carrying a broadcloth loom and a spinning jenny both operated by English artisans added color and significance to the event. Mechanics carrying an "appropriate flag" marched along; a band furnished music, and four marshals headed by the sheriff and mounted on gray horses conducted the half-mile procession.

The third and fourth Berkshire exhibitions grew both by elaboration of old features and by addition of new ones.[20] The 1812 show was marked by a three-fold increase in the amount awarded in prizes, $50 going to Watson for the "best piece of superfine broadcloth," and $150 for live stock. In 1813, seventeen prizes were awarded to agriculture, fifteen to women's domestic manufactures, eleven to men's domestic manufactures and twenty to live stock. But not only was the prize list expanding. At the 1812 show Watson, convinced of the appropriateness of acknowledging divine blessings and believing incidentally "that this measure would tend to give popularity to the society, among the graver class of the community," persuaded one of the reticent clergy to preface the annual address and the public announcement of prizes with what proved to be "an animated, pastoral prayer." [21] And the next year Watson induced the young men of the community to plan a grand agricultural ball to close the exhibition. ". . . Many farmers' daughters graced the floor" and "the officers of the society, and many respectable visitors, attended to give countenance to the measure." [22] Before the women would participate whole-heartedly in these shows, Watson found it necessary to hold a special exhibition for domestic manufactures. A large display was produced on the appointed day in the winter of 1813, but no women appeared to claim their prizes until Watson went home for

[20] *Ibid., passim.*   [21] *Ibid.*, p. 125.   [22] *Ibid.*, pp. 131-32.

his wife, brought her to the exhibition hall and then sent messengers to tell the other women of the village that she waited for them. His efforts were successful, and when the women had assembled he made one of his inevitable addresses and proceeded to the public announcement and the awarding of the prizes.

The Berkshire Agricultural Society was the prototype of the so-called practical agricultural societies, or those organized on the Berkshire plan. The chief differences between them and the earlier learned agricultural societies lay in their membership and in their methods of encouraging agricultural improvement. Working farmers could become members of the Berkshire societies upon the payment of small annual dues, in return for which they received a certificate of membership. The greatest difference, however, was that the Berkshire societies held an annual cattle show, or as it came to be known later, agricultural fair, and relied on this institution and the interest aroused and prizes awarded at it, to encourage agriculture. The plan of these fairs was no doubt subjected to local modifications, but in general the fairs consisted of a competitive display of live stock, agricultural products and domestic manufactures, for the best specimens of which prizes of money or silver plate were awarded and certified by elaborate certificates. At the earlier fairs prayers were usually offered by a local minister, pastoral odes were sung by a choir, and the annual address was delivered by some man of prominence. Various other features were introduced, the most common of which were parades and plowing matches; and the fairs usually closed with a grand agricultural ball. These were the principal features of the institution as adopted by Watson and recommended by him as the Berkshire system. His scheme for popularizing agricultural improvement sought first to arouse the attention and emulation of the whole body of farmers.

That task accomplished by contests, addresses and festivities, Watson believed that farmers would turn naturally to more scientific endeavor in which books and experiments would play an important part.

For fifteen years after the organization of the Berkshire Agricultural Society, other societies modeled on this plan sprang up rapidly. Watson sold his farm and in 1816 returned to Albany, but he continued to labor indefatigably to establish a society in every county. To this end he sent pamphlets explaining and extolling his plan to the prominent agriculturists, governors and other public men in the whole nation. He himself made visits and addresses in behalf of the movement. The result was gratifying for not only did he succeed in spreading his societies over a great part of New York and New England but to many parts of the South and West. He had witnessed the comparative failure of the early learned agricultural societies to enlist the interest of the working farmers. Though he as well as the founders of the old societies could be classed as a gentleman farmer, he gave to his activities such a practical turn, made his appeal so broad, and enlisted the coöperation of the working farmers so completely that by comparison his work marks the definite creation of a new type of agricultural organization. He contrasted the European and the early American societies with his own with due deference to the good that the former had wrought, but he showed himself fully aware of the defects of their methods in making effective appeals to the working farmers. He diagnosed the failure of their leaders, "scientific and literary gentlemen, moving within the walks of *classic ground*," as due to the fact that they did not utilize American habits and did not take into account the state of contemporary American society. He realized that the American population was young and scattered, and that the common American farmer was "just beginning to lisp," to use his own phrase, "those fascinating words" botany, chemistry and agricultural science. "The great object with us, . . ." he wrote, "is to contemplate society in its actual state of existence, — not as we could wish it. . . ." [23] He sought a more intimate way of reaching the common farmers than by pamphlets, dissertations, memoirs and grandiose premiums. He sought to reach their underlying desires — as he puts it, "to seize upon the human heart." [24] He knew the motivating power of competitive emulation, of personal ambition, personal interest and personal pride, and at the same time he placed their rewards within the reach of those whom he sought to influence. Gradually the older societies, too, became more democratic and began using the annual exhibitions as a means to disseminate their information and to arouse the common farmer. In 1812 Watson wrote to John Adams, then president of the old Massachusetts Society for Promoting Agriculture, soliciting aid from its unused premium fund.[25] He received a scorching reply: "You will get no aid from Boston, — commerce, literature, theology, are all against *you*; nay, medicine, history, and university, and universal politics might be added. — I cannot, I will not be more explicit." [26] But four years later when the Massachusetts society adopted the plan of holding an exhibition and cattle show, John Lowell was magnanimous enough to acknowledge in his address to the society their indebtedness to the Berkshire system,[27] and Adams himself in a subsequent letter to Watson stated that his curt remarks had been influenced by the belief that his society should institute public exhibitions of their own.[28]

[23] *Ibid.*, p. 178.   [24] *Ibid.*, p. 160.
[25] It often happened that the premiums offered by the learned societies lay unclaimed for years, so difficult was it for the farmers to meet their conditions.
[26] Quoted, *ibid.*, p. 133.   [27] *Ibid.*, p. 179.
[28] Watson, Elkanah, *Men and Times of the Revolution*, New York, 1857, p. 499.

for personal prestige was fully reflected upon the background of public approval. The cereal farmer, the live-stock fancier, the women, all shared in the awarding of prizes and the public attention paid to them. The sanction of the clergy and "the graver class of the community" blessed these events — often with the spirit of thanksgiving for the bountiful harvest. The agricultural balls must have been gala occasions for the young people and undoubtedly won Watson many an enthusiastic acclaimer. All these activities recognized "the windings of the human heart," to the tracing of which Watson attributed his success.

Certainly few men succeed as Watson did in stamping an institution with lasting characteristics. He completed the transition of agricultural gatherings of this type to a basis of competitive display. He so zealously propagated his type of society and the annual exhibition which it sponsored that he is justly named "the father of the agricultural fair."

The monument erected over his grave bore the inscription: [32]

HERE LIE THE REMAINS

O F

ELKANAH WATSON,
The Founder and First President of

THE BERKSHIRE AGRICULTURAL SOCIETY.

MAY GENERATIONS YET UNBORN
Learn by his Example
TO LOVE THEIR COUNTRY.

The Decline of Agricultural Organization in the 1820's

The movement set on foot by Watson proved, however, to be a mushroom growth. It is impossible to know the

[32] *Men and Times,* p. 527.

number of societies founded on the Berkshire plan, but Watson aided personally in the organization of numerous associations in New York and New England, and by his correspondence and propagandist activities stimulated the formation of others over the entire country. Accepting his own account, we may assume that in 1819 all the counties of the New England states with the exception of those of Rhode Island had organized societies. The movement was also spreading rapidly in North Carolina, Virginia, Maryland, Kentucky, Ohio and Illinois. In Pennsylvania and South Carolina it was just commencing. And Watson with his unquenchable enthusiasm was hopeful of the future.[33]

Yet he admitted that the struggle had not been altogether easy. The question of ways and means had intruded itself vigorously, as it usually does in most movements of this kind. Time and again Watson was repulsed in his efforts to secure public funds for his society, to establish a state board of agriculture or enlist the support of public men. The question of state aid was one that had to be settled affirmatively if agricultural societies were to be established on a large scale. Many of the members of the New York legislature "appeared to approach it with loathing"[34] and, though $10,000 was granted by this body in 1819 for the work of the agricultural societies, the agitation for a state board of agriculture was dropped by its advocates till a more auspicious time. The period of low prices following the War of 1812 seems to have effected a temporary increase in the number and membership of the practical societies. Bidwell and Falconer suggest[35] that the farmers turned to the societies with the vague hope that somehow they could find economic relief through them. Instead they

---

[33] *History of Agricultural Societies*, p. 180.
[34] *Ibid.*, p. 161.
[35] *History of Agriculture in the Northern United States, 1620-1860*, Washington, 1925, pp. 191 *et seq.*

found only ideas of raising more and better crops and fatter
live stock. Prizes still were awarded without regard to cost
of production. And it was still the gentlemen farmers who
benefited most from the societies. Many of the working
farmers turned away in disappointment and perhaps disgust.
Though Watson's plan made a direct appeal to the interests
of the practical farmers, and compared to that of the earlier
learned societies achieved remarkable success, it admittedly
depended upon the support of a small group of public-
spirited men in each community. In 1820 the farmers were
still, generally speaking, without a market, and the appeal
for greater production and higher quality was still, as in
colonial times, a matter that did not greatly excite them.

The first wave of the formation of societies on the Berkshire plan reached its crest in the period from 1820 to 1825.
In 1822 New Hampshire discontinued the state aid that it
had granted in 1817, and in a few years all its societies had
disappeared. A wholesale collapse of the movement in New
York followed the withdrawal of state funds, and in 1830
only one society still survived. Most of the societies in Pennsylvania and Connecticut disbanded after 1825, and though
state aid was not wholly withdrawn in Massachusetts no
new societies were formed in that state between 1823 and
1839. The decade of the thirties witnessed some revival of
interest, but on the whole agricultural organization remained
on a generally low level. Maine and Ohio, for example,
granted state aid early in the decade to societies formed
within their borders, and a state agricultural society, organized in New York in 1832, made sporadic and largely
unsuccessful attempts to hold state fairs. Not until 1840
did agricultural interest, both public and private, give unmistakable signs of a revival of the industry, but the next
decade, as we shall see, ushered in a new period of agricultural expansion.

IV

THE GOLDEN AGE AND AFTER

NEVER before in human history had the common man achieved the social status that was his in mid-nineteenth-century America. Land and natural resources appeared limitless. Farming as an occupation, therefore, quickly shed its peasant tradition on the one hand and its baronial-landlord tradition on the other; and the farmer attained to a place of middle-class prominence. He became a man of property, and his psychology began to reflect the implications of that status. The laborer, likewise, enjoyed a uniquely favorable position. Whether he chose the field of urban industry or that of pioneer settlement, he had little difficulty in finding more opportunities than he could avail himself of. The nation became a great farmer-mechanic democracy, its people possessing an economic status, political powers, educational opportunities, and qualities of independence, ambition and individualism quite novel in the history of the world.

THE SETTING FOR THE GOLDEN AGE

It is with certain qualifications that a specific date is chosen as the beginning of any new era of social history. An evolutionary analysis warns the student against the division of historical and social development into rigidly fixed periods. Nevertheless, the year 1840 revealed a number of important trends in American agriculture, and marked the approximate date of a number of specific events significant in the evolution of agricultural organization.

We have already noted that after the peak reached in the period from 1820 to 1825, agricultural organization fell into a rapid decline, and throughout the decade of the thirties remained generally inconspicuous. Here and there of course notable efforts were made to keep the movement alive or to inject new vigor into it. In other respects, too, the period is not entirely without significance for an evolutionary analysis of the agricultural fair. Agricultural associations began to differentiate. Public concern for agricultural improvement increased rapidly. State-wide agricultural organization on the Berkshire plan began to emerge.

For the half century following 1840 American agriculture enjoyed an unprecedented period of expansion. It was of course only a phase of the general national expansion taking place throughout the country, stimulating intellectual activity no less than technological advancement and rewarding all with material prosperity. Early in the period classical studies began to feel the pressure of interest in science. The discoveries of Liebig, first announced in 1840, heralded the rôle soon to be played by chemistry and other sciences in scientific agricultural experimentation. Popular works on science prepared the way for great benefits in its application, and the prospects of new scientific inventions increased the popular interest. The rapidity with which lines of steam transportation and telegraphic communication were thrown across the country evidenced something of the energy with which vast areas of the national domain were opened to settlement and exploitation, as well as being expressive of closer social cohesion of the people and the diffusion over wider areas of their social possessions. All these activities accelerated agricultural expansion and reverberated in agricultural organization.

The prevailing need of the expanding agricultural economy was information regarding live stock, crops, machinery and other agricultural matters, a need which, as we shall see, was filled by the agricultural fair, with its educational emphasis, more completely than by any other agency. The problem was again how to grow more and better products; for it must be remembered that the twenty years preceding the Civil War witnessed an expending market for farm products as well as the development of numerous means which enabled farmers to supply that market.[1] The Northeast, especially New England, was becoming more and more industrialized. Here an increasing population was becoming more urbanized, thereby widening the domestic market for agricultural products from the West. At first of course, the competition of western products was resented in the East, but in the readjustments necessitated in eastern agriculture, the eastern farmer was driven more and more to specialization or to the abandonment of his rocky and exhausted soil to seek for himself the richer and more fertile lands of the West. At the same time numerous events transpired in Europe to increase the foreign market for agricultural products. American grain and other foodstuffs were allowed to enter England free of duty after the repeal of the corn laws in 1846. For the previous three-quarters of a century England had turned definitely toward industrialization and her population had increased enormously. The Irish potato famine of 1846 had two significant results for the American agricultural market: it impelled the importation of great quantities of food into Ireland and it sent tens of thousands of Irish immigrants to the cities of the American East.[2] The European revolutions of 1848 and the Crimean War of 1854 increased the dependence of European countries upon American food supplies. By 1845 the prices of western wheat, corn, pork and beef had already swung into an upward trend, and the discovery of gold in California a few

[1] Carver, Thomas Nixon, *Principles of Rural Economics*, Boston, c. 1911, pp. 84 *et seq.*; Bidwell and Falconer, *op. cit., passim.*

[2] During the eight years from 1847 to 1854 Irish immigrants coming into the United States averaged more than 148,000 a year. Cf. Stephenson, George M., *A History of American Immigration, 1820-1924*, Boston, c. 1926, Chaps. V-XI.

years later further stimulated the rising prices. The American farmer feasted as never before at prosperity's table.

At the same time the means were being made more available for the farmers to bring the West rapidly to productivity and to meet the enlarging demand for their products. The passage of a general preëmption act in 1841 inaugurated a period of twenty years during which the number of actual settlers steadily increased on the easily settled and immediately cultivatable prairies of the Upper Mississippi Valley. Though land was abundant, labor was comparatively scarce and high-priced. Hence the mad scramble to secure labor-saving machinery that would enable the farmer quickly to bring large areas under cultivation. By 1840 it was pretty generally the cast-iron plow that turned the prairie sod, in spite of the frequent objection that iron poisoned the soil. In 1837 John Deere made the first steel plow from an old saw blade. William Manning had patented a mowing machine in 1831, and Obed Hussey and Cyrus H. McCormick soon afterward took out patents on reapers, the former in 1833 and the latter in 1834. By 1845 threshing machines that threshed and separated the grain were in common use in wheat-growing sections, and after 1850 corn planters and cultivators tremendously extended the farmer's ability to raise corn. Improved live stock also received its share of attention. The Ohio Importing Company made importations of Shorthorn cattle in 1834, 1835 and 1836, the most important step in the introduction of improved cattle up to that time; and there were improvements in numerous other breeds of cattle and horses.

The introduction of labor-saving machinery and improved live stock was not the most important factor, however, in the expansion of American agriculture. In opening up new territories to settlement, in providing the means of sending produce to market and in breaking down the traditional self-sufficient agriculture, the leading rôle was played by the agencies of transportation and communication. The canal-building period prior to 1840, important though it was, was completely overshadowed by the railroad-building period that followed and by the advent of cheap ocean transportation. From some 2,000 miles of railroad in 1840 the network of steel tracks grew to some 30,000 miles by 1860. Railroads were regarded with great favor by the western pioneers; millions of acres of public lands were granted to the railroads in order to insure the blessings they were able to bestow. How railway promoters and operators financially fleeced the farmer need not concern us here; but that they were the predominant factor in the expansion of American agriculture after 1840 there can be no doubt. They enabled the farmer to become a specialist; they carried to him his live stock and his machinery; most important of all, they allowed him to send his products to market and to exchange them for the manufactured goods of the industrial centers. The railroads, moreover, enabled the farmer to learn of the new things in agriculture; current ideas reached him with increasing ease; he could organize in larger and more far-reaching groups, he could indulge his predilection for travel by taking the train to the multiplying fairs and conventions.

A number of specific events help to justify, so far as such a procedure is permissible, the use of the year 1840 to mark a revival of agricultural interest. Most of the agricultural societies had either disbanded or were struggling along haltingly after 1825. But in response to state aid granted by Maine in 1832 and by Ohio in 1833, six and fifteen county societies respectively, had been organized in these states by 1840.[3] Massachusetts and Maine revived, toward the end of the same decade, the old policy of appropriating public

[3] Bidwell and Falconer, *op. cit.*, pp. 189 *et seq.*

funds for bounties on certain crops, such as wheat, corn and raw silk, which it was deemed wise to encourage as a part of the agricultural economy of the state. Ill-advised and ineffective as these bounties were, they served nevertheless to stimulate the renewed attempts of state governments to aid the agriculture of New England.[4] In New York, too, a legislative grant of $40,000 in 1841 precipitated a rapid increase in the number of local agricultural societies. By the close of the year the state had thirty-two county societies, a number which a year later had increased to forty-two.[5] These were the opening lines of the great drama of agricultural organization that was to be played against the background of prosperous agricultural expansion from 1840 to 1870.

A second mark of agricultural revival was the appropriation in 1839 of the first Federal funds for the promotion of the industry. An alarming exhaustion of the soil in all the Atlantic seaboard states, augmented by general crop failures in the years 1837 and 1838 and necessitating the importation of large quantities of foodstuffs, aroused the apprehension of many public men. Among them was Henry L. Ellsworth, the Commissioner of Patents, at whose suggestion Congress appropriated $1,000 in 1839 to be expended by the Patent Office for "the collection of agricultural statistics, investigations for promoting agriculture and rural economy, and the procurement of cuttings and seeds for gratuitous distribution among the farmers. . . ."[6] The appropriation was not made in 1840 or 1841 but was renewed in 1842. In 1843 and 1844 it was raised to $2,000 a year, in 1845 to $3,000; following another lapse in 1846 it was made regularly and gradually increased in accordance with the work to be undertaken. The first Federal agricultural report, though a meager document

[4] *Ibid.*, p. 193.   [5] *Ibid.*, p. 317.
[6] Commissioner of Patents, *Report*, 1857, *Agriculture*, Washington, p. 24.

of fifty-four pages, marks a significant point in the development of agricultural organization in the United States.

A third important event of this period was the convening of a national agricultural convention in Washington in 1841. This convention, attended by the leading agriculturists of the day was prompted by the desire to secure for agricultural purposes the fund bequeathed to the United States in 1826 by James Smithson to found an institution for the "increase and diffusion of knowledge among men." The agricultural leaders, however, failed to secure this fund, Congress establishing instead the Smithsonian Institution in 1846. The more permanent organization of a national agricultural society awaited a second effort in 1852.[7]

Still another event of 1841 may be cited, indicating agricultural revival and the accompanying evolution of agricultural organization. This was the holding of the first state fair worthy of the name. It resulted directly from the reorganization of the New York Agricultural Society earlier in the same year. This society, which attempted to embrace the agriculturists of the entire state, was first organized in 1832 "at a time when there was in the state of New York absolutely no other organization devoting itself to the interests of farming and rural life."[8] It made little progress, however, because of the feeble response accorded it by the public. It appears to have sponsored several minor exhibitions between 1834 and 1841, but they attracted so little attention that they were not even recorded in the society's printed records. The executive committee, meeting in Albany in February, 1841, reorganized the society, revised the constitution, put in force a system of annual dues with life membership privileges rated at $50, passed a resolution providing for the holding of the fair at Syracuse in

[7] Cf. Poore, *op. cit.*, p. 525.
[8] "The New York State Agricultural Society," New York State Department of Farms and Markets, *Bulletin 161*, Albany, 1924, p. 5.

THE GRANDSTAND AT THE ROCKVILLE FAIR

MARYLAND

September and prepared a memorial to the legislature asking for appropriations to aid in the promotion of agriculture.[9]

The question of the adjustment of public and private
agricultural interests had arisen, therefore, before 1840.
People come into a fuller realization of their own organic
and psychic desires and a fuller participation in society's
affairs through countless modes of associated effort corre-
sponding to the countless varieties of human interests. These
associated efforts may, for our immediate purposes, be
divided into the voluntary and the compulsory, the private
and the public. Early agricultural interests in America were
served, through the private or voluntary efforts of men who
either out of personal interest or from their conception of
public welfare united to attain certain ends. But as American
social organization became more complex many agricultural
interests became so general or so important that they could
be served completely only by public or compulsory organization utilizing the authority and the resources of the state.
Private organizations early began to solicit public support,
seeking to transfer certain functions to governmental authority and to secure the indirect support of all the people by
exacting governmental privileges and aid. Since the state
is the only all-inclusive association in society and the only
one vested with the power of compulsory action, its sanction,
authority and purse were the objects of appeal by the pro-
ponents of agricultural interests.[10]

[9] Another state agricultural society was organized at New Brunswick, New
Jersey, in 1839, and in 1841 it, too, held its first fair. The New Jersey state
society was not so fortunate as the New York state society, however, in securing a subsidy from the state and it apparently did not long survive. It was
not until 1855 that a permanent series of annual state fairs was inaugurated
in New Jersey. Woodward, Carl R., "Odd Bits of Agricultural History;
Early Fairs of State Agricultural Society," New Jersey Agriculture, Oct.,
1931, p. 15.
[10] Cf. Wiest, Edward, Agricultural Organization in the United States, Lexington, 1923, Chap. I.

A few minor grants of public aid were made by the colonial legislatures for the promotion of certain branches of colonial agriculture — notably silk, hops, indigo, hemp, lumber, pitch, tar and sheep. Washington advocated the creation of a national board of agriculture, a body that would have been in large measure at least a public agency. The increasing appropriation of public funds to private agricultural societies and the creation by certain states of state boards of agriculture, made up usually of delegates from the county agricultural societies, characterized the early period of transition in which many of the functions of agricultural organization were transferred from private to public hands. In 1820, the New Hampshire legislature created a state board of agriculture consisting of the president of each county society and one other delegate from each. A high mortality of the local societies followed the withdrawal of state aid in 1822, however, and with their demise the state board of agriculture became extinct.[11] In New York, too, a state board of agriculture had existed between 1820 and 1826, taking the place, in fact, in the year of its creation, of the old state agricultural society. Between 1826 and 1832 there was no state-wide agricultural agency at all in New York, and not until the action of the New York legislature in 1841 [12] was public support again secured for agricultural activities.[13] These boards of agriculture were semipublic bodies usually composed of representatives of the local agricultural societies to which the state had delegated certain administrative functions of an agricultural nature. In later years the functions of agricultural organizations have multiplied tremendously and have been performed by countless other agencies: by public agencies such as agricul-

[11] "History of Our Rural Organizations," Commissioner of Agriculture, *Report*, 1875, Washington, pp. 455 *et seq.*
[12] Cf. *supra*, p. 77.
[13] Commissioner of Agriculture, *Report*, 1875, *op. cit.*, pp. 456 *et seq.*

tural schools, agricultural extension services and departments of agriculture, state and national; and by new private agencies such as breed associations, coöperative marketing and buying associations and numerous political and social groups that have come into being to serve new agricultural interests.

Throughout the middle part of the nineteenth century, however, agricultural organization remained essentially private. Public support when given was for the most part in the form of grants of public funds for promoting the work of the voluntary societies. After 1840 hundreds of state and local associations sprang to life, at once reflecting the expansion of American agriculture and constituting important agencies in its development. This was especially true after 1850. So rapid was their increase and so widespread their distribution that Kenyon L. Butterfield has been prompted to designate the period from 1850 to 1870 as "the golden age of the agricultural fair." [14] The golden age flourished against a background of material prosperity — a rich national domain, an intense enthusiasm for new machinery, new crops and new breeds of live stock, an expanding market. It was ushered in by a revival of interest in private agricultural organization and an increasing provision of public support by state and national governments.

The agricultural societies were the predominant form of association among American farmers of the middle nineteenth century. They were therefore the chief medium for the formation and expression of rural opinion and the conservation of rural interests. The period was one in which the farmers of the Middle West especially became the arch disciples of rugged individualism. The vast expanses of fertile soil invited the pioneers to bring the region into

[14] "Farmers' Social Organizations," Bailey, L. H., (ed.), *Cyclopedia of American Agriculture*, New York, 1909, IV, 292.

cultivation at once and to build a great agricultural and industrial civilization. Whatever stayed their hands they resented with hearty impatience; whatever new ideas, tools, equipment or agency made for the expansion of the national domain or for its more rapid settlement and cultivation they seized upon avidly. A rapidly expanding social organization was the natural concomitant of a rapidly expanding economy. Nearly every state, and for that matter nearly every county, organized its agricultural society, and often its horticultural society as well. The fairs that were held by practically all the societies were the means of broadening the farmers' information concerning live stock, machinery, crops and agricultural practices. The exhibits which were to be seen at the fairs stimulated the introduction and greater use of improved animals, implements, and crops, and these in turn were the things that constituted a renewed and growing agricultural display at the fairs.

THE GOLDEN AGE AT ITS ZENITH

The golden age began to reach its zenith with the rapid multiplication of state and local societies following 1850. The Commissioner of Patents reported in 1857 that state agricultural societies had been incorporated in Alabama, California, Connecticut, Georgia, Illinois, Iowa, Kentucky, Maine, Maryland, Michigan, Minnesota, Mississippi, New Hampshire, New Jersey, New York, North Carolina, Pennsylvania, Rhode Island, South Carolina, Vermont and Wisconsin, and state boards of agriculture in Indiana, Massachusetts, Ohio and Tennessee.[15] As to the exact number of local societies we have no knowledge but we do know that they increased rapidly. In 1858 the Commissioner of Patents had compiled a list of 912 state and county societies dedicated to the promotion of agricultural or horticultural

[15] *Report*, 1857, *Agriculture, op. cit.*, p. 24.

interests, and in 1868 the Department of Agriculture had a
list of 1,367 state, district, county and township societies of
this character. Butterfield estimates that at least five-sixths
of those existing in 1858 were established after 1849.[16] And
of 993 reporting their date of organization in 1868 over
86 percent were formed after 1850.[17]

These two lists compiled by the Federal Government in
1858 and 1868 are probably not complete, but they furnish
us with material for several significant analyses of the agricultural organization of the golden age. In the first place,
the geographic distribution of the societies is important.
In 1858 New York possessed 97; the New England states
together had 95; in Illinois there were 94; and Indiana,
Iowa, Ohio and Pennsylvania followed with 77, 74, 74 and
71 respectively. The states of the old Northwest — Ohio,
Indiana, Illinois, Michigan and Wisconsin — possessed
together 308, and when to these are added those of Minnesota, Iowa and Missouri the total number of societies in the
area that comprises, roughly speaking, the present Middle
West, was 443. The entire group of southern states —
Delaware, Maryland, Virginia, North Carolina, South
Carolina, Georgia, Kentucky, Tennessee, Alabama, Mississippi, Arkansas, Louisiana and Texas — that reported
societies in 1858 had 165. The societies were pretty evenly
distributed over the southern states; Virginia with 33 had
the largest number, and was followed in order by Texas
with 24, Tennessee with 20, Mississippi with 16, Kentucky
with 14, South Carolina with 13, and Georgia and Maryland with 10 each. It will be seen by a glance at Table I that
New England had 10.4 percent of the societies (we are assuming that the number of fairs was in close correspondence

[16] Bailey, L. H., (ed.), *Cyclopedia of American Agriculture*, p. 292.
[17] Cf. "Agricultural and Horticultural Societies and Clubs," Commissioner
of Agriculture, *Report*, 1867, Washington, pp. 364 *et seq.*

with the number of societies) in 1858; the Middle Atlantic group had 20.1 percent; the East North Central states had 33.7 percent; Iowa, Minnesota and Missouri had 14.8 percent; the South had 18 percent; the Pacific states had 1.3 percent; and the remaining 1.4 percent of the societies were scattered in other states and territories. Nearly half the societies, 48.5 percent to be exact, were located in the eight states of the Middle West.

TABLE I

DISTRIBUTION OF AGRICULTURAL AND HORTICULTURAL SOCIETIES, 1858

NUMBERS AND PERCENTAGES OF THE STATE AND LOCAL AGRICULTURAL AND HORTICULTURAL SOCIETIES REPORTED TO THE UNITED STATES COMMISSIONER OF PATENTS IN 1858 AND THE NUMBERS AND PERCENTAGES OF THE TOTAL POPULATION IN 1860, BY GEOGRAPHIC DIVISION [a]

Geographic Division	Numbers		Percentages	
	Population 1860 [b]	*Societies 1858*	*Population 1860*	*Societies 1858*
New England	3,135,283	95	9.9	10.4
Middle Atlantic States	7,458,985	184	23.7	20.1
East North Central States	6,926,884	308	22.0	33.7
Iowa, Minn., Mo.	2,028,948	135	6.4	14.8
South	11,133,361	165	35.4	18.0
Pacific States	444,053	12	1.4	1.3
All Other Territory	315,807	13	1.0	1.4
Total	31,443,321	912	100.0	100.0

[a] Compiled from Commissioner of Patents, *Report*, 1858, *Agriculture*, Washington, p. 91 and United States *Census.*
[b] The total population rather than the rural population is used here, since in matters of initiative, financial support and attendance, the fair was to a very appreciable extent an urban as well as a rural enterprise.

A comparison of the number of societies with the population of the various groups of states is also significant. Table I presents a comparison between the numbers and percentages by geographic divisions of the agricultural societies of

1858 and of the population in 1860, the nearest census year. Note that New England, with 10.4 percent of the societies and 9.9 percent of the total population showed a close correspondence between the two. The same was true of the Pacific Coast group. In the Middle Atlantic states the societies were slightly less numerous than an equal distribution according to population would have made them. Great contrasts are observable, however, between the number of societies and the size of population in the South and the Middle West. The South with more than one-third of the population in the entire country had only 18 percent of the agricultural societies. That these societies with their annual fairs were part and parcel of the expansion of the great agricultural Middle West is shown by the fact that the states of the old Northwest — Ohio, Indiana, Illinois, Michigan and Wisconsin — with 22 percent of the population had 33.7 percent of the societies; and that the three frontier states of Iowa, Minnesota and Missouri with only 6.4 percent of the nation's population had 14.8 percent of its agricultural societies. The agricultural-society movement spread from east to west, but pretty largely through the northern states. Initiated along the Atlantic seaboard, it turned westward principally through western New York and Pennsylvania into the great valleys of the Ohio, the Upper Mississippi and the Missouri. The agricultural civilization of this region was largely a creation of the East. New Englanders, New Yorkers and Pennsylvanians, moving westward into these fertile valleys, brought with them the idea of the agricultural society and its fair as a part of their social heritage. And the type of farming that they developed permitted the utilization of the fair in a particularly successful manner. Life in the scattered pioneer homesteads of the West demanded institutions of social intercourse; the need of efficient machinery, live stock and crops to make possible the possession of the land required an agency of popular agricultural instruction and extension.

TABLE II

DISTRIBUTION OF AGRICULTURAL AND HORTICULTURAL SOCIETIES, 1868

NUMBERS AND PERCENTAGES OF THE STATE AND LOCAL AGRICUL-
TURAL AND HORTICULTURAL SOCIETIES REPORTED TO THE UNITED
STATES COMMISSIONER OF AGRICULTURE IN 1868 AND THE NUMBERS
AND PERCENTAGES OF THE TOTAL POPULATION IN 1870 WITH THE
PERCENTAGE INCREASE IN NUMBERS OF SOCIETIES AND POPULATION
OVER 1858 AND 1860 RESPECTIVELY, BY GEOGRAPHIC DIVISION [a]

Geographic Division	Numbers		Percentages		Percentage Increase	
	Population 1870 [b]	Societies 1868	Population 1870	Societies 1868	Population over 1860	Societies over 1858
New England	3,487,924	139	9.0	13.4	11.2	46.3
Middle Atlantic States	8,810,806	186	22.8	18.0	18.1	1.0
East North Central States	9,124,517	390	23.6	37.7	31.7	26.6
Iowa, Minn., Mo.	3,355,021	181	8.7	17.5	65.3	34.0
South	12,288,020	62	31.8	6.0	10.3	−62.4 [d]
Pacific States	675,125	6	1.7	.5	52.0	−50.0 [d]
All Other Territory	816,958	68	2.1	6.5	158.6	423.0
Total	38,558,371	1,032 [c]	100.0	100.0	22.6	13.1 [c]

[a] Compiled from Commissioner of Agriculture, *Report*, 1867, pp. 364 *et seq.* and United States *Census.*
[b] See note [b], Table I.
[c] The Department of Agriculture had on its records 1,367 organizations, of which 1,052 had made reports in response to a questionnaire sent out by the department. The published list, however, contains only 1,032 with the information necessary for inclusion in this tabulation.
[d] Decrease.

Table II presents the distribution of agricultural societies in 1868 and of the population in 1870. The societies it will be observed, had become relatively more numerous in the New England states and relatively less numerous in the Middle Atlantic states. In the South they had suffered a decided diminution, those of the entire region constituting only 6 percent of the total; in absolute numbers they decreased from 165 to 62, or 62.4 percent, significant of the distress and disorganization following the Civil War.[18] The Middle West is seen still to be the stronghold of agricultural societies and fairs. The eight states comprising this group had among them 55.3 percent of the societies, though only 32.3 percent of the population. The increase of the societies in this region was not so rapid of course as the increase of population, but it maintained a fairly even pace. Ohio led all the other states in the number of societies reporting in 1868. There were 118 within her borders. Iowa was close behind with 116, and New York, Illinois and Indiana followed with 107, 102 and 86 respectively.

The Civil War put a sudden end to a great many of the agricultural societies. Their decimation in the South has already been noted; but it was more than offset by the increase in the New England and the western states. Table III shows that of 993 societies reporting their date of organization in 1868 almost nine-tenths came into existence

TABLE III

DATE OF ORGANIZATION OF AGRICULTURAL SOCIETIES

NUMBERS AND PERCENTAGES OF AGRICULTURAL SOCIETIES REPORTING DATE OF ORGANIZATION TO THE UNITED STATES DEPARTMENT OF AGRICULTURE IN 1868, BY FIVE-YEAR PERIODS [a]

	Numbers	Percentages
Before 1841	40	4.0
1841-45	30	3.0
1846-50	68	6.8
1851-55	185	18.6
1856-60	250	25.1
1861-65	178	17.9
1866-68 [b]	242	24.3
Total	993	100.0

[a] Compiled from Commissioner of Agriculture, *Report*, 1867, pp. 364 *et seq.*
[b] A period of about two and a half years.

[18] It is possible of course that, owing to the political situation, a larger proportion of societies failed to report from this section than from others in 1868.

after 1850. Each five-year period, except that in which the Civil War occurred, showed a steady increase in the number organized.

Almost the whole burden of agricultural experimentation, instruction, recreation and social life fell upon these agricultural societies of the golden age. Some of them owned and conducted experimental farms or trial grounds; most of them published their transactions in annual or biennial volumes or, if less prosperous, in local newspapers. Some of the societies held monthly meetings for discussion and debate; some engaged in the importation and breeding of improved live stock and seeds; most of them attempted the collection of an agricultural library. The Bethel Farmers' Club in Oxford County, Maine, reported to the Patent Office in 1858,

We meet semi-monthly, in the winter, to discuss agricultural and horticultural subjects. Reports of these meetings are published in our village, county and State papers.[19]

The Farmers' and Mechanics' Benevolent Reform Association in Marshall County, Iowa, reported a monthly meeting to discuss various subjects. "Four members, two of each sex, are appointed at each meeting to address the Society at the next, on agriculture, or any subject of interest and importance which they may select." [20] The Elm Dale Agricultural Society in Weakley County, Tennessee, owned a thirty-acre experimental farm equipped with live stock and machinery, on which scientific experiments were conducted.[21] Agricultural implements were imported for trial by the Massachusetts Society for Promoting Agriculture and, if found usable, were recommended to manufacturers for introduction. This society also maintained a herd of Ayrshire cattle, the offspring of which it proposed to distribute throughout the state.[22] The Boone County Agricultural and Industrial

[19] Commissioner of Patents, *Report*, 1858, *Agriculture, op. cit.*, p. 133.
[20] *Ibid.*, p. 128.   [21] *Ibid.*, p. 206.   [22] *Ibid.*, p. 135.

Society, in Iowa, reported the ownership of Durham and Devon cattle and Byefield and Suffolk swine kept for breeding purposes.[23]

It is impossible to know just what proportion of these societies held fairs, but their reports indicate that most of them did. Certainly on the whole that was their main business. The agricultural society was the paramount form of collective activity among the rural population and the fair the dominant institutionalized expression of that activity. In general the fairs performed two major functions for those who took part in them. They were first the agencies through which a vast amount of information was distributed to the people in the communities in which they were held. Second, and undoubtedly no less important, they were the occasion of an annual celebration for farm folks, who lived a comparatively prosaic, if strenuous, life, especially in the newer regions of the West. Christmas, the Fourth of July and the county fair, varied by an occasional picnic or circus, long remained the traditional holidays of rural America. But Christmas was a day of decidedly private character — a family affair of cousins and uncles and aunts and grandchildren. The Fourth of July in spite of its crowds, noise and spread-eagle oratory did not effect a very close tie-up with the tyrannies of George III. Life, liberty, and the pursuit of happiness would take care of themselves if only the farmer could get hold of more efficient reapers and plows, better breeds of cattle and horses and hogs and sheep, and more productive grain. It was at the county fair that the farmer not only saw the means by which agricultural expansion was taking place and which he could use advantageously in bringing the land to a fuller productivity, but also gained a conception of his own importance and the inspiration for participating still more actively in agricultural expansion.

[23] *Ibid.*, p. 123.

This was an occasion connected intimately with the pressing problems of his everyday work.

The farmer, especially the pioneer farmer, may have enjoyed his recreation and amusement, but he usually justified them in terms of earnest labor. Always at the fair there was a decidedly serious purpose, for it was here that the majority of farmers had their greatest opportunity of the year to learn of the advances being made in the agricultural world. Here the farmers' problems were more fully met and dealt with than by any other agency. There were agricultural journals to be sure, but after all they lacked the element of personal contact. Their descriptions of Fawkes' steam plow or Wood's mower or Brown's corn planter or McCormick's reaper or of the Shorthorns and Devons and Berkshires and Merinos could at best but whet the farmers' desire to attend the fairs where these new machines and animals might be seen. Their discussions of agricultural problems lacked the give-and-take of the group of farmers gathered at the stock pens or implement trial grounds or the evening discussion meetings at the fair. Pure-bred live stock was so scarce that many people never saw improved animals until they attended their first fair. There the farmers could ascertain what types and breeds were coming into popular use and could get acquainted with breeders and importers. In 1867 a group of fifteen farmers in Washington County, Iowa, having contributed after many pros and cons, $10 each toward the buying of a pure-bred bull to improve their brindle scrub cattle, were at a loss to know where to go to make their purchase until the keeper of the county-seat livery stable, who had attended the state fair, directed them to a breeder some hundred miles distant.[24] About the same time a few pure-bred hogs were brought into the neighborhood, and the next year saw the organization

[24] Iowa State Fair and Exposition, *Report*, 1929, Des Moines, pp. 112 *et seq.*

of the first county fair in Washington County. The scarcity of labor was a very real problem for the farmer; an examination of the machines on exhibition at the fairs gave him an idea of the machinery best suited to his needs. Cyrus H. McCormick received his first award in the Mississippi Valley, when in 1844 his reaper was given a certificate of merit at the Hamilton County, Ohio, fair, the judging committee relying upon testimonials from New York and Virginia.[25]

I saw at the Fair held at Rochester in 1864, an agricultural boiler for steaming food for cattle — what has become of it? . . . I would like very much to obtain such an apparatus if it answers a good purpose,

wrote a subscriber to the *Cultivator and Country Gentleman*,[26] echoing the interest of thousands of farmers in all sorts of mechanical contraptions as well as in the more necessary farm implements.

Formal annual addresses and evening discussion meetings as well as the displays of live stock and machinery were prominent features of the fairs in the golden age. The visitors at various New York state fairs included such celebrities as Daniel Webster, Martin Van Buren, William H. Seward, Millard Fillmore, John Tyler, Henry Clay, Stephen A. Douglas, Josiah Quincy, Hamilton Fish and George Bancroft, the historian, many of whom addressed the assembled crowds.[27] At the Delhi, New York, Town Society fair in 1867, "the Address by Luther H. Tucker, Esq., [publisher of the *Cultivator and Country Gentleman*], was listened to with more than usual attention" by a "large number of persons that remained quiet, . . . most of them standing for more than an hour. . . ."[28] The speech of J. Stanton Gould of

[25] Hutchinson, William T., *Cyrus Hall McCormick*, New York, c. 1930, p. 211.
[26] June 17, 1866, p. 384.
[27] New York State Department of Farms and Markets, *Bulletin 161, loc. cit.*, *passim*.
[28] *Cultivator and Country Gentleman*, Oct. 17, 1867, p. 256.

Hudson, New York, at the Union Agricultural Society fair in 1870 was "full of practical suggestions, which if acted on, would be better for the country." [29] But the golden age had its disappointments as far as the annual address as a feature of the fair was concerned. As early as 1864, one orator repeatedly refused invitations to speak, because he had seen how "pitiably better men than he" had competed with the animals the public came to see.[30] A reporter of the Vermont state fair in 1870 lamented the fact that President Grant had disappointed the fair two years in succession by his failure to appear as scheduled.

These distinguished public functionaries [ran the comment], should not excite the expectations of the people without gratifying it if possible. But it is a settled fact that public men do not always keep their promises.[31]

At the Iowa state fair in 1874 President A. S. Welsh, of Iowa State Agricultural College, delivered his address on the race track between the heats of the race while the horses were cooling off.[32] The larger fairs especially sponsored evening discussion meetings where spirited debate raged over every conceivable sort of agricultural problem. No less a personage than President Andrew D. White, of Cornell University, attended the meetings at the New York state fair in 1874 to see whether he could learn anything of benefit for his school.[33]

Various other agricultural matters also received attention. A visitor reporting the Montgomery County, New York, fair in 1874 feared, after viewing the culinary displays, the pictures and household exhibits, that farmers might justly deserve the accusation that they were lazy, or

[29] *Ibid.*, Oct. 13, 1870, p. 649.
[30] Michigan State Board of Agriculture, *Annual Report*, 1879, Lansing, p. 452.
[31] *Cultivator and Country Gentleman*, Sept. 29, 1870, p. 620.
[32] *Ibid.*, Oct. 1, 1874, p. 628.
[33] *Ibid.*, Oct. 1, 1874, p. 627.

at least that they took things too easily.[34] At a New Hampshire county fair in 1872 "the dairy was fully represented, as many of the farmers' wives and daughters still retain the knowledge of manufacturing first rate butter and cheese, as also white and brown bread." [35] An Ontario, Canada, local fair enjoyed, besides several addresses, essays read by two young ladies on the requirements of a good farmer's wife.[36] At the Minnesota state fair in 1874 "the best exhibition of vegetables was by the Lake Superior and Mississippi Railroad...." [37] The railroads often made concessions to the exhibitors and visitors attending the fair, though the New York Central apparently reduced temporarily the number of exhibits at the state fair when in 1874 it decided to give free transportation only one way instead of both.[38] On the other hand, the Long Island Railroad, carrying articles and cattle free of charge to and from the Queens County fair, was praised for having "had not a single accident during the entire week." [39]

The golden age saw, too, the beginnings of a bitter conflict between the old educational features of fairs and the newer types of amusements, particularly those centering around the horse race.[40] In both East and West, race track and show ring tried to outbid each other for popular support. In spite of the "inevitable race horse" at the 1867 New Jersey state fair, it was claimed that "the 'better part' was appreciated by the 'select few'." [41] But at the Champaign County, Illinois, fair in 1870, drawing a pitiably small agricultural display except for the local exhibits of apples and Berkshire hogs, "there was a raft of racky-boney pacers and trotters gathered together from the ends of the earth,

[34] *Ibid.*, Oct. 8, 1874, p. 645. [35] *Ibid.*, Oct. 31, 1872, p. 693.
[36] *Ibid.*, Dec. 6, 1866, p. 365. [37] *Ibid.*, Sept. 24, 1874, p. 612.
[38] *Ibid.*, Sept. 24, 1874, p. 616. [39] *Ibid.*, Oct. 22, 1874, p. 676.
[40] Cf. *infra*, Chap. VII.
[41] *Cultivator and Country Gentleman*, Oct. 31, 1867, p. 285.

and there was riding, pacing, racing and trotting every day, and nearly every hour of the day. . . ."[42] By 1875 the question was seriously discussed whether fairs had not fallen into the hands of wealthy and ambitious men eager to use their positions as stepping-stones to political and social advancement, and a "ring" of fine stock breeders and holders of valuable patents on agricultural implements.[43]

A few state fairs had been held before the golden age and the movement to establish them gained force rapidly in the early fifties. Necessarily the early societies both learned and practical were local in character; a society organized on the Berkshire plan comprised usually the county as a geographical unit. But state societies followed gradually; the spirit of agricultural expansion soon extended beyond county boundaries. We have already noted that New York and New Jersey held so-called state fairs in the thirties. Pennsylvania, after several more or less unhappy attempts about the same time, established a successful state fair in 1851. In the Middle West the organization of state societies followed upon that of county societies and the state exhibitions were held accordingly.[44] Michigan held its first state fair at Detroit in 1849. The first state fairs in Ohio and Wisconsin were held in 1851, at Cincinnati and Janesville respectively. Indiana followed with her first state fair at Indianapolis in 1852; Illinois, at Springfield in 1853; Iowa, at Fairfield in 1854; and Minnesota, at Fort Snelling in 1860. Even in far-away San Francisco, so-called state fairs were held from 1851 to 1853, and with the organization of a state agricultural society in 1854 an official California state fair was established.

[42] *Ibid.*, Sept. 22, 1870, p. 596.
[43] *Ibid.*, Sept. 30, 1875, p. 612.
[44] Cf. Ross, Earle D., "The Evolution of the Agricultural Fair in the Northwest," *Iowa Journal of History and Politics*, July, 1926, pp. 449 *et seq.*; Commissioner of Agriculture, *Report*, 1875, *op. cit.*, pp. 437 *et seq.*

In the southern states, both old and new, agricultural improvement moved somewhat more slowly. The organization of societies for holding fairs did not become general until about 1855. But in that year state fairs were held in Alabama, Georgia,[45] Kentucky, Maryland, North Carolina, Virginia and Tennessee. Kentucky held the best of the southern fairs before 1861, a fact easily understood when we remember that they were often combined with the races so popular in that state and that in the famous Kentucky blue-grass pastures grazed the finest live stock of the South, if not of the entire nation.[46]

These early state fairs were conducted by state agricultural societies or, as in the case of Ohio and Indiana, by state boards of agriculture, the semipublic form given to state agricultural organization in some of the states. Upon the reorganization of the New York State Agricultural Society, the state fair embarked upon an uninterrupted course of development. The first fair was held at Syracuse and lasted two days. The courthouse was thrown open to the displays of farm products, implements and domestic manufactures. A train load of twenty-five cars of live stock from Albany and the river counties arrived at Syracuse the day before the opening of the fair. It was estimated that from 10,000 to 15,000 people visited the fair; President Nott, of Union College, gave the principal address; the village of Syracuse provided homemade amusements; and a plowing contest and a farmers' dinner were notable events.[47]

---

[45] The first Georgia state fair, so-called, followed immediately upon the organization of a state agricultural society at Stone Mountain in 1846. The local hotel owner made the only exhibits, a jack and a jennet — somewhat after the manner of Elkanah Watson's exhibition of his two Merino sheep at Pittsfield in 1807. Cf. Commissioner of Agriculture, *Report*, 1875, *op. cit.*, p. 439.

[46] Francis, David R., "Southern Agricultural Fairs and Expositions," *The South in the Building of the Nation*, Richmond, c. 1909, V, 587 *et seq*.

[47] New York State Department of Farms and Markets, *Bulletin 161, loc. cit., passim*.

In Iowa, the state society and the state fair were the direct outgrowth of county societies and fairs in one corner of the state. The Jefferson County society, taking the initiative, offered its grounds for the state exhibition. The state society was organized in 1853 by fifteen delegates from five counties, who, adopting the premium list of the Pennsylvania state society, offered $1,100 in prizes and set the date for the fair in 1854. The fair was apparently a success in every way except financially; it closed with a deficit which was made up by the president. From 7,000 to 10,000 people, it was estimated, attended the fair, a notable gathering for this frontier state, since the means of transportation were limited to walking, horseback, two-wheeled oxcarts and covered wagons. Many families are reported to have camped during their stay at the fair, as well as along the way to and from Fairfield. A representative exhibit of live stock, grains, agricultural machinery and handwork was shown. Prizes were still awarded for such entries as the best ox yoke and the best grain cradle. Many of the implements displayed were not yet produced for the market but were only models which acquainted the visitors with the advancement being made.[48]

In Minnesota, the Minnesota Territorial Agricultural Society and the Hennepin County Agricultural Society were both organized in 1853, and in 1855 they united in holding a fair at Minneapolis which drew exhibits from three counties. Several other fairs were held thereafter, before Minnesota became a state in 1858. Failing to raise the necessary money, the territorial society could not hold a fair that year, but it united with the Hennepin County Agricultural Society in 1859 to hold its last joint fair. The Minnesota legislature in 1860 incorporated the Minnesota State Agri-

[48] Iowa State Department of Agriculture, *Yearbook*, 1904, Des Moines, pp. 618 *et seq.* Cf. also Ross, *op. cit.*, pp. 450 *et seq.*; and Ross, Earle D., ["The Iowa State Fair"] *Palimpsest*, Aug., 1929, *passim*.

cultural Society, stipulating that it should hold an annual fair. In spite of the fact that no state aid was provided, subscriptions amounting to over $1,000 were made, the fair was generously advertised by the press of the state, and the largest assemblage of people in Minnesota up to that time gathered at Fort Snelling. A total of 775 entries was on display, as well as many other spectacular features which included a combined reaper and mower, fire engines and a hog that weighed 640 pounds.[49]

These reviews of the first state fairs in New York, Iowa and Minnesota, brief though they are, present typical cases of the establishment of the institution throughout the country. Probably the greatest fairs of the golden age were held by the United States Agricultural Society. The temporary organization effected in 1841 to solicit the Smithson fund [50] was revived in 1852 when representatives from twenty-three states and territories meeting at Washington formed a society to "improve the agriculture of the country, by attracting attention, eliciting the views, and confirming the efforts of that great class composing the agricultural community, and to secure the advantages of a better organization and more extended usefulness among all State, county, and other agricultural societies." [51] Functioning really as a Federal board of agriculture, this society carried on investigations of implements and agricultural practices in other lands, published transactions, periodicals and reports, and assembled in annual conventions in different parts of the country. Finally it held national fairs and field trials — at Boston and Springfield, Massachusetts; at Springfield, Ohio, and at Philadelphia, Richmond, Louisville, Chicago and

[49] Hall, Darwin S. and R. I. Holcombe, *History of the Minnesota State Agricultural Society from Its Organization in 1854 to the Annual Meeting of 1910*, St. Paul, 1910, *passim*.

[50] Cf. *supra*, p. 78.

[51] Poore, Commissioner of Agriculture, *Report*, 1866, *op. cit.*, p. 525. Cf. pp. 525-26 for further discussion of the society's activities.

Cincinnati. The activities of this society undoubtedly stimulated greatly state and local fairs throughout the nation.

In many respects all the early state fairs were little more than local exhibitions. Transportation facilities were too limited to permit exhibits from every corner of the state. The exhibits were often poorly classified, the lists frequently being copied, as in the case of the first Iowa state fair, from those of fairs in older regions. The grounds on which the fairs were held were small and inadequately equipped. Many of the county societies, though they often owned their exhibition grounds, had pitiably meager permanent equipment, and the state fairs, always transient exhibitions, had practically none. The state societies conceived it as their duty to rotate the fair among different parts of the state so that periodically each section might share in its advantages. Obviously an institution seeking to serve an entire state was confronted with the problem of making contacts with all the people, and under undeveloped conditions of travel and transportation it was easier to take the fair to the people than to bring the people to the fair. Even so, thousands of people were yearly prevented by lack of transportation facilities from attending the state fairs. At the New York state fair held at Saratoga in 1866, for example, the attendance was cut because the one railroad serving the village refused to run excursion trains.[52] The transient state fair permitted the exhibitors — the extensive breeders of live stock and the manufacturers of implements or other articles — to reach a new group of buyers every year. Farmers in different sections of the state were also given an opportunity to exhibit their products every few years, as well as periodically to learn of the advances in agriculture without being compelled to make an extended and costly journey. Though this plan best met the needs of pioneer

[52] *Cultivator and Country Gentleman*, Sept. 20, 1866, p. 192.

society, the development of the railroad and later of the automobile made the itinerant state fair less necessary.

THE PERIOD OF READJUSTMENT, 1870-1900

The designation of the period from 1850 to 1870 as "the golden age of the agricultural fair" is undoubtedly justified, but only in a qualified sense. The agricultural societies of the period, being by far the chief forms of agricultural coöperation and organization, served the combined interests of the rural population — educational, economic, social, recreational and sometimes even political. The holding of fairs was the chief means of promoting these interests. Some of the societies existed for no other immediate purpose. In the less differentiated agricultural order then prevailing, the fair served practically all rural interests, and in a day when the fair was able to serve all these interests it did assume in the social life of rural people a relatively more important rôle than it does today. By 1870 a noticeable differentiation had begun among agricultural interests, and consequently in agricultural organization; and the fair as a mode of expression of the agricultural society assumed, as we shall see, a more specialized place in the rural social scheme. As a social institution the fair served many of the same interests in a different way; social differentiation resulted in the development of agricultural schools, departments of agriculture and coöperative and social organizations like the Grange, the Farmers' Union and the Farm Bureau, which have taken over many of the functions previously performed by the agricultural societies. The period from 1850 to 1870 constitutes the most important and the most clearly defined stage in the evolution of the agricultural fair since the period of 1810 to 1825 when Elkanah Watson was propagating his practical Berkshire societies and cattle shows.

During the last three decades of the nineteenth century,

and indeed to the present day, agricultural fairs have not only increased in number but have rapidly differentiated into complex and specialized forms. New social and economic needs arose calling for different types of rural associations. Political problems of a peculiarly rural character clamored for solution. Private enterprise became incapable of providing adequate means of experimentation and dissemination of agricultural information. Agricultural specialization began to call for specialized associations to promote particular branches of the industry. More and more, government agencies, state and national, were created to take over many of the functions of the agricultural societies. The solicitation of public funds necessitated as time went on a more complete control by the government of societies receiving such aid, as well as the assumption of many of the societies' activities. During the course of the century several of the states — New York and New Hampshire in 1820, and Ohio, Massachusetts and Indiana near the middle of the century — created state boards of agriculture, semipublic bodies often exercising some measure of official control over county societies, carrying on some elementary forms of agricultural education, and sometimes, as in the case of Ohio and Indiana, conducting the state fair. In most of the states, however, the state agricultural societies performed the functions of a board of agriculture, acting as agencies through which public contributions to the promotion of agriculture were distributed. In either case a more or less uniform type of state agricultural organization emerged, namely, a state department of agriculture ranking as a centralized administrative department of the state government, headed by a popularly elected or appointed secretary or commissioner, and performing a wide variety of administrative duties.[53] This type of organization developed first

[53] Cf. Wiest, *Agricultural Organization in the United States*, pp. 601-11,

in the South after the Civil War and spread to other parts of the country as a part of increasing government regulation extending to agriculture as well as to industry and commerce. This trend was facilitated by the fact that agricultural experimentation, research and education had reached such enormous proportions that private organization could no longer conduct them.

In 1862 two notable steps were taken by the Federal Government which were indicative of the tendency to aid agriculture. These were the establishment of the United States Department of Agriculture and the passage of the Morrill Act providing for land-grant colleges. The first was the fruition of agitation begun by George Washington's advocacy of a national board of agriculture and concluded by the persistent labors of the United States Agricultural Society.[54] At every national convention of this organization the creation of a Federal department of agriculture had been urged, and when this was finally accomplished in 1862, the society, relieved of many of its self-imposed functions, ceased to exist. The organization and development of public instruction under the terms of the Morrill Act obviously placed in public hands almost all the functions of instruction and research, formerly carried on by the private agricultural societies largely through their fairs. This act was the first of a number of Federal acts designed to provide more fully for carrying on agricultural education, research and extension. Most important were the Hatch Act of 1887, establishing agricultural experiment stations, and the Smith-Lever Act of 1914, providing for coöperative extension work between the agricultural colleges and the Federal Department of Agriculture. In addition there have been countless acts

for a comparatively recent tabulation of the agricultural departmental organization in the different states.

[54] Cf. *supra*, p. 97.

passed by the various states, assuming the same type of function within their respective borders.

The differentiation of agricultural organization was not confined, however, to the increase of public control. Private societies of all sorts arose rapidly after 1870 to promote special agricultural interests. Economic, social and political interests were served by such organizations as the Grange, founded in 1867, and the Farmers' Alliance, founded in 1875, groups that eventuated in the Populist movement. A new set of agricultural conditions came into being after 1870. Big business, the farmers saw, had attained its eminence partly at least, by denying them their share of the profits of rapid expansion and exploitation. A new set of economic and political issues loomed on the horizon — issues that inevitably became the warp and woof of partisan politics and which called forth new types of agricultural associations. The countless agricultural unions, wheels, clubs and alliances organized between 1870 and 1896 represented a large part of the structural aspect of the politically militant farmers' movement.

Other types of private agricultural societies also differentiated during the century. Horticultural societies were the earliest to branch off from the general agricultural societies. A state horticultural society was formed in Pennsylvania in 1828, which held for many years thereafter a semiannual show; and in 1829 the Massachusetts Horticultural Society was organized, which from the beginning held shows weekly during the summer and autumn with a grand annual show in September and a special rose show in June.[55] During the middle of the century horticultural societies rivaled agricultural societies in number and in activity. Many of them held exhibitions in connection with their annual or semiannual conventions, as did the Illinois Northern Horti-

[55] Commissioner of Agriculture, *Report*, 1875, *op. cit.*, pp. 449 *et seq.*

cultural Society. At its meetings were to be seen displays of fruits, flowers, vegetables, wines, cordials and ciders.[56] Others united with regularly organized fairs to hold an exhibition of their products, as did the Michigan State Pomological Society in 1870 and for several years thereafter with the Kent County Agricultural Society.[57] The next type of agricultural organization to break away from the parent stem was the woolgrowers' association. This organization was interested primarily in promoting legislation and education favorable to the woolgrowing industry. Initiated in Ohio in 1863 it spread westward, especially to Missouri and Kansas.[58] It, too, held numerous sheep shows and sheep-shearings. Nor should we overlook the dairymen's association. The Vermont Dairymen's Association was formed in 1869 to resist the competition offered by the dairy products of other regions. Two similar organizations followed in New York in 1871.[59] Still another type of association serving a specialized agricultural interest was the poultry association. The formation of the American Poultry Association in 1873 helped to unify and standardize the poultry exhibitions that were beginning to be held.[60] Yet another differentiation took place when the breeders' registry associations began to be organized for the purpose of recording the pedigrees of pure-bred live stock and promoting its increase and extension. Some forty or fifty of these breed associations were formed in the United States during the thirty years following 1870.[61] Financed by membership fees and registration fees collected from the owners of pure-bred animals, they have since devoted their energies to popularizing the breed of stock in which they are particularly interested.

[56] *Ibid.*, p. 443.   [57] *Ibid.*, p. 452.   [58] *Ibid., passim.*   [59] *Ibid., passim.*
[60] Jull, Morley A., *Poultry Husbandry*, New York, 1930, p. 31.
[61] Plumb, Charles S., *Types and Breeds of Farm Animals*, Boston, c. 1906, *passim.*

Agricultural social organization has thus evolved concurrently with the physical, technical and economic development of the industry. This increasing specialization did not react, however, to the permanent detriment of the agricultural fair. The fair merely became a more specialized institution itself. Left free to perform those functions for which it is best adapted, it forms a focusing point where all the specialized agricultural associations coöperate in making a grand display to the people. No longer the all-inclusive agricultural institution, itself serving directly the entire complex of agricultural interests, it has become an agency through which a hundred other associations make a popular appeal. The present day fair association usually exists for no other purpose than to conduct the fair, furnishing thereby one of the media by which the government departments of agriculture, the agricultural colleges, the breed associations and manufacturers and merchants reach a popular audience.

The fair was therefore compelled to undergo a period of radical readjustment following 1870. From that date to 1900 it struggled to define its relationship to other agricultural organizations and to articulate a policy for its own development. Just as the American frontier came to an end about 1890 and American energies turned somewhat from vehement expansion to the internal refinement of social organization already initiated, so the agricultural fair lessened its geographical expansion and evolved new types, new methods and new purposes wherever it was organized. Fairs always operate with varying degrees of success. They are affected by the weather, the crops, the price level and, though to a diminishing degree, the transportation facilities. According to the report of the United States Commissioner of Agriculture in 1875, Indiana was so delighted with the success of her state fair that a thirty-day exposition was held, while at the same time the state board of agriculture in Kansas was attempting to dispense with such "expensive luxuries," and was directing all its energies to the collection and publication of agricultural and industrial statistics.[62] In the period of readjustment there was always the question of the extent to which public funds should be used to maintain the fairs. No less vexing was the problem of what features should be emphasized and what excluded. Many fairs operated at a financial loss during the years of economic depression; there was constant agitation for state aid both to rescue them from temporary financial distress and to provide for their permanent development. Many of the states made loans or appropriations for the partial payment of indebtedness, and some instituted more or less well defined policies of regular state aid; constructive policies of governmental support became general only after 1900.

The development of state fairs had been considerably retarded by the necessity of their yearly migrations. Many persons contended that the permanently located state fair was likely to be permanently dominated by one branch of agriculture. The main agricultural interests of New York, for example, were dairying, fruit growing and truck farming; those of Minnesota were wheat raising and live-stock breeding; would it not be difficult, therefore, argued some, to make the stationary state fair representative of state-wide agriculture? A transient fair, however, could not attain the stability of a permanently located fair. Obviously it could acquire no permanent grounds and but little permanent equipment. The state capitol building was utilized as an exhibition hall for the Maine state fair in 1870, while the live stock was shown in pens erected in a park across the street.[63] Often the transient state fair had to depend upon

---

[62] *Op. cit.*, pp. 444, 446. It is interesting to note that at the present time there are two state fairs in Kansas.

[63] *Cultivator and Country Gentleman*, Oct. 6, 1870, p. 628.

the facilities of a local society, already meager enough. Furthermore, it was too often the cause of sectional rivalry and jealousy that boded ill for the social unity of the state. Dependent also upon local support, the fair was usually held at the city which promised (but not necessarily actually paid) most in the way of financial assistance. These early state fairs led a precarious existence, but the more mobile the population became as a result of improved transportation facilities, the more fully could the fairs settle down to the development of a constructive program, the building of a permanent physical plant and the execution of a definite policy.

Most of the county fairs acquired permanent grounds earlier than the state fairs, but the latter had largely done so by 1900. The New York state fair was located at Syracuse in 1890, after that city had donated one hundred acres of land for the fair's permanent home.[64] In 1884 the Iowa legislature appropriated $50,000 for the purchase of a state fair grounds upon condition that the city of Des Moines raise an equal sum for improvements.[65] A long and bitter contest between Minneapolis and St. Paul for the possession of the Minnesota state fair came to a close in 1885, when the state was presented with two hundred acres of land at Hamline, midway between the two cities, and the state legislature appropriated $100,000 for buildings and improvements.[66] In 1895 the Illinois legislature appropriated $212,500 for the purchase of grounds and the construction of permanent buildings.[67] The Indiana state fair was established permanently at Indianapolis in 1868, the Ohio state fair at

[64] New York State Department of Farms and Markets, *Bulletin 161, loc. cit.*, p. 16.
[65] Ross, *Palimpsest, loc. cit.*, p. 302.
[66] Hall and Holcombe, *op. cit., passim.*
[67] Illinois State Department of Agriculture, *Transactions*, 1896, Springfield, p. 289.

Columbus in 1883 and the Wisconsin state fair at Milwaukee in 1891.[68] At the same time, however, the Pennsylvania state fair was discontinued in 1895, and not until 1917 did this state have another state-wide agricultural exhibition — conducted, significantly, upon entirely original lines.[69]

The location of state fairs on permanent sites near urban centers gave rise to many new problems, particularly in the matter of entertainment and recreation. Naturally many activities that would have been extraneous to the fairs of the golden age attached themselves to the institution when it was compelled to readjust itself to the changing social order. By 1888 the Rhode Island state fair was described as a "worldly fair":

a variety fair as well as an agricultural fair; but if the farmer, after a year's battling with soil and crops, demands entertainment — something not seen on the farm, a glimpse of the outside world — he has had it. He has seen a "grand tournament" of bicyclers, a balloon ascension, "a young and handsome couple" married in the balloon and sent off in it, polo games, steeple chasing, football match, and racing by wheelbarrows, greased poles, sacks and horses.[70]

Professional horse racing and, especially after the Chicago World's Fair in 1893, the midway with its galaxy of side shows, threatened to eclipse all other features. Many of the fairs came into the hands of jockey clubs and sporting associations; consequently, the purposes of the fairs were more and more called into question and many of them lost a considerable measure of popular support. They were boycotted by that class of people represented by the correspondent of the *Cultivator and Country Gentleman* who wrote: "The writer does not claim to perfection in morality; yet he withdrew his support from his County Fair some

[68] Ross, *Iowa Journal of History and Politics, op. cit.,* p. 464.
[69] Pennsylvania State Farm Products Show Commission, *Premium List*, 1932, Harrisburg, p. 6.
[70] *Cultivator and Country Gentleman*, Oct. 4, 1888, p. 740.

years ago, because he could not conscientiously support an institution that does so little to encourage the honest sons of toil and so much for horse-racing, which is one species of gambling." [71] At the same time, however, it was reported that the Clinton County, New York, fair had been forced to abandon its grounds and sell its fixtures at auction, because a jockey club, thinking to profit by the fair's crowd, established a race track near-by and distributed hand bills advertising races "in connection with the Fair." [72] And in 1872 a trotting association held a race meet at Elmira simultaneously with the New York state fair and attracted many city people who would have otherwise attended the fair.[73]

In spite of the fact, however, that many local associations ceased to hold fairs in the nineties, the institution as a whole entered into a new phase of development with the beginning of the twentieth century. By 1900 most of the older states were holding a relatively constant number of fairs each year, paying on the whole gradually increasing amounts of prize money to exhibitors, and drawing, consequently, gradually increasing numbers of exhibits. With the increasing number of visitors and exhibitors, the added expenditure of funds for permanent equipment and prizes, the expansion of activities and the growth of government control, the management of fairs came to be a specialized business. Not only did this give rise to a group of professional fair managers but it also necessitated a system of interfair relationships. In many of the states associations of local fairs were formed, which acted as a kind of clearing house for the discussion of common problems, the formulation of policies, the adoption of common standards and rules of conduct, and the settlement of such immediate problems as the setting of nonconflicting dates and the utilization of certain popular

[71] Oct. 20, 1870, p. 661.
[72] *Ibid.*, July 28, 1870, p. 468.   [73] *Ibid.*, Oct. 10, 1872, p. 648.

exhibits. In 1891 the International Association of Fairs and Expositions was organized to perform these functions for the larger fairs of the United States and Canada.

By the close of the nineteenth century, therefore, the fair showed several more or less definite trends. Unquestionably it was turning from a period of geographic expansion to one of refined institutional evolution: first, by redefining its purposes in the light of social differentiation; second, by coöperating with the new agricultural associations which that differentiation had created; third, by assuming the aspects of a specialized business, adopting the methods of modern business institutions; and finally, by developing constructive programs of providing permanent physical equipment and utilizing public financial aid.

V

THE FAIR IN THE TWENTIETH CENTURY

SINCE 1900 the agricultural fair in America has shown four main tendencies: first, the various shiftings of importance between the state and county fairs and the consequent changes in the kinds of activities which they have carried on; second, the development of specialized fairs and shows serving the interests of particular branches of the agricultural industry; third, the increasing emphasis upon the so-called community fair, a more or less conscious effort to adapt the fair idea to a local neighborhood and to make it the agent for the social participation of intimate neighborhood groups; and fourth, the increasingly important place in the fair scheme filled by boys' and girls' agricultural club activities. At the risk of some repetition we shall consider each of these tendencies in turn.

The State Fair and the County Fair

The period from 1900 to 1920 was, on the whole, one of accelerative prosperity for all classes of American people. This prosperity was rooted in the period of the late nineties. Not only did the economic assets of American business expand to unheard of degrees during these years but, even more significant, the American people became increasingly imbued with the notion that economic prosperity was *the* standard of worth-while achievement, and business enterprise *the* means of attaining that standard. As far as farmers were concerned this prosperity terminated at the close of the World War. In spite of increasing absolute numbers, farmers and the amount of agricultural capital were becoming relatively less important as compared to other classes of

the population and the economic assets with which the latter
worked. Even before 1914 it was becoming increasingly
evident that agriculture was not sharing proportionately in
the general prosperity. Whatever the general trends, however, they were obscured by the cataclysmic eruptions of the
World War, and whatever agricultural difficulties may have
been in the offing were postponed by the temporary inflation
of all economic activity during the war years. Since agricultural fairs are dependent partly upon the attendance of large
crowds of both rural and urban people, partly upon the
appropriation of public funds and partly upon the patronage
of the live-stock breeders, farmers, merchants and manufacturers who exhibit their products, they prospered generally from 1900 on.

The extent to which the older state fairs had acquired
permanent locations by 1900 has already been noted. The
advisability of such a plan was not wholly accepted, however, for at least another decade. In spite of the fact that
many of the state fairs had long been permanently located
and considerable money spent to secure and equip permanent
grounds, the reports of agricultural fair associations abound
from 1890 to 1910 in earnest discussions regarding the
merits of the stationary state fair as compared to those of
its transient predecessor. But the objectors constituted a
dwindling minority. The generally increasing success which
attended each successive year of a particular fair was
pointed out as allaying the misgivings of those who opposed
the change to a permanent site. The state fairs increasingly
prepared to remain in fixed locations. Flimsy wooden buildings, which were necessarily supplemented during fair week
by tents and temporary sheds and pens, gave way gradually
on every state fair ground to massive and substantial structures of brick and steel and concrete, planned to serve the
special purposes of all the fair's activities. As rapidly as

appropriations could be secured from state legislatures or profits made from the annual exhibitions, they were turned into live-stock barns, judging arenas, machinery halls, administration buildings, agricultural halls, women's and children's buildings, amphitheaters and a dozen lesser buildings to house the different parts of the fair. Landscape architects were called in to beautify the grounds; sidewalks and pavements were laid; electric current, water systems and sanitary equipment were provided. Though at the present time it is still necessary to erect temporary wooden buildings and tents for use during the exhibition at even the best equipped state fairs, almost all states have developed pretty definite programs of providing permanent equipment for all the attractions of the fair; and the amounts of money spent for such purposes have, in general, followed an upward trend.[1]

The new improvements not only resulted in a greater willingness of exhibitors to patronize the fairs but also facilitated the more comfortable and safer entertainment of the visitors. Live-stock breeders became more willing to exhibit their valuable animals;[2] the exhibitors of machinery and other manufactured articles found in the new exhibition

[1] For example, from 1901 to 1930 the average annual expenditure by five-year periods for improvements and permanent repairs on the Iowa state fair ground was as follows (Compiled from Iowa State Department of Agriculture, *Yearbook*, 1930, Des Moines, p. 477): 1901-5, $33,259; 1906-10, $74,946; 1911-15, $75,742; 1916-20, $82,945; 1921-25, $39,128; 1926-30, $93,191.

Statistical information in respect to both state and local fairs is extremely fragmentary. In only a few of the states have anything like complete records been kept, and what reports are available show a disheartening lack of uniformity from state to state and often a lack of continuity from year to year in the same state. Figures quoted in this chapter must be read, therefore, with some qualification. They are used, however, only when they are believed to be truly reflective of the point under consideration and descriptive of noncontroversial tendencies.

[2] It was no less a complaint of the live-stock exhibitors in the first years of the century that their animals often contracted diseases at the fairs, than of public health officials that fairs, through their failure to provide such necessities as pure drinking water, often left a trail of typhoid behind them.

THE MIDWAY AT A COUNTY FAIR

halls facilities for displaying their products more advantageously to the public. The task of presenting their exhibits was made easier; but more important than this, there were ever increasing crowds (as may be seen by referring to Table IV), to which an appeal might be made. The new grand stands or amphitheaters provided the means by which larger

TABLE IV

STATE FAIR ATTENDANCE

THE AVERAGE ANNUAL ATTENDANCE BY FIVE-YEAR PERIODS AT THE NEW YORK, WISCONSIN, IOWA AND MINNESOTA STATE FAIRS, 1906-31

New York [a]		Wisconsin [b]		Iowa [c]		Minnesota [d]	
Years	Attendance	Years	Attendance	Years	Attendance	Years	Attendance
				1908-11[e]	231,538	1906-10	311,125
		1912-16	126,098	1912-16	272,519	1911-15	323,909
1918-22	205,760	1917-21	236,796	1917-21	351,936	1916-20	454,357
1923-27	226,555	1922-26	239,910	1922-26	367,742	1921-25	419,606
1928-30[f]	229,141	1927-31	270,453	1927-31	381,150	1926-30	440,922

[a] Compiled from New York State Department of Agriculture and Markets, *Annual Reports*, Albany.
[b] Compiled from Wisconsin State Department of Agriculture, *Biennial Reports*, Madison.
[c] Compiled from Iowa State Department of Agriculture, *Yearbooks*.
[d] Compiled from Minnesota State Agricultural Society, *Annual Reports*, Minneapolis.
[e] Four-year period.   [f] Three-year period.

crowds could witness the racing and the free attractions staged by the management. It provided, furthermore, a new way of augmenting the fair treasury by the charging of admission fees for amphitheater seats, and incidentally indicated a trend in the type of entertainment which state fairs were furnishing their patrons. Moreover, the extent to which the construction of permanent buildings progressed gave some measure of the degree to which fairs were removed from the mercy of the weather. Rainy days have ever been one of the principal bogies hovering over the fair. But the construction of substantial fairground equipment, coupled with the building of hard-surfaced roads, has greatly mitigated the losses from that source. More and more have the exhibitors been relieved of the danger of being routed by a rain storm in the middle of the night and compelled to move their live stock or other exhibits to new quarters; less and less often have visitors been subjected to the indignities of wading ankle deep in mud to quit the grounds following an afternoon thundershower.

The local fairs (still organized largely with a county constituency, at least until the war period) followed the example of the larger fairs in so far as their funds permitted. In general, they were compelled to depend more than state fairs upon individual initiative. They usually acquired permanent grounds and equipment somewhat earlier than state fairs, but since they were only small agricultural units and were only beginning by 1900 to organize into state-wide groups, their command of state funds was somewhat more limited. They were financed usually by stock companies owned by local merchants and farmers. Most of the states granted them a certain measure of public aid, but usually with the stipulation that such money was to be distributed as prizes for agricultural products rather than used to acquire physical equipment. The local fair associations did, however, improve their grounds so far as they were able. Their limited resources confined them to less pretentious efforts, but the policy of providing a permanent physical basis of the fair was as pronounced in the local as in the state institutions.

The amount of money spent by the fairs for physical plants is representative of that spent in many other directions; all is indicative of the fact that they were becoming in the twentieth century business enterprises of greater or lesser proportions. This tendency was apparent in the matter of providing more lavish and spectacular entertainment, of offering more prize money, of using more state aid, of adopting modern methods of business management and of engaging in carefully laid advertising campaigns designed, to use the not infrequent phrase of some fair managers, "to sell the fair to the people." The state fairs particularly began to solicit the attendance of large crowds. The fact that most of them acquired permanent locations near the larger cities made their urbanization almost inevitable.[3] The residents of the city constituted a group that the fair managers could not afford to ignore. Properly interested they could swell the gate receipts materially. But often their interest in the fair was not identical with that of rural visitors. Their experiences, generally speaking, were wider and their sophistications more pronounced than those of their rural neighbors. If the state fair was to profit by their presence it was compelled, therefore, to cater to urban interests, a tendency that materialized largely in the growth of commercialized amusements. On the whole, the new type of entertainment appealed to both urban and rural visitors; for many of both classes it became an increasingly important point of attraction, and consequently, an increasingly important source of revenue for the fair. So it was that music (Sousa's band, for example, played at numerous state fairs), hippodrome acts, spectacular fireworks displays, automobile races, airplane demonstrations, even such bizarre attractions as head-on railroad train collisions, came to be customary features of the entertainment program. The recreational aspect of the fair is of course as old as the institution itself, but only in the present century has it come to involve lavish expenditure in the manner of providing periodic popular spectacles. The Iowa state fair, which spent $3,000 in 1900 for music and attractions, spent $25,520 in 1910, $37,506 in 1920 and $37,125 in 1930.[4]

[3] Cf. Wisconsin State Board of Agriculture, *Annual Report*, 1906, Madison, pp. 316 *et seq.*   [4] Iowa State Department of Agriculture, *Yearbooks.*

The state fair in this and other states took on many of the characteristics of a modern urban amusement park. In days when the automobile was permitting rural people to go to state fairs in larger and larger numbers, these amusement features benefited fairs by giving this group diversion not only different in amount from what they had known before, but different in kind as well. These changes in amusement particularly at the larger fairs are part and parcel of the processes of urbanization and commercialization so characteristic of twentieth-century American social life.

The competitive displays, unlike the amusement programs, continued on the whole to serve agricultural interests. But they, too, commanded generously increased sums of prize money. The average annual sum expended for prizes at the Illinois state fair in the five-year period from 1901 to 1905 was $33,753; in that from 1911 to 1915 it was $66,275; while in the period from 1926 to 1930 it had risen to $150,562. The average annual expenditures for prizes at the Iowa state fair during the corresponding five-year periods were $23,635, $62,219 and $124,256 respectively.[5] The increased prize money was probably both cause and effect of an increased number of entries in the various competitive classes. The general tendency was to extend the prize money to reward the winners of lower places as well as those of the first few, a plan that was feasible in the light of increased entries and a generally improved quality of practically all agricultural products.

The state fairs of the country have come to be well established state institutions, usually conducted by a bureau in the state department of agriculture or by a special state fair board responsible to the state government. But the men in charge of the fairs conceive their duties very much in the

[5] Compiled from Illinois State Department of Agriculture, *Transactions* and *Annual Reports*, Springfield, and Iowa State Department of Agriculture, *Yearbooks*.

manner of business promoters. The International Association of Fairs and Expositions, as pointed out before, acts as a clearing house for the problems of fair managers. The activities of this organization are numerous, and indicative of the establishment of fairs on the basis of business enterprise. Aside from holding annual meetings, the association held in 1924 a so-called School in Fair Management, with the aid of the School of Commerce and Administration of the University of Chicago; it has issued from time to time special studies dealing with such subjects as budgeting, accounting and advertising applied to fairs; it has more than once sent its representatives to Washington to act as lobbyists before the Federal Government. The state fairs, however, remain under the control of the state, supported by the state, often owned by the state, and in all cases regarded as essential parts of the state's system of agricultural promotion and education.

TABLE V

COUNTY AND DISTRICT FAIR TRENDS, 1901 TO 1930

THE AVERAGE NUMBER OF COUNTY AND DISTRICT FAIRS HELD ANNUALLY IN IOWA, TOGETHER WITH THEIR AVERAGE ANNUAL ATTENDANCE, AVERAGE ANNUAL NUMBERS OF EXHIBITORS, AVERAGE ANNUAL TOTAL DISBURSEMENTS, AVERAGE ANNUAL EXPENDITURES FOR PRIZES AND AVERAGE ANNUAL EXPENDITURES FOR AMUSEMENTS, BY FIVE-YEAR PERIODS, 1901-30 [a]

Years	Average Number of Fairs	Average Annual Attendance	Average Annual Number of Exhibitors	Average Annual Total Disbursements	Average Annual Expenditures for Prizes	Average Annual Expenditures for Amusements
1901-5	78			$3,212	$1,626	
1906-10	88			3,914	1,823	
1911-15	91	10,638	197[b]	5,899	2,333	$1,141[c]
1916-20	94	15,250	254	12,256	3,556	2,247
1921-25	95	16,367	364	16,707	5,502	2,903
1926-30	87	18,817	399	16,080	5,330	2,887

[a] Compiled from Iowa State Department of Agriculture, *Yearbooks.*
[b] Three-year period, 1913-15.   [c] Two-year period, 1914-15.

The county fairs have followed in the twentieth century a somewhat less steady and prosperous course. In actual numbers they seem to have been slightly on the decline. In those states, however, for which the data are available it appears that county fairs have expended generally increasing sums of money for prizes, for entertainment and for the acquisition and equipment of physical plants, and at the same time have drawn increased numbers of entries, exhibitors and visitors.[6] More complete data of this character are available for the local fairs of Iowa than for those of any other state. Iowa fairs have probably been representative of those in all the states, at least of the great agricultural Middle West where the institution, on the whole, flourishes most luxuriantly. Various phases of the course followed by the county and district fairs in this state may be judged by reference to Table V. Note that the average annual attendance and the average annual number of exhibitors have increased consistently to the end of the period, while the average annual expenditures for various purposes showed a consistent increase only to about 1925. These decreased expenditures may be explained partly by a lowered general price level, but the fact that the average number of fairs held annually has decreased leads to the suggestion that county fairs may be losing something of their pristine importance.

The county fair has, in fact, been ground between an upper and a nether millstone — between the larger state and district fairs and the smaller neighborhood fairs and boys' and girls' club shows, the former providing for both rural and urban people more spectacular entertainment and varied displays of agricultural products than the county fair has been able to furnish, and the latter arising as an

[6] A generalization that possibly needs qualification in the light of the financial depression of the last few years.

occasion for the intimate, primary-group participation of rural neighbors in a neighborhood festival and exhibit of neighborhood products. An analysis of this trend has many ramifications, most of which must be left for consideration in a later chapter. We may indicate here, however, that it is intimately connected in this period, as in the golden age, with the means of transportation. In the golden age it was the railroad that indirectly aided the growth of fairs by virtue of its being the dominant means of agricultural expansion. Sixty years later it was the automobile that created a condition tending to put the county fair at a disadvantage compared to the larger and more brilliant state fair. The anticipation with which the annual visit to the county fair is viewed loses much of its tang in an age of movies, amusement parks, golf courses, and a whole series of urbanized contacts. This situation has led to numerous suggestions — some of them from official sources such as state departments of agriculture — that several counties combine in holding an annual district fair instead of each county's holding its own county fair. The extent to which this suggestion may eventually be acted upon will depend primarily upon two things: first, the trend of economic conditions, whch will determine in large measure all phases of the support upon which fairs depend; and second, the attitude of government administrative agents who may control the conduct of the fairs and especially the amount of public financial assistance given them.

Some notion of certain of the fair's sources of income may be gained by reference to Table VI. The table shows the average annual percentages of the total receipts which certain important items contribute to the revenue of the fairs in two Middle Western states. The largest single source of income is the gate receipts — admission fees paid by visitors upon entering the grounds, plus the admission

fees paid by those who sit in the grand stand while watching
the races and vaudeville acts. Other important items of
income, for which data are available, are grants of state
aid, fees collected from concessionaires who set up shows
and booths on the grounds, and, in the case of the Iowa
state fair, entry fees and stall rents collected from live-
stock exhibitors, plus special prize money donated by promotive associations.

If any pronounced trends were discoverable in these items
of income, we should be in a position to predict something
as to the probable future of the fair. Our conclusions in this
respect, however, must be extremely tentative, both because
of the scarcity of data and because of the lack of decisive
trends in those which are available. But we may point out
that the percentages which the admission fees constitute of
the total receipts of the fair appear to have been dwindling
in recent years. There is, on the other hand, a slight tendency
for the percentages which state aid constitutes of the total
receipts to increase. The same incipient tendency is apparent
in concessionaires' fees and entry and stall fees. In other
words, it would appear that fair visitors are coming to pay a
smaller proportion of the total cost of the enterprise at the
same time that government subsidies and exhibitors are
coming to account for a larger proportion.[7] In the case of
county fairs in both Iowa and Minnesota this downward
trend of admission fees and the accompanying upward trend
of state aid have been steady for nearly two decades. These
tendencies, slight though they are, suggest again that the

[7] The depression beginning in 1929 may result in drastic reductions of state
aid to fairs. The Budget Advisory Board of New York State, for example,
in a report to Governor Lehman in Dec., 1933, recommended that state aid
for local agricultural fairs be withdrawn in the 1935-36 budget, and that
steps be taken to place the state fair on a self-supporting basis. The committee maintained that local fairs have outlived their usefulness. Cf. New
York *Times*, Dec. 31, 1933.

TABLE VI

SOURCES OF INCOME OF FAIRS

AVERAGE ANNUAL PERCENTAGES OF TOTAL RECEIPTS CONTRIBUTED BY CERTAIN SOURCES OF INCOME TO THE STATE FAIRS AND THE COUNTY AND DISTRICT FAIRS IN IOWA AND MINNESOTA, BY FIVE-YEAR PERIODS, 1901-30

Years	Iowa State Fair [a]				Minnesota State Fair [b]			Iowa County and District Fairs [c]			Minnesota County and District Fairs [d]		
	State Grant	Concessions	Admissions	Entry Fees, Stall Rent, Donated Prizes, etc.	State Grant	Concessions	Admissions	State Grant	Concessions	Admissions	State Grant	Concessions	Admissions
1901-05	12.70	5.32[e]	40.08[e]	11.94	2.13	8.38	54.37						
1906-10	14.30	9.25	45.44	13.60	8.51	11.54	51.47						
1911-15	15.36	9.38	48.07	14.82	4.94	10.83	56.06	6.35[f]	10.66[f]	65.36[f]	12.18[g]	5.65[g]	36.84[g]
1916-20	12.96	10.49	51.50	16.96	12.53	8.97	49.94	7.84	10.35	66.72	13.27	7.45	36.95
1921-25	6.40	12.45	50.60	16.18	8.88	9.54	44.59	13.11	10.59	59.00	16.16[h]	8.71[h]	32.66[h]
1926-30	14.54	11.77	43.80		10.92	10.06	41.99	14.26	12.11	58.17			

a Compiled from Iowa State Department of Agriculture, *Yearbooks*.
b Compiled from Minnesota State Agricultural Society, *Annual Reports*.
c Compiled from Iowa State Department of Agriculture, *Yearbooks*.
d Compiled from Minnesota State Agricultural Society, *Annual Reports*.

e Four-year period, 1902-5.
f Two-year period, 1914-15.
g Four-year period, 1917-20.
h Five-year period, 1927-31.

county fair is probably coming, slowly but rather surely, to stand less and less on its own feet.

In summary it may be said that state fairs have grown considerably larger and financially stronger in the present century, partly at least at the expense of the county fairs. Not only have the state fairs become definitely established institutions, but their immediate future seems to be more or less assured by the responsibility which the states assume for them. The county fairs on the other hand, though still widespread, have become relatively less important than formerly, especially in so far as their services to the agricultural population are concerned.

THE SPECIALIZED LIVE-STOCK SHOW

The history of the agricultural fair in the twentieth century has been characterized, in the second place, by the growth of specialized fairs or shows. This differentiation naturally accompanied the evolution of the agricultural industry. With the development of technological tools and processes, the opening up of new markets and the introduction of other changes to rural economy, new divisions of labor and new forms of association constantly emerged in rural society. These new types of associations, as we saw in the preceding chapter, served new types of agricultural interests, educational, economic and political; and the agricultural fair was virtually compelled to make certain readjustments to meet these new conditions. One of the phases of this readjustment was the appearance of the specialized fair or show, more limited in its activities and serving narrower interests, but making a much more intensive appeal than the older agricultural fairs. Usually the specialized show emphasizes some more or less narrow branch of the agricultural industry, though it rarely does so to the complete exclusion of other branches, or of certain more or less universal interests, such as the economic, recreational or educational. The specialized show represents a differentiation of fair types just as the economic, political, educational or technological associations represent a differentiation of agricultural organization.

The horticultural, woolgrowers' and dairymen's associations that began to emerge in the nineteenth century [8] often held special exhibits that in some measure foreshadowed the specialized agricultural shows so numerous in the present century. Poultry shows, too, were held as early as 1849, and have since become not only well established institutions in the field of poultry husbandry, but also the most widespread type of specialized agricultural show. In 1873 the American Poultry Association was organized to formulate and adopt a standard of excellence to be used by other associations in awarding prizes to exhibition poultry. Though periodically revised, this first "Standard of Perfection" has existed from its publication in 1874 to the present.[9] Hundreds of small towns or local neighborhoods all over the United States hold their annual winter shows, sponsored by a local poultry fanciers' association or by a loose and temporary organization formed by a few interested individuals for the purpose of conducting the show. There are also large state, national and international poultry shows, New York, Boston, Chicago and St. Louis holding the most important. The most famous of these, the Madison Square Garden Poultry Show, established in 1872 and held annually in New York City, attracts poultry fanciers from all over the world. They come to advertise their stock, to compete for prizes, to discuss their problems and otherwise to promote their interests.

Less widespread than poultry shows are numerous other

---

[8] Cf. *supra*, Chap. IV.
[9] Jull, Morley A., *Poultry Husbandry*, New York, 1930, p. 31.

exhibits representing specialized branches of the agricultural industry. Corn shows, grain shows, fruit shows and pet stock shows are common events in sections of the country where these particular products are grown. Flower shows, dog shows and the so-called society horse shows constitute a type of specialized show representing a unique combination of agricultural and urban interests. While their exhibits are products of the same general type as those shown and emphasized at the agricultural fair or show and are often made a part of these more general shows, the interests which are served thereby are decidedly more urban than rural. The activities so represented are prone to become urban hobbies as regards not only participation in the shows and membership in associations but also the actual growing and preparation of the product.

But the specialized agricultural shows which to date top all others in America are the various exhibitions serving and representing the live-stock industry. These shows, although they bid for urban support by adding attractions that appeal to urban as well as to rural people, remain essentially rural in their basic interests. The agricultural products shown are produced on the farms and ranches of the country; the manufacturers' and merchants' displays and those of the coöperating educational institutions, government agencies, breeders' associations and propagandist organizations present machines, articles or processes intended for use primarily by rural people, particularly those engaged in the branch of agriculture which the show represents.

Exhibits of farm animals have always constituted a prominent feature of American agricultural fairs from the days of the Washington, Columbian and Berkshire fairs to the present. As the agricultural fairs multiplied during the golden age and after, live stock became perhaps the most universal feature. Indeed the period from 1866 to 1886 has been called "the golden age of animal husbandry," [10] because it witnessed an astonishing development not only of new breeds of pure-bred stock, but also of new kinds of feed, new methods of management and new associations and journals to promote the industry. In this period began the first specialized live-stock show of long-standing importance — the American Fat Stock Show — held in Chicago from 1878 to 1897. It was established by the Illinois State Board of Agriculture and was granted state aid by the Illinois legislature. It was exclusively a fat-stock show, patterned after the fat-stock show at Smithfield, England. Fat beeves, sheep and hogs and the dressed carcasses of these meat animals made up the exhibits. The American Fat Stock Show was perhaps ahead of its time, so to speak, for it is reported that "lack of support" caused its discontinuance in 1897. Primarily a display of animals and meat prepared especially for the holiday city butcher trade, it rested of course on a relatively narrow base of both technical and popular interest. It was perhaps, therefore, a differentiated form of the fair institution, too specialized to claim sufficiently strong support to insure its perpetuation from year to year.

The show which followed on the same ground after three years, while essentially a reorganization of the old fat-stock show and sponsored by many of the same group of men, was cast on decidedly broader lines. It served from its inauguration a far greater variety of interests than its predecessor, and in its development has continued to serve many added rural interests and a few urban ones as well. In 1899 representatives of the live-stock registry associations, live-stock breeders and officials of the Chicago Union Stock Yards Company met to plan a new show to represent the meat-producing industry. On December 1, 1900, the Inter-

[10] Gras, Norman Scott Brien, *A History of Agriculture in Europe and America*, New York, 1925, p. 319.

national Live Stock Exposition was opened with an exhibit of all kinds of beef cattle, hogs and sheep and draft horses, the broader base of the new show being apparent in the fact that it was a combined display of fat stock prepared for the butcher's block, breeding stock aimed to improve the type of such meat-producing animals, and horses productive of one of the farmer's most important sources of power. It was and has remained the primary object of the show to display the improvement made in live-stock production and to furnish incentives for further improvement in the breeds and types of farm animals.

In carrying out this primary object the show has developed along four principal lines: first, an exhibit of pure-bred cattle, sheep and hogs which are the means of improving the type of market animals, supplemented by the display of pure-bred horses; second, the exhibit of prime fat stock fitted for the market, admirably near at hand in Chicago's packing houses, presenting the types of and the methods of producing market-topping beef, pork and mutton animals; third, a range-cattle display which serves an essentially commercial interest in that it constitutes a market through which the western ranchman sells his unfattened cattle to the grain-belt feeder; and fourth, a whole series of demonstrations, displays and contests conducted by agricultural colleges, experiment stations, extension services, breeders' associations and other agricultural organizations designed to teach lessons of live-stock breeding, feeding, management and selection purporting in some way to improve the industry. Each year there come to the International Live Stock Exposition great crowds of live-stock breeders, especially from the Middle West and the range countries, to exhibit their animals, to study the new types of animals and methods of production being developed and to keep in intimate touch with other members of their industry. The social intercourse which this and similar exhibitions afford develops a wider acquaintance among live-stock men, casts a certain halo of significance and sentiment about the art of animal breeding, and makes of the prize-winning specimens a kind of animal royalty commanding the homage of their owners, their keepers and their admirers. Although the International has advanced in general along the four lines named above, it has added certain entertainment features, relatively extraneous, for the purpose of attracting urban as well as rural visitors. These have taken the form principally of society horse shows, which are held in the evening and bid for the attendance largely of urban patrons.

The International, like the county and state fairs, began its career in temporary quarters. Unlike the state fairs and some of the other specialized shows, it has never been a transient exhibition. It was first held in scattered, inconvenient buildings improvised for the occasion at the Chicago stockyards. As it became more firmly established as an institution among live-stock breeders, a permanent home was provided in the form of a huge concrete and steel amphitheater and necessary stock pens. Even so, part of the exhibits overflow into the stockyards and the property of other coöperating agencies.[11]

In general most of the other specialized live-stock shows follow the same plan as does the International. Perhaps the second event in importance is the American Royal Live Stock Show, held at Kansas City. It was inaugurated as an exhibition of pure-bred beef cattle, and while such animals have continued to constitute the major exhibits of the show,

[11] Cf., Plumb, C. S., "International Live Stock Exposition," *Book of Rural Life*, Chicago, c. 1925, V, 2921-23; J. E. P., "The International Anniversary Show," *Breeder's Gazette*, Nov. 27, 1919, pp. 1147-48. Following the disastrous stockyards fire of May 19, 1934, in which the International Amphitheater was destroyed, the International management began the erection of an elaborate set of structures designed to house the complete show.

it has since come to include all other kinds of live stock, and, like the International, to cater to urban patronage by introducing society horse shows and other entertainment features. Because of its location nearer to the range country, the interests of ranchmen loom relatively larger at this show than at the International. Several other lesser live-stock shows also are patterned on this same general plan, the most notable being the Ak-Sar-Ben Live Stock Show at Omaha, the National Western Live Stock Show at Denver and the Southwestern Exposition and Fat Stock Show at Fort Worth.

The National Dairy Show is the largest of the specialized shows serving the dairy industry. Founded in 1906 by a group of men interested in promoting dairying by the same method used by the International in advancing the meat-producing industry, this organization had an interesting career. The first show was held at Chicago and for twenty-two years thereafter it was a transient exhibition, Columbus, Springfield (Massachusetts), Milwaukee, St. Paul, Memphis, and St. Louis being among the cities to entertain it. Finally in 1929 a number of St. Louis business men formed the National Exhibition Company and contracted with the National Dairy Association to hold the show at St. Louis. A permanent exposition building was erected and the show embarked on a program both of developing a permanent plant and of enlarging its means of popular appeal.[12] The show itself, devoted to the dairy industry, has been promoted along three principal lines: first, a competitive exhibit of pure-bred dairy cattle; second, a display of dairy machinery, ranging from such things as cream separators and dairy-barn equipment, which is of interest principally to the farmer and breeder, to machinery

[12] The National Dairy Show has not been held since 1931, admittedly because of the business depression. Whether this marks a permanent or only temporary lapse of the institution remains of course to be revealed.

used in the manufacture of butter, ice cream, cheese, condensed milk and other dairy products; and third, the exhibits of dairymen's associations, agricultural colleges, experiment stations, departments of agriculture and state and city boards of health, presenting lessons in the use of dairy products.[13] Some of these items, it should be noted, are of interest to urban as well as to rural people.

The swine industry also has produced its specialized show. The National Swine Show was first held at Omaha in 1916 under the auspices of the National Swine Growers' Association in coöperation with the Omaha Board of Trade. Later shows were held at Cedar Rapids and Des Moines, Iowa; at Peoria and Springfield, Illinois; and at Indianapolis, Indiana. While the show seems to have become a firmly established institution among swine producers, it cannot yet be said with certainty that it has become permanently located. The National Swine Growers' Association has repeatedly held its show in connection with one of the leading Middle Western state fairs, the fair profiting by the added attraction of a national event and the swine show profiting by the use of the state fair buildings and grounds and the presence of large numbers of people who would not be sufficiently interested in the swine show alone to visit it were it held separately. Since 1931 the National Swine Show has been held in connection with the Illinois state fair at Springfield, though whether this marks the end of the show's nomadic career is not certain.[14]

Initial steps toward the creation of other specialized national live-stock shows have been taken by several breed organizations. This has usually been done by designating one of the state fairs or national live-stock shows as the seat

13 Cf. *Breeder's Gazette*, Nov., 1929, p. 7; Eckles, C. H., "National Dairy Show," *Book of Rural Life*, VI, 3750-52.
14 Cf. Ferrin, E. F., "National Swine Show," *Book of Rural Life*, VI, 3756.

for the year of a special breed show, the breeders' association then offering special prizes or otherwise contributing to the scope and to the ultimate success of the show. For example, the American Hereford Cattle Breeders' Association in 1932 celebrated the fiftieth anniversary of its organization by holding a "Golden Jubilee" Hereford cattle show in connection with the regular exhibition of the American Royal at Kansas City, when the largest sum of prize money ever offered for one breed of cattle drew the largest aggregation of pure-bred cattle of one breed ever assembled in an American show ring. Approximately 1,000 head of pure-bred Herefords competed for $75,000 in prizes. Another twentieth-century development of the specialized live-stock show is a combination show and auction sale of pure-bred breeding stock usually conducted by state or national breeders' associations. A typical example is the National Shorthorn Congress established at Chicago in 1918 by the American Shorthorn Breeders' Association. Entries of Shorthorn cattle are solicited from breeders all over the country; at the Congress the cattle are first shown for prizes in their respective classes and later are sold at auction. Countless similar events, most of them on a smaller scale of course, are conducted by state or local breed associations, and while they serve primarily a commercial interest by providing a central market for surplus breeding stock, they nevertheless, by virtue of their competitive exhibit features, become specialized live-stock shows, thus contributing to the aggregate importance of this type of agricultural exhibition.

THE NEIGHBORHOOD FAIR

The third point which merits consideration in any discussion of the twentieth-century fair is the development of the so-called community fair, or as we shall refer to it here,

the neighborhood fair.[15] It is given a variety of names —
school fair, grange fair, township fair, farmers' fair, fall
festival, etc., but the underlying plan is the same for all.
The neighborhood fair arises characteristically as a festival
of the rural neighborhood, expanded to include as far as
possible the whole range of the community's economic and
social life. It is hailed as a return to the old type of agricultural fair, principally because it is relatively free from
the commercialization which characterizes the larger fairs
particularly in their recreational aspects. In most cases there
is a definite attempt to make the neighborhood fair appeal to
all members of the neighborhood by urging them to become
active participants instead of passive spectators, and by
providing the means, in the way of sports, contests and
exhibits, whereby they can do so. There are few gaudy
displays, few breath-taking thrills at such a fair; it is almost
entirely free from horse racing, commercialized side shows
and entertainment, professional fair managers and stock-
holders. The residents of the neighborhood usually provide
their own amusements and their own simple organization.
The exhibits are not the property of professional exhibitors
from another county or another state, but are displays of
local products made or raised by neighbors to neighbors. The
neighborhood fair, therefore, is a more or less spontaneous
revelation of neighborhood spirit, in which intimate contacts
are fostered which in turn provide the means of creating
and sustaining a primary-group socialization among the

[15] Cf. Rubinow, S. G., "The Organization and Management of Fairs," and
"Fairs and Their Educational Value," North Carolina Agricultural Extension
Service, *Circulars* 68 and 69, 1918; Moran, J. Sterling, "The Community
Fair," United States Department of Agriculture, *Farmers' Bulletin* 870, 1917;
Taylor, E. H., "Country Fairs," *Country Gentleman*, July 17, 1920, pp. 11
et seq., July 31, 1920, pp. 8 *et seq.*, Aug. 7, 1920, pp. 22 *et seq.*, Aug. 21, 1920,
pp. 9 *et seq.*; Galpin, C. J. and Emily F. Hoag, "The Rural Community
Fair," University of Wisconsin Agricultural Experiment Station, *Bulletin* 307,
1919; "Planning the Community Fair Exhibit," *Wallaces' Farmer*, Aug. 13,
1926, p. 1065.

members of the neighborhood. Like the larger fairs, the neighborhood fair satisfies certain desires of its constituents — the desire to pleasure together, the desire to excel in some form of endeavor, the desire to learn — but it does so in a more intimate way, first because a larger proportion of the residents of a neighborhood participate in its activities, and second, because almost all of them are personally and intimately acquainted with one another.

At the neighborhood fair are displayed agricultural and domestic products — live stock, poultry, vegetables, fruits, grains, canned goods, sewing, etc., varied of course according to local interests or facilities — grown or made in a particular neighborhood. Opportunity is afforded for some educational or extension agency, particularly the agricultural college or the vocational agriculture department of the local high school, to do some first-hand work among the people of the neighborhood. Many of the agricultural colleges have coöperated with neighborhood fairs by providing standardized premium lists and classifications for entries, by appointing members of their teaching or extension staffs to act as judges of the products exhibited, and by sending extension workers to the fairs to conduct demonstrations of various farm and home processes being developed or tested at the schools.

The neighborhood fair is in many respects a rural playday, a time of friendly social intercourse between rural neighbors. As such it furnishes the opportunity to make of it more than an occasion for neighborhood gossip or mere idle visiting; it can be made the beginning or the fruition of a planned neighborhood program of rural recreation. Here again some of the larger agencies of rural service have coöperated in the development and conduct of this type of fair; the schools, the agricultural extension services and the farm bureau, for example, have furnished many of the plans and much of the leadership in directing the recreational activities of the neighborhood fair. Simple pageants and plays are often presented and all sorts of games and contests are conducted in which the visitors can take part. At perhaps no other type of fair is social integration through recreational interests promoted so readily.

The neighborhood fair is commonly a one-day event. Its structural organization is simple and usually temporary. Rarely is an admission fee charged; the small expenses incurred are generally met by the contributions of interested individuals or the merchants of a near-by town, or in a few cases by grants of public funds. Such a fair requires little expenditure in operation, none in upkeep. Most often perhaps it is held at the neighborhood school center, though sometimes at the neighborhood church or trading center. In 1919 only 5 of the 210 neighborhood fairs in North Carolina were held at railroad stops; the rest were held in the open country.[16] The significance of the neighborhood fair is not measured by its size, but by the satisfaction that its participants receive from the intimate social interaction with their immediate neighbors, in which a high degree of coöperative participation may be achieved and neighborhood and individual resources and efforts may be seen in the light of neighborhood betterment.

The neighborhood fair is of comparatively recent development. Since it lends itself even less than state and county fairs to the accumulation of statistics, there is no way of knowing how many are held annually throughout the nation. It is, however, widely scattered as a type; and has probably thrived more vigorously in the South than in any other section. Though still the region of small things agriculturally, the South has recently made giant strides in agricultural and home improvement; and undoubtedly the neighborhood

[16] Taylor, *Country Gentleman, op. cit.,* July 17, 1920, p. 11.

fairs are again both a manifestation of this activity and an agency of its stimulation.

The neighborhood fair is often a definite part of the state's system of agricultural encouragement. It has benefited noticeably from the public aid to agriculture given through the Federal Government in coöperation with the state governments in the form of extension services and vocational agriculture courses in the public schools. The fair, in many instances, centers around the activities of the rural school, though it usually includes the active participation of adults as well as children. As the status of rural education has advanced, therefore, the neighborhood fair has grown in importance and extent. In 1918 the state of North Carolina, through its fair committee, limited state-aided neighborhood fairs to four in each county in order that sufficient funds and competent judges might be provided. At the same time it inaugurated a systematic policy of state aid for all classes of fairs — neighborhood, county, district and state — stipulating that all grants were to be distributed over four divisions of exhibits; namely, live stock, farm and field crops, horticulture, and home economics.[17] Largely as a consequence of this action North Carolina became one of the leading agricultural states of the South, her system of fairs rating among the highest in the entire nation.

In certain instances the neighborhood fair has developed into a county fair, and in many others it has acted as a feeder to the larger fairs. One of the popular features of many county fairs is the competition between neighborhood booths, which has very often been stimulated by a neighborhood fair. In this and similar cases the county fair provides the opportunity for competition between neighborhoods and thus forms a link in interindividual and intergroup rivalry which

[17] *Ibid.*, p. 11.

expresses itself in progressively enlarged rural exhibitions. The neighborhood fair movement, however, has not had a completely happy effect on county fairs as a whole. Often it has tended to displace the county fair as the occasion of a local rural fall festival. The neighborhood fair is the one evidence of decentralization discernible in the recent social changes which fairs have undergone.

The Influence of Boys' and Girls' Agricultural Clubs

The fourth significant development of the twentieth-century fair has to do with boys' and girls' agricultural club activities. This development is doubly important. In the first place it records the growth of boys' and girls' fairs, at which the junior club members are the principal if not the sole exhibitors. Secondly it indicates the increasing import-ance of the junior divisions of the well established fairs and shows throughout the country. The boys' and girls' club show often constitutes in reality one type of neighborhood fair, yet the club movement has had such a far-reaching effect upon the fair as an institution that it merits a separate treatment.

The phenomenal growth in recent years of boys' and girls' clubs is the result of the Smith-Lever Act of 1914, granting Federal aid to agricultural extension work, and the Smith-Hughes Act of 1917, providing Federal assistance for rural vocational education. These Acts, however, were not with-out historical antecedents. The introduction of nature study into both rural and urban schools prior to 1900 was the result of a growing demand on the part of rural people for the teaching of agricultural subjects in the public schools. Then from 1900 to 1905 farmers' institutes multiplied rapidly, many of them coöperating closely with the county superintendents of schools in providing agricultural projects for rural boys and girls. Meanwhile the modern club idea began to take form. In 1899 W. B. Otwell, president of the farmers' institute in Macoupin County, Illinois, having failed to enlist the interest of adult farmers, determined to center his attention on the boys and girls of the county. He distributed one ounce of high-grade seed corn to every boy and girl in the county who promised to plant the seed and exhibit the produce at the next farmers' institute. Five hundred boys and girls accepted and almost the entire number appeared in 1900 with their corn exhibits. After Otwell had attracted national attention to his boys' and girls' corn club at the Louisiana Purchase Exposition in 1904, by displaying a huge corn pyramid made up of the exhibits of a thousand Illinois club members, similar club work was begun in other states and with other products. There was, however, no uniformity in the conduct of the clubs and they depended largely upon the initiative of private individuals in the various communities. The Smith-Lever Act not only provided funds to take over practically all the junior agricultural club work in the country and to extend the system further, but it also created a single extension system which made club work relatively uniform in all the states. Competent leadership was provided for state and county club work; the number and kinds of projects were increased; boys and girls were organized into definitely interrelated clubs; and the demonstration team was developed as a means of presenting to the people of the community the methods used in improving farm and home practices.[18]

Of the numerous clubs organized, the 4-H club is in many respects, most widely known.[19] The 4-H club work is con-

[18] Cf. Farrell, George E., "Boys' and Girls' 4-H Club Work Under the Smith-Lever Act, 1914-1924," United States Department of Agriculture, *Miscellaneous Circular* No. 85, Washington, 1926, pp. 9 *et seq.*; True, Alfred Charles, "A History of Agricultural Education in the United States, 1785-1925," United States Department of Agriculture, *Miscellaneous Publication* No. 36, Washington, 1929, pp. 393 *et seq.*

[19] The name 4-H signifies the training and use of four faculties — head,

ducted among boys and girls between ten and twenty years of age, usually in groups of from ten to twenty members. The clubs meet regularly, conduct literary programs and business meetings, report the status of the members' projects and take part in numerous social and recreational activities. Each member of a club selects one or more agricultural or home economics projects in which he or she engages under the direction of local and state club leaders. There are dozens of different kinds of projects, almost as many as there are farm products and home economics activities. There are projects having to do with all kinds of animals — calves, pigs, lambs, colts and poultry, and with all kinds of crops — corn, cotton, fruit, vegetables, etc. Girls participate in these as well as other projects, canning and preserving fruit and vegetables, making articles of clothing, beautifying homes, gardens or lawns, remodeling furniture, studying child care and training, home management, foods and nutrition.

The Smith-Hughes Act provided for the organization of vocational agriculture courses and projects in the rural public schools. Many phases of this work are identical with that of the 4-H clubs; the principal distinction lies in the fact that the Smith-Hughes vocational agriculture work is conducted through the public school system while the 4-H club work is conducted by an extension service — the coöperative effort of the United States Department of Agriculture, the state agricultural colleges and the local farm bureaus.

The stimulus to the unification and the extension of club work furnished by the Smith-Lever Act resulted in a temporary inflation during the World War. Many city boys and

---

heart, health and hands — the head to reason, think and plan; the heart to be kindly and sympathetic; the health to insure efficiency and enjoyment; the hands to perform skillful work. The emblem of the clubs is a four-leaf clover with an H on each leaflet. Cf. Farrell, "Boys' and Girls' 4-H Club Work," *op. cit.*, p. 1 n.

girls were enrolled in clubs in an effort to increase the production and conservation of war-time necessities. After a postwar deflation period, club work began to enjoy a gradual expansion. Table VII presents the growth of the 4-H club movement from 1923 to 1930.

TABLE VII

GROWTH OF THE 4-H CLUB MOVEMENT

THE NUMBER OF 4-H CLUBS IN THE UNITED STATES, THE NUMBER OF BOYS AND GIRLS ENROLLED AND THE NUMBER COMPLETING THEIR PROJECTS, TOGETHER WITH THE NUMBER OF PROJECTS STARTED AND THE NUMBER OF PROJECTS COMPLETED, 1923-30.[a]

Year	Number of Clubs	Number of Boys and Girls Enrolled	Number of Boys and Girls Completing Projects	Number of Projects Started	Number of Projects Completed
1923	32,673	459,074	249,416	722,508	428,746
1924	38,120	510,355	283,283	945,663	489,262
1925	41,286	565,046	329,574	1,079,604	589,440
1926	41,234	586,156	368,305	1,161,024	673,997
1927	44,188	619,712	399,107	1,330,239	776,029
1928	46,671	663,940	447,579	1,466,584	882,795
1929	52,180	756,096	507,487	1,614,149	995,262
1930	56,180	822,714	554,345	1,535,619	971,308

[a] United States Department of Agriculture, *Yearbook*, 1932, Washington, p. 954; Smith, Clarence Beaman and Meredith Chester Wilson, *The Agricultural Extension System of the United States*, New York, 1930, p. 195.

The encouragement of young people's activities by agricultural fairs had a few scattered protoypes in the nineteenth century,[20] but the wide-spread recognition of club work at the fairs is almost entirely a development of the last fifteen years. Club activities at practically all fairs have become one of the leading parts of the program, and at not a few, the principal if not the sole nucleus around which the fair is organized. County fairs, state fairs and the larger special-

[20] Horace Greeley offered prizes at the 1856 New York state fair at Watertown for the best farming efforts of boys under eighteen years of age. Cf. Morrish, R. W., *A History of Fairs*, Chicago, n.d., p. 35.

ized shows have made generous provision in the way of
prize money, club equipment and programs designed to
promote club activities at their respective exhibitions. In
many cases county fairs, particularly those that have become
financially weak, have elevated club work to a dominant
position or have practically reorganized as junior fairs, thus
becoming a county-wide agency of coöperation between the
extension services responsible for club work and local individuals interested in holding some sort of county agricultural exhibition. In addition to these provisions by the well
established fairs for the recognition of club work and to the
reorganization of certain fairs on an almost exclusive club
basis, nearly all the 4-H clubs hold an annual county-wide
achievement day at the close of the club year, which in many
respects deserves to be ranked as a type of agricultural fair.
The vocational agriculture students in many schools hold a
public display of the same general character. Whatever
forms the exhibition of junior products and the demonstration of junior activities take, they constitute the most
significant aspect of the evolution of agricultural fairs in
the present century.

The typical 4-H achievement day is a county-wide meeting of club members and club leaders, attended usually by
any other interested persons. On these occasions the club
projects are reported, competitive demonstrations of an
educational nature are conducted, and the products of the
club members are exhibited for prizes or are selected to be
sent to larger fairs or club meetings. The program of the
day often includes an inspirational address, music, plays
and pageants, dinners and picnics. The scope and importance to the community of the 4-H achievement day often
depend upon whether it is merely an elimination contest to
select the best products or club teams for later county, state
or national competition, or an event which, constituting an

end in itself, presents to the county a more or less final exhibit of club work. In counties where no regular agricultural fair is held, the achievement day is likely to assume the latter significance. In such cases it takes the place of the agricultural fair; and in addition to the exhibition of club products and demonstrations, it often includes certain other features furnished by the merchants and the social or civic organizations of the towns in the county. Boys' and girls' club work, organized as it is as a part of the national agricultural extension system, demands progressive elimination contests for the selection of winners in the different competitions. The national club shows, demonstrations or contests are usually held in connection with such shows as the International, the American Royal or the National Dairy Show. The local elimination show, however, may take one of several forms: a club exhibit at the regular county fair, an achievement-day show that acts solely as an elimination contest, or an achievement-day event that combines club displays with entertainment and recreation of a much broader appeal, and thereby becomes essentially a new type of county fair.

County fairs, state fairs and the larger specialized shows, finding the 4-H club department the means of injecting new and powerful forces into their exhibitions, have devoted increasing attention to the enlargement of this phase of the fair. County and state fairs have not only increased the amount of prize money offered for boys' and girls' exhibits, but they have in numerous cases erected special club buildings as a part of their permanent equipment. A number of fairs have conducted 4-H camps quartering the club members on the fairground during the fair, where under the supervision of club leaders they show their exhibits, engage in their contests, attend leadership training schools and participate in other fair and camp activities. A national

BABY BEEVES ON THEIR WAY TO THE SHOW RING, CLUB FAIR

4-H club congress is held each year during the International at which state and local winners are the guests of the show as a reward for outstanding accomplishments in the various kinds of club work; a similar national meeting of the vocational agriculture schools is held during the American Royal. The scope of 4-H club work as it relates to fairs may be seen in the range of junior activities outlined for the 1932 International. The calves, pigs and lambs fitted by the boys and girls for the junior live-stock feeding contest were classified. Competitive exhibits were also arranged for cotton, potatoes, sweet potatoes, peanuts, corn, eggs, canned goods, clothing and home furnishings. A style show, a health contest, leadership and achievement-record contests, and judging contests of live stock, crops, meat, bread, canned goods, clothing and home furnishings represented another phase of the show. Special awards in the form of money, merchandise, medals, trophies and scholarships at agricultural colleges were offered by live-stock breeders' associations, the Chicago Live Stock Exchange, the Union Stock Yard and Transit Company, the Chicago Association of Commerce, the *Country Gentleman* and Thomas E. Wilson, the packer.[21] Appreciating the genuine and abiding interest in club work, fair managers, the country over, have been only too happy to collaborate with these organizations. Their publicity value alone is a source of strength to any fair.

A comparison of the sums of money spent by various fairs in the last decade or so gives some indication of the growing emphasis placed upon 4-H work. This comparison becomes more significant when we note the percentages of the total amount of prize money represented by the sums paid for club work. It will be seen in Table VIII that the

[21] International Live Stock Exposition, *Preliminary Classification*, 1932, Chicago, pp. 70 and *passim*.

TABLE VIII

PRIZE MONEY PAID TO JUNIOR EXHIBITORS

TOTAL AMOUNTS OF PRIZE MONEY PAID, AMOUNTS AND PERCENTAGES OF TOTAL PAID TO JUNIOR EXHIBITORS AT SELECTED STATE FAIRS AND AT COUNTY AND DISTRICT FAIRS IN IOWA AND WISCONSIN, 1920-31

Year	New York State Fair [a] Total Amount Paid	Paid to Junior Exhibits Amount	Percentage	Iowa State Fair [b] Total Amount Paid	Paid to Junior Exhibits Amount	Percentage	Wisconsin State Fair [c] Total Amount Paid	Paid to Junior Exhibits Amount	Percentage	Illinois State Fair [d] Total Amount Paid	Paid to Junior Exhibits Amount	Percentage	Iowa County and District Fairs [e] Total Amount Paid	Paid to Junior Exhibits Amount	Percentage	Wisconsin County and District Fairs [f] Total Amount Paid	Paid to Junior Exhibits Amount	Percentage
1920				$112,620	$4,508	4.00	$72,733	$2,749	3.77				$462,295	$14,172	3.06			
1921				120,428	6,045	5.01	95,469	2,478	2.59				516,124	18,691	3.62			
1922	$64,615	$956	1.47	104,522	6,155	5.88	93,544	2,407	2.57				520,683	23,055	4.42			
1923	65,375	1,752	2.67	105,886	7,721	7.29	92,659	3,191	3.44	$110,835	$2,169	1.95	527,639	29,945	5.67			
1924	70,956	2,150	3.03	120,676	9,589	7.94	94,589	2,533	2.67	102,643	3,369	3.28	509,735	37,320	7.32			
1925	63,165	2,166	3.42	112,067	8,939	7.97	103,701	3,083	2.97	123,957	3,317	2.67	538,928	43,626	8.09			
1926	71,144	4,291	6.03	122,959	10,048	8.17	88,062	5,515	6.26	142,449	5,650	3.96	500,311	44,963	8.98			
1927	76,766	4,985	6.49	119,606	9,476	7.92	90,582	5,974	6.59	108,086	4,377	4.04	474,412	45,876	9.67			
1928	79,284	5,287	6.66	122,220	11,234	9.19	92,822	6,029	6.49	149,766	6,883	4.59	446,004	49,847	11.17			
1929	82,962	5,810	7.00	127,943	12,029	9.40	93,859	6,119	6.51	160,755	10,090	6.27	444,825	48,216	10.83	$411,162	$54,699	13.30
1930				128,553	13,228	10.28	96,009	7,242	7.54	162,619	12,656	7.78	449,988	54,134	12.03	412,851	69,209	16.76
1931				120,013	13,285	11.06				171,584	10,185	5.93	403,612	57,974	14.36	394,901	73,061	18.50

[a] Compiled from New York State Department of Agriculture and Markets, *Annual Reports.*

[b] Compiled from Iowa State Fair, *Report*, 1931, Des Moines, pp. 48-49.

[c] Compiled from Wisconsin State Department of Agriculture, *Biennial Reports.*

[d] Compiled from Illinois State Department of Agriculture, *Annual Reports.*

[e] Compiled from Iowa County and District Fair Managers Association, *Proceedings*, 1931, Des Moines, p. 205.

[f] Compiled from Wisconsin State Department of Agriculture, *County and District Fair Reports*, Madison.

New York state fair, for example, in 1923 paid 1.47 percent of its total prize money to boy and girl exhibitors, while in 1930 it paid them 7 percent of the total. The Iowa state fair, paying 4 percent of its total prize money to junior exhibitors in 1920, paid them 11.06 percent in 1931. Likewise, the Illinois and Wisconsin state fairs have made a general, though less steady, increase in the percentages of total prize money paid to boys and girls. The growing recognition of club work is shown even more strikingly in a consideration of the county and district fairs of Iowa and Wisconsin. In the former state, where records are available over a longer period of years, the prize money paid to junior exhibitors showed a proportionate increase of nearly fivefold from 1920 to 1931; in Wisconsin it increased from 13.3 percent in 1929 to 18.5 percent in 1931. The state of Illinois, in recognizing such work, has enacted a law organizing fifteen vocational agriculture section fairs and providing state funds to the extent of $1,500 for each section for their support. As a rule each section holds a live-stock show and a grain show, the vocational agriculture schools in the section sending their representatives to compete for prizes. By further legislative enactments (1929) Illinois provides state aid for the partial payment of prizes to 4-H club exhibits in each county, such exhibits either constituting an independent 4-H fair or a section of the regular county fair. State funds for these junior fairs as well as for the other agricultural fairs are paid from a fund known as the "State, County Fair and Agricultural Extension Club Premium Fund," which is accumulated from the license fees and admission tax collected from the race tracks of the state.[22] This increase, both absolute and proportionate, in the amount

22 Cf. Illinois Department of Agriculture, *Reports of the 4-H Club Exhibits, 1930,* Springfield; Illinois State Board for Vocational Education, "Report of the Vocational Agriculture Section Fairs, 1931-1932," *Bulletin* No. 54, Springfield, 1932.

of prize money paid to club exhibitors, means not only that
the prize awards for the winning products or articles shown
by them are larger, but that thousands more boys and girls
are availing themselves of the opportunity to exhibit at the
fairs. The number of club entries [23] at the New York state
fair, for example, increased from 496 in 1923 to 3,927 in
1930.[24] The same trend is apparent in other cases where
the figures have been published.

It is evident, therefore, that on the whole there has been
in the last decade a steady progression in the amount of
recognition given by fairs of all classes to boys' and girls'
club work. For many fairs it has undoubtedly been a "life-
saver"; for all it has been the means of extending their
services, both by coöperating with certain educational
agencies and by serving a new type of rural interest. At
practically every meeting of fair managers, in almost every
survey of fair conditions, the junior exhibitors receive their
share of commendation for whatever measure of success the
fairs attain. As early as 1920 it was said that "the boys'
and girls' club work is the life blood of the present-day
fair." [25] Probably few fair men would share the combined
optimism and pessimism of one who, writing of the boys'
and girls' exhibits, said, "Without them our tables would
be bare — our stalls and pens empty," but went on to say
that "this is truly a most encouraging and stimulating
sign." [26] But probably all would agree, and correctly, that

[23] An entry does not necessarily imply either an individual boy or girl or
an individual product. One exhibitor may make several entries; one product
may be entered in several classes. The number of entries is, however, a rough
indication of both the number of exhibitors and the number of products
exhibited.
[24] Compiled from New York State Department of Agriculture and Markets,
Annual Reports.
[25] Rummell, L. L., "Lessons of the County Fairs," *Ohio Farmer*, Oct. 30, 1920,
p. 525.
[26] Boston, L. B., [Director of the Division of Reclamation, Soil Survey and
Fairs], Massachusetts Department of Agriculture, *Monthly Fairs Letter*,
Boston, Feb., 1932, p. 6.

"in the fostering of boys' and girls' club work alone, and in providing a medium of competition for these junior farmers, our fairs of the last decade have made a contribution to the future of agriculture, the magnitude of which no one now living can fully estimate." [27] Boys' and girls' club activities, as well as the intimate participation of neighbors in the neighborhood fair, are looked upon in many quarters as a purging as well as an invigorating factor in the conduct of fairs. Certainly there is at present scarcely any commercialization of their features; club work in its present organization rests in such large measure upon government aid and government sponsorship (in reality it is a part of the public educational system) that in its exhibitive, educational and recreational aspects it remains close to the interests of rural people and the utilization of their own efforts. Not only does it represent a new differentiation of the agricultural fair, but it illustrates pointedly the ever-new process of social evolution or change.

A Classification of Agricultural Fairs

Proceeding from the thesis that the core of the fair as an institution is the competitive display of agricultural products as a means of promoting the improvement of the agricultural industry, we are now ready to propose a classification of agricultural exhibitions. They fall into three main categories, — general, specialized and subsidiary. The general agricultural fair is so called because it endeavors, through a display of practically all agricultural products in which the farmers of its area have an interest, duly to recognize all branches of the industry to a degree commensurate with their importance in a particular community. The specialized agricultural show, in the offering of prizes and in the acceptance of educational, commercial and industrial ex-

[27] Cameron, C. E., [President of the Iowa State Fair Board], Iowa State Agricultural Convention, *Proceedings*, 1931, Des Moines, p. 115.

hibits, serves specifically and emphatically one or more
branches of the industry, though it may or may not thereby

TABLE IX

CLASSIFICATION OF THE AGRICULTURAL FAIRS IN THE
UNITED STATES [a]

I. General agricultural fairs
    A. State and regional fairs
    B. District fairs (serving several counties)
    C. County fairs
    D. Neighborhood fairs (including school, grange, township
       and farmers' fairs and fall festivals)
    E. Boys' and girls' club achievement days
II. Specialized agricultural shows
    A. Horticultural shows
    B. Poultry shows
    C. Crop shows (including corn shows, hay and grain shows,
       etc.)
    D. Live-stock shows (ranging from inclusive live-stock shows
       displaying most, if not all, varieties of live stock to
       highly specialized shows featuring only one breed)
III. Subsidiary agricultural exhibits (held as adjuncts of the great
     world's fairs or commemorative expositions, such as those at
     Chicago, Buffalo, St. Louis, San Francisco and Philadelphia)

[a] As pointed out earlier in this chapter, society horse shows, dog shows,
flower shows, etc., while presenting displays of essentially the same character
as many of the specialized agricultural shows, appeal primarily to urban
rather than to rural interests, and therefore are not here considered as types
of agricultural fairs or shows.

exclude other interests primarily urban. A specialized agricultural show obtains when its avowed primary purpose is
the promotion of a particular branch of agricultural activity,
such as live stock, poultry, fruit or farm crops or subdivi-
sions thereof. The subsidiary agricultural exhibition can be
dismissed with brief mention. It forms a part of a larger
industrial and commercial exposition known as the world's
fair, the preëminent characteristic of which is not agricultural, either in intent or in reality. The functional aspects
of such agricultural displays differ in no respect from those

of the regularly organized agricultural fair of the same magnitude, and therefore merit no separate treatment in the present analysis.

The distinction between the general agricultural fair and the specialized agricultural show is perhaps more a matter of degree than of kind, since few specialized shows serve exclusively a specialized interest. There is, however, a rather subtle implication in the distinction, an implication recognized in the common usage of the words "fair" and "show" and seeming to turn chiefly on the emphasis laid upon the amusement features by the two types of exhibition. The etymology of the word "fair," it will be recalled,[28] lends to the institution the significance of the "holiday" or "festival." The holiday or festive aspects of the general agricultural fair have ever been of great importance, though they have usually been subordinate in intent at least to the educational or promotive aspects. The display of agricultural products competing for prizes, accompanied in later years by the demonstration of improved processes of farming and rural home-making, has been in all agricultural fairs the professed primary purpose. Yet from the beginning the opportunity for social intercourse and recreation has constituted the chief interest of many fair visitors and one of at least secondary importance to practically all others. It may be a far cry from Elkanah Watson's program of pastoral odes sung in the Pittsfield village church to a modern state fair music festival, or from his agricultural ball to a 4-H club pageant, yet these new features are indicative of the vast amount of the spirit of harvest festivity and celebration retained by the general agricultural fairs. Traditionally they have been held in the autumn, at the close of the harvest season, and both in their displays of products and in their recreational activities they have been invested with the

28 Cf. *supra*, Chap. I.

spirit of merrymaking and festal celebration almost if not as much as with more sober purposes.

The specialized agricultural shows, on the other hand, betoken, as has already been noted, a differentiation of the fair institution, serving specialized interests of the agricultural industry. Having developed at a later time, when rural recreational needs were being increasingly well met, and representing, as they did, more highly differentiated technological, economic and social interests, the activities of these specialized shows have been limited much more than those of the older fairs to the competitive display and the agricultural demonstration features. The effort to broaden the supporting base of these shows has led to the purposeful introduction of certain entertainment features, such as the society horse shows at the International Live Stock Exposition or the American Royal Live Stock Show; and any gathering of individuals in pursuit of a common interest inevitably affords, furthermore, a certain kind and a certain measure of recreational activity in the social intercourse thus created. The specialized agricultural shows, therefore, cannot be said to serve either an exclusively agricultural or an exclusively educational interest. But the fact remains that they are established essentially as displays or exhibits, and that whatever aspect of festivity they possess is largely incidental.

The competitive display of agricultural products remains the core of both the general and the specialized agricultural fairs. The general agricultural fair affords the means of displaying the products raised in, or interesting to, the community which it serves. The resources of the community, whether it be a local rural neighborhood or a state, set the only limits to the scope of the fair. The great state fairs, such as those of Illinois, Iowa, Minnesota, Ohio or New York, or a great regional fair, such as the Eastern States'

Exposition at Springfield, Massachusetts, in which the New England and the Middle Atlantic states coöperate, are grand pageants of state and national agricultural activity. They seek to present a complete picture of the agriculture of their respective communities as well as to present at least a partial picture of that portion of commercial and industrial activity which is rooted in agriculture. These fairs (and the same is true of the larger specialized shows) represent chiefly an idealization of agriculture. They are places for the most part for professional exhibitors of live stock and agricultural products, for larger manufacturers, merchants and advertisers, and to a very great extent for professional entertainers. The great fairs and shows remain essentially spectacles. Members of the average rural family are perhaps little more than spectators or imaginative participants, though there are indications that rural people in larger and larger numbers are finding opportunities to play an active rôle in the state fair program. The introduction of boys' and girls' exhibits and contests as definite phases of the larger fairs and shows, the increasingly large place made for amateur sports, theatrical performances, music festivals and contests and demonstrations by rural people themselves under the direction of agricultural educational institutions and extension agencies are evidences of such a trend.

The district fairs, which serve several counties or in a few cases parts of two or three states, and the county fairs, which serve as a rule only one county, are really miniature state fairs. Their exhibits are less numerous and usually less varied, though their premium lists make essentially the same classifications as do those of the state and regional fairs. Their amusement programs — the races, the midway, the free acts, the music, etc. — follow the same general pattern as those prevailing at the larger fairs. The exhibits come from smaller geographical areas, the crowds from shorter distances. In general, the smaller the fair, ranging down through state, district, county and neighborhood, the less pageantry and professionalism and the more free and more complete participation of rural and small-town people. This tendency becomes most pronounced in the case of the neighborhood fair, which as we have seen, is usually conducted by a simple and temporary organization, provides for the exhibition of products of only the immediate neighborhood and in its recreational aspects becomes a rural neighborhood playday. Such a fair, however, small though it may be, usually includes several classes of agricultural products, and therefore falls into our category of general agricultural fairs. Likewise the exhibits shown at boys' and girls' club achievement days are usually limited to the results of the projects that the members have carried on during their club year, but the variety of the projects — live stock, crops and home economics — is usually sufficiently wide to cause the exhibition to partake of the nature of a general agricultural fair.

The specialized agricultural shows represent various degrees of specialization. A poultry show or a corn show, for instance, may be nothing more than a competitive exhibit of poultry or corn, or the National Swine Show nothing more than a competitive exhibit of swine and demonstrations interesting almost exclusively to swine growers. The International Live Stock Exposition, on the other hand, includes many kinds of live stock, crops and club exhibits, and does something also in the way of pure amusement; but the emphasis of this show is so clearly and so strongly focused upon live stock and live-stock production that it belongs in the category of specialized shows.

The classification of agricultural exhibitions proposed in Table IX should not be regarded too rigidly; there is much overlapping, and few of the types appear in their pure form.

Boys' and girls' club achievement days, for example, are often organized within county limits; numerous specialized shows are established to serve certain branches of agriculture within particular counties or states. The classification, it is hoped, will prove suggestive and helpful, in the pages which follow, where fuller consideration is given to the functional aspects of the fair as a social institution.

PART III

THE FUNCTIONAL ASPECTS OF THE AGRICULTURAL FAIR

VI

THE EDUCATIONAL ASPECT OF THE FAIR

THE first and most common claim of the agricultural fair is that it is an educational institution. In considering this aspect of the fair we shall not attempt any extended discussion of the social philosophy underlying education, a delineation of its aims and objectives, an exact evaluation of its methods and practices or a critical examination of the learning process. We shall be concerned chiefly with the organization and functions of the fair as a social institution in those respects in which it serves an educational interest itself or furnishes the means whereby other agencies do so.

It may be remarked in passing that education may denote in general one or both of two processes. Broadly speaking, it may mean the process by which the individual develops his own personality and grows into the culture of his social group. So considered it is as broad as the learning process itself, progressing through the individual's participation in any kind of activity and lasting as long as his experiences continue to broaden. On the other hand, education may mean a process denoting a deliberate attempt to train and direct the individual in acquiring the fundamental ideas, attitudes and techniques by which he is enabled to function as a member of society. So considered it is a socially initiated attempt to shape the experiences of the individual or to transmit to him accepted ideals for purposes of social control or of preparation for social participation; it is a purposeful process of making him a participant in the institutional life of society. This latter conception of the educative process implies the existence and functioning of definite educational groups or associations serving educational interests, agencies admittedly purposing a directional molding of the individual's social becoming. The school is of course the modern type form of educational association, but there are many others wholly or partially devoted to educational interests. The agricultural fair is one such agency. It may itself initiate certain educational activities, or, far more frequently as in recent years, constitute a medium for displaying the results of the year's agricultural education through exhibits, contests, demonstrations and programs. It has come to operate most significantly as an agency which other organizations can and do utilize in their educational functioning.

Obviously the fair in whatever age and of whatever type has furnished informally the opportunity for broadening the experiences of those who have in one way or another participated in it. This is especially true of fairs in any degree cosmopolitan — the great medieval commercial fairs, the world's fairs and expositions and, more pertinently, the great agricultural fairs. Often they have constituted an important, if not the sole, point of vivid personal contact with the larger world. As such they have been and still are a source of information and social intercourse, no less than a means of serving some more clearly defined end or ends. Our interest at the moment lies, however, in the more purposeful educational activities of the fair and the agencies coöperating with it.

The Fair's Educational Tradition

Any discussion of the more formal educational aspect of the fair must be in the nature of a consideration of the organization of the institution along definitely educational lines and of the delineation of the types of stimuli to which the visitors are subjected. Traditionally, the fair has been an agency of agricultural stimulation, inspiration and

information, and it remains in our social structure as a widely accepted means of rural service. No fair can fulfill the
ideal of "a university education crowded into ten days," [1]
but the fact that thousands of people participate as exhibitors and demonstrators and that millions participate as spectators indicates that the fair points the way constructively
to the attainment of ideals in agricultural production and
practice and individual and social living. In performing its
educational functions the fair of course possesses no compulsory control over its constituents. It is rather a place
where visitors may exercise a considerable choice among the
educational opportunities provided for their benefit. It con-
ducts on the whole no extended course of training, discloses
only the most rudimentary outlines of a formal curriculum,
and does not endeavor to solve problems by scientific investi-
gation and research. It is rather a time of commencement,
so to speak, when the results of the year's work are drawn
together from countless sources and set before the public
for the purpose both of capturing public recognition and of
popularizing the activities of agricultural improvement. The
fair, therefore, fills a unique position in the agricultural
educational system.

The evaluation of the fair as a composite educational
institution apart from other activities of the educational or
semi-educational organizations that coöperate in its conduct
is impossible. Agricultural education could quite conceivably
proceed in its absence. We must be wary, too, in assuming
that visitors who attend the fair for amusement purposes
will acquire a significant amount of agricultural information
or inspiration *per se*. Institutions traditionally as rich in
ritual and accouterments as is the fair usually have considerable difficulty in maintaining pure forms of interests as

[1] Cf. advertisement for the 1917 National Dairy Show, *Field Illustrated*,
Oct., 1917, pp. 790-91.

seriously purposeful as the educational. Nevertheless, the
fair does year after year provide a concentrated survey of
agricultural activity, idealizing the accomplishments of
agriculture, setting forth a vast number of visual educational stimuli and pointing the direction of agricultural
improvement. The large fairs particularly show what has
been and what can be accomplished in agricultural production. In countless cases, no doubt, they awaken admiration
for certain agricultural achievements and a determination
to learn the techniques and arts that have made these
possible. The exhibits, contests and demonstrations at the
fairs also provide the opportunity of acquiring certain
types of information and instruction for many people who
do not benefit directly from such means of agricultural
education as farm periodicals, bulletins of the agricultural
colleges and departments, the extension services of the
government, or the farm improvement associations.

Very few fair associations have been able to operate as
self-supporting organizations. The admission fees collected
at the gate, the concessionaires' fees collected from the
operators of side shows, refreshment stands and certain
display booths, and the entrance fees and stall rent collected
from the exhibitors of agricultural products, do not total a
sum sufficient to meet the expenses of the fair. Consequently,
other sources of revenue must be sought; it may be from
private individuals, from specialized promotive associations,
or from the public purse. The policy of the state in granting
very liberal aid, particularly to the general agricultural fairs,
raises repeatedly very involved questions not only of the
extent to which fairs may be looked upon as educational
institutions but also of their educational efficacy when they
are so regarded. The construction and maintenance of
elaborate physical plants, most of which lie idle except for
perhaps an average of one week in the year; the upkeep of a

more or less complete organization; the payment of handsome sums of prize money to the exhibitors of agricultural
products — all these challenge a justification on the part
of the fair's adherents. Usually that justification takes the
outward form at least of defending the fair as an educational institution that cannot be expected to pay financial
returns any more than a university, a museum, an art gallery
or a church. "It is only a question as to what value the City,
Governments, or other sponsors place upon the indirect
returns [of a fair] and how much they are willing to invest
to secure these returns." [2] Since no other educational agency
is conducted on a profit-making basis and since no other
institution serves so wide a range of public interests,

Why worry [ask the fair managers] about an occasional loss? Why
feel like a mendicant when the legislature is called upon to tide over
a bad spot? [3]

We have already noted [4] the extension of government
control to numerous of the fair's activities as a result of the
state aid granted for its maintenance. This question has
given rise to a related group of complications, the extent
to which entertainment should be featured as a part of the
fair's program and the kinds of amusement attractions that
should be brought or allowed to come to the fair. This of
course is an old problem, by no means settled as yet, arising
from the process of social change which the fair undergoes.
It is quite certain that many visitors are attracted to the
fair almost solely by the amusement program. They constitute a group potentially capable of being aroused to
appreciation of the accomplishments of agriculture, and of
being instructed in the processes of agricultural improve-

[2] International Association of Fairs and Expositions, *Report of Thirty-ninth
Annual Meeting*, 1929, p. 83.
[3] *Ibid., Report of Forty-first Annual Meeting*, 1932, p. 14. Cf. also p. 25.
[4] Cf. *supra*, Chaps. IV and V.

ment. To reward agricultural achievement and to stimulate among all classes of rural people interest in agricultural improvement, public funds are usually not begrudged the fair as long as the amusement interest is kept incidental. The demand for public aid is certain to be unpopular, however, if the fair is to be scarcely more than an amusement center. Unless it may be regarded as serving some more fundamental purpose, it is generally agreed that it should receive little state support.

In commendation of fair managers it should be said that in numberless cases they have outdone public appreciation in providing educational exhibits and demonstrations. "The public . . . wants . . . *even its education* served up in the latest approved style," [5] is a premise upon which most of the fairs, so far as possible, are built.

Justification for [their] existence . . . is vested in [their] display of live stock and other farm products, human interest exhibits, and the general array of modern and serviceable merchandise which [are termed] industrial exhibits. Each . . . of these exhibits should present a message of educational value to the Fair visitor. [6]

Therefore, "the Fair is justified in demanding from each exhibitor a display of interest and attractiveness to its patrons." [7] The secretary of the Minnesota state fair, expressing in such phrases the aims of fair managers in general, reveals how applications for entry or exhibit space at his fair are scrutinized and suggestions made in the light of what the management believes the average fair visitor will be interested in seeing in connection with the proposed display. The tractor exhibitors, for example, were encouraged to give actual demonstrations of their machines doing a good job of plowing. The implement manufacturer brought a painter to his booth to show the visitors how

[5] International Association of Fairs and Expositions, *Report of Forty-first Annual Meeting*, 1932, p. 42.   [6] *Ibid.*, p. 42.   [7] *Ibid.*, p. 43.

wagon boxes are striped, and the clay-products exhibitor set up a turntable in his exhibit space to demonstrate the process of molding tiles. In the fat-cattle department a cut meat show was set up; in the apiary department pretty girls tempted the visitors' palate by making delicacies from honey. Crowds who formerly hurried past the wool exhibit lingered and gave the fleeces closer inspection as they witnessed the sheepshearing contest.[8]

Several of the most important of the recent trends in the fair system might well be considered in the light of this adjustment to educational purposes. The specialized agricultural shows are predominantly for the exhibition of agricultural products and the demonstration of methods and practices bearing upon certain branches of the industry. Such shows usually receive their major support from technical or commercial associations, and their exhibits and displays serve, therefore, pretty consistently and completely a general educational purpose. There is little question raised concerning the expenditure of public funds, for, if state support is given at all, it is distributed directly in the form of prizes that amount to a bounty on improved products, and the educational purpose of the exhibition is adhered to rather strictly. The neighborhood fair, too, represents in its educational aspects a more or less definite effort to combine the benefits of agricultural exhibits and the consequent comparison of products, with the first-hand demonstration of agricultural methods for, and often by, the members of the neighborhood primary group. The educational purposes of the whole event profit from the large degree of freedom from the commercialism and professionalism so noticeable in the larger fairs. Finally, the boys' and girls' club work constitutes a type of agricultural activity that is clearly educational; and the fairs in so far as they have embraced

8 *Ibid.*, pp. 43 *et seq.*

this work have set out on a definitely educational program. Since 4-H club work and Smith-Hughes vocational agriculture work form parts of our public educational system, they are supported largely by public funds, quite aside from any inherent connection they may have with fairs. It is significant, however, that the grand finale of the activities engaged in by this branch of our educational system almost invariably takes the form of an exhibit consisting of displays of products, and demonstrations and explanations of processes followed by the clubs or schools in their project work.

From their establishment agricultural fairs were looked upon as a means of promoting agriculture. The first agencies for agricultural education that had a popular appeal, they were conducted on the theory that competitive displays of products would prompt the farmers to improve their live stock and crops and to adopt the new agricultural machinery. The educational activities of the early fairs were largely embraced in the judging of live stock and farm products, the machinery demonstrations and contests, and the discussion meetings and lectures sponsored usually by the fair association itself. It was not until the latter part of the nineteenth century that the breeds of live stock became in any sense standardized, or that they came to be promoted by special associations. The farmer visited the fair to see the new breeds of live stock and the new varieties of fruit, grain and vegetables, and to discuss the qualifications each possessed for serving his needs. Often the exhibitors were required to make a statement of the breeding and the methods of care and feeding used in developing their animals, or of the seeds and methods of cultivation and harvesting used in producing their prize crops. The judging committees made more or less extended reports to the society embodying the reasons for their decisions and recommendations for the adoption of the various products by the farmers of the community. For example, at the 1869 Ohio state fair the committee passing upon the potato exhibit announced in its report that it considered the White Peach Blow "the best table potato, although not so early as some." The Early Goodrich it condemned as "unprofitable, because it [was] imperfect inside, yield [ed] poorly, and cook [ed] watery." But the Early Rose it pronounced *"smooth, uniform in size, and the earliest potato,"* and the Jersey Peach Blow it commended as "one of the best." [9] Such comments, amateurish though they may seem now, were not to be depreciated in a day of rare opportunities for agricultural education.

The fairs performed important educational services also in the development and use of agricultural machinery. The plowing match had been a time-honored feature of many a fair since Elkanah Watson's day, and when, after 1830, other agricultural implements began to be developed, the same principles were followed in testing and demonstrating at field trials and fairs. The trials and demonstrations at the fairs made the visiting farmers acquainted with the machines and their operation, functions especially important as the Middle Western farmers sought to bring the great virgin prairies rapidly to cultivation. The societies sought to encourage the invention and improvement of machinery by offering prizes. At the 1858 Illinois state fair, for example, the executive committee awarded a prize of $500 to J. W. Fawkes, the inventor of Fawkes' steam plow, which was on exhibition, although the machine was admittedly not a success.[10] On the other hand, the committee at the Ohio state fair of 1869 awarded but one premium in the class for reapers and mowers. "By unanimous consent of committee

[9] Ohio State Board of Agriculture, *Annual Report,* 1869, Columbus, pp. 177 *et seq.* Reported from Cincinnati *Chronicle.*
[10] Illinois Department of Agriculture, *Transactions,* 1871, Springfield, p. 228.

and exhibiters [*sic*], it was agreed that, there being such numerous competitors and close competition for the other premiums, it was just as well to settle the difficulty by awarding no premium to any one." [11]

The third general educational feature of early fairs was the discussion meetings and lectures, a feature that has come to consist at present largely of the demonstrations and talks by representatives of the agricultural schools and farm organizations, instead of the annual meeting of the agricultural society or the popular evening meeting with its informal discussions, its formal addresses by agricultural experts, and its so-called annual address, or inspirational lecture given by the most famous speaker that could be secured.[12] Practically all these features were sponsored by the agricultural societies themselves. When other agricultural associations became differentiated, they began to coöperate within the ambit of the fair by conducting certain of their educational activities at the annual exhibition. In the latter part of the nineteenth century, when the manufacture of agricultural machinery came to be a more perfected and more of a commercial industry, the trial of implements as a definitely educational feature was discontinued. The conception of the machinery display changed from a matter of fostering invention to a matter of commercial advertising. The evening discussion meetings gave way to farmers' institutes and agricultural college exhibits. Hundreds of new associations vied with one another in utilizing the fair crowd to promote their interests, many of which may be regarded as educational or semi-educational in nature.[13]

At a time when the agricultural societies were almost

[11] Ohio State Board of Agriculture, *Annual Report*, 1869, p. 180. Reported from Cincinnati *Chronicle*.
[12] Ross, Earle D., "The Evolution of the Agricultural Fair in the Northwest," *Iowa Journal of History and Politics*, July, 1926, pp. 455 *et seq.*
[13] Cf. *ibid.*, pp. 468 *et seq.*

solely responsible for agricultural experimentation, instruction and popularization, the educational importance of the fair may be readily appreciated. It was with considerable truth, if with somewhat ornate language, that it was said:

The county societies are the *primary schools* of agriculture and kindred arts — the state societies, our only AGRICULTURAL COLLEGES, and the productive classes could just as easily obtain their modicum of "reading, writing and arithmetic," without the use of common schools, as they can a reasonable and reliable amount of knowledge, in the way of their vocations, from any existing source apart from the exhibitions of these societies.[14]

The agricultural societies of the middle nineteenth century were partly responsible, both directly and indirectly, for the widespread interest in agriculture which led finally to the establishment of the United States Department of Agriculture, the land-grant colleges and the experiment stations, all performing definitely educational functions.

THE EDUCATIONAL FUNCTIONS OF COMPETITIVE DISPLAYS

If the competitive display of agricultural products constitutes the essential element of the agricultural fair, what, it may be asked, are the educational services rendered by such exhibits? The earlier fairs definitely set many standards of agricultural production. The present-day fair, however, tends more and more to function as an interpreter of standards. Other agencies are now better able to determine the standards by keeping in close touch with market demands and by seeking efficient methods of meeting them. But the fair remains, both traditionally and rationally, a most effective place for bringing such standards to the attention of farmers: traditionally because it is expected that the ideal in agricultural production is to be seen at the fair, rationally because in spite of the fact that standards are set ultimately

[14] Illinois State Agricultural Society, *Transactions*, 1853-54, Springfield, p. 168.

by the market, few producers have become familiar directly with its nicest requirements. Despite the multiplication of schools, colleges, experiment stations and extension services, countless farmers are as yet little influenced by these agencies. Until comparatively recently the standards upheld by fairs were frequently size and curiosity; prizes for the largest pumpkin, the most curiously shaped potato, the longest watermelon or the largest steer, tended to weight exhibits all too heavily in favor of the freakish and the useless. In response to the more exacting demands of the market, the researches and experiments of the agricultural colleges and experiment stations, and the efforts of influential live-stock breeders, farmers and horticulturists, quality, utility and beauty have become the criteria of agricultural production. The market demand for light weight, early maturing and well finished cattle, hogs and sheep has helped to effect an ideal type of animal, trimmer and more compact than those shown in earlier years in both the market and the breeding classes at the fairs.[15] The demand for the "apartment-house roast" filters back through the live-stock markets, the agricultural colleges and experiment stations and is reflected finally in the ideal animal types shown at the fairs and stock shows. Here the farmer is aided immensely by the direct visual demonstration of the standards which the market more or less compels him to meet. New measuring sticks are set up from time to time in response to changing factors; the fair is often the quickest and most effective avenue by which the farmer may be reached.[16]

15 Des Moines, Iowa, *Tribune*, June 18, 1932, p. 5 a.
16 The manner in which the fair interprets standards to the agricultural public was illustrated in the writer's presence at a county fair in 1932. Sheep are judged in the show ring on the basis both of their wool-producing and mutton-producing qualities. The judge of the sheep, an agricultural college instructor, was rating the mutton-producing qualities relatively higher than the wool-producing qualities, and in his comments to the exhibitors and spectators explained that he was doing so because the market

The breeds of live stock and the varieties of grain, vegetables and fruit fall into fairly well standardized types bred
to meet certain purposes. The creators of these types have
been breeders who, holding in mind some more or less
definite ideal, have sought by discriminating selection and
careful management to bring their products into conformity
with that ideal. In the last half century they have enjoyed
to an increasing degree the aid of the agricultural colleges,
both in determining the ideal and in developing methods
of attaining it. They have organized, further, into specialized associations for promoting their interests along the
same lines of endeavor. The standards that have thus been
created have been shaped ultimately by two sets of factors:
physical factors — the conditions of the soil, climate and
natural resources; and a social factor — the conditions and
demands of the market. In a less evolved rural society than
we know today, the diffusion of these standards progressed
at a relatively slow rate. In such a situation the fair served,
as did no other kind of rural coöperative effort, the purposes
of those who were trying to improve their products and their
methods of farming. It was the first great meeting place of
the breeders of improved agricultural products; it was a
place of comparison for those who were trying to establish
types. From the competitions and the discussions stimulated
by them, standards of agricultural excellence gradually took
form. The more or less vague biological maxim "like
begets like" came to be supplemented by scientific conclusions regarding heredity and care, feeding or cultivation, as
the work of new experimental and educational agencies
began to be known. But the fairs probably until well into
the twentieth century remained the most important coöperative agencies through which the breeds of live stock and

price of mutton at that time was consistently running relatively higher than
the market price of wool.

the varieties of farm crops came by their accepted standards of excellence. This was especially true of breeding stock — animals, seeds and plants — through which farmers and breeders attempt to bring about the improvement of products that supply the commercial market. Though the agricultural colleges and experiment stations have assumed a great deal of the task of determining, and sometimes creating, the varieties and types of products fitted to meet certain requirements of the market or of soil and climatic conditions, the standard-setting functions of the fair have been by no means lost. The specialized agricultural shows particularly are in large part the efforts of certain groups of breeders to promote their industry by creating the ideals of their production, by displaying both their individual and associative progress in attaining those ideals, and by disseminating their stock to the public. The recent differentiation of the fair in the direction of the specialized show would indicate, furthermore, that this type of fair may continue as an important means of setting standards, though other agencies may coöperate increasingly, as they have done in the past, in utilizing the fair, both in this and in other forms, to interpret to the public standards that are being evolved.

The great educational function performed by the competitive display of agricultural products in creating standards and interpreting them to the public is revealed at two distinct points: the classification of products and the judging of exhibits. It is obvious that certain kinds of crops or live stock are better suited than others to certain natural, or even social, environments. It is clear, also, that in some regions there is a dearth of certain kinds of crops that might profitably be incorporated into the agricultural scheme. A historic case in point is the overwhelming emphasis in the South upon cotton and tobacco, to the neglect of live-stock production.

Taking for granted the desirability of diversified farming in the South, the fairs in that region, by the differential distribution of prize money through carefully constructed classifications of live-stock entries are able to encourage the introduction of farm animals and thereby advance the cause of diversification. Likewise, the fairs in southern California may stimulate live-stock raising in the fruit-growing sections of that state. On the other hand, in the Middle West, where the most suitable general branches of agriculture have become more or less well established, the fairs by revising their classifications and adjusting their awards can encourage greater improvement in the principal products already grown in their communities. Here, during the period of agricultural expansion, premium lists were enlarged in order to insure the introduction of a greater number of products into the region. The experimentation thus fostered by the fairs made of them essentially a sort of popular testing ground for the trial of many kinds of products, in the hope of determining those most suitable for adoption in their respective communities. Owing, however, to the changes brought about in the numerous phases of agricultural development, such premium lists are now, in many instances, in need of revision to reward the improvement of a smaller number of standardized and proved varieties.

The agricultural colleges have been a potent force in recent revisions of fair classifications. The state and regional fairs, backed by more capital and commanding the services of the better trained agriculturists, have been more alert to the needs of their communities than have the smaller county and neighborhood fairs. Most states are adapted to, and actually produce, a diverse array of agricultural products; and the state fairs have correctly taken cognizance of these facts in their classifications and awards. The agricultural colleges have been especially helpful to the smaller fairs, their experts drawing up and publishing standard classifications in accord with their conceptions of what the fairs should most encourage.[17] At the same time they have often made regulations, particularly as regards grains, fruits and vegetables, in order to insure the awarding of prizes to samples representative of the entire crop. For example, a sheaf of grain may be required to accompany the threshed product in order to prevent the purchase of select samples to fill an exhibit; or it must be certified that the sample comes from a crop grown on a plot of a certain number of acres in order to preclude the exhibition of products from specially cultivated display grounds. At certain fairs in North Carolina, hay may be exhibited only if it is baled — a requirement that aids in making the farmer realize the advantages of baling as a means both of preserving his crop and of preparing it for market.[18] Thus is the fair, by a closely regulated system of awards, able to encourage the introduction of desirable crops into a region and the improvement of those crops when introduced.

The actual judging of the products during the course of the fair marks another point in the public interpretation of agricultural standards. The judges at the early fairs had no accepted standards. The breeds of live stock and the varieties of farm crops were themselves only slowly and somewhat haphazardly being developed. Their purposes were not fully understood by anyone. The judges usually constituted impromptu "viewing committees," sometimes even drawn on short notice from the assembled spectators, and

[17] In North Carolina a standard premium list was adopted for neighborhood fairs, designating the various crops that could command prizes and the section of the state — coastal, Piedmont or mountain — to which each was best suited. Cf. Taylor, E. H., "Country Fairs," *Country Gentleman*, July 17, 1920, p. 11.
[18] *Ibid.*, p. 11.

almost inevitably from the fair officials' circle of personal acquaintances. The majority of them were slow-moving, indecisive groups, lax in enforcing the exhibition rules and possessed of little basis for the standards they espoused. Repeatedly, committees of three judges, unable to agree in their decisions, called in alternates to decide the issue; in one case on record the members of the committee numbered seventeen before a verdict was reached.[19] Such bungled performances could not but cause disgruntled exhibitors and confused onlookers. Cyrus H. McCormick is said to have come to avoid fairs, when exhibiting his reapers, except under the most favorable circumstances, because of the unfairness and incompetence of the judges.[20] The agricultural societies made various attempts to remedy the situation. In some cases the judges were not allowed to argue, were required to vote by ballot and were supposed to keep their identity unknown to the competitors till after the decision.[21] Sometimes they were appointed several months before the fair and their names printed in the premium list, but even then, it was complained, not one in ten appeared at the appointed time to assume his duties.[22] In the seventies a concerted movement got under way to change entirely the system of judging by securing one expert judge to act in each department of the fair and remunerating him for his services. A committee of the Michigan State Board of Agriculture recommended that at least one member of each "viewing committee" be appointed from outside the state and that his expenses be paid.[23] and similar recommendations

[19] Iowa State Agricultural Society, *Report*, 1881, Des Moines, p. 203.
[20] Hutchinson, William T., *Cyrus Hall McCormick*, New York, c. 1930, p. 348.
[21] Cf. Michigan State Board of Agriculture, *Annual Report*, 1880, Lansing, p. 381.
[22] Wisconsin State Agricultural Society, *Transactions*, 1883-84, Madison, p. 40.
[23] Michigan State Board of Agriculture, *Annual Report*, 1877, p. 497.

were made in other states till the practice of hiring single expert judges has become almost universal.[24]

The system of judging at fairs is still undergoing significant changes, but several notable well defined trends are discernible. In numerous respects the judges have become better qualified for their tasks. Men who by experience and training are acquainted with the purposes and the qualities of the products which they pass upon have supplanted the old amateur committees. Often breeders, farmers and horticulturists who have spent their lifetimes in the practical production of the animals or crops in which they are interested, are called upon to officiate, particularly at the larger fairs. More and more are the representatives of agricultural colleges and stations — professors, herdsmen and extension agents — summoned to the judging rings of both great and small fairs. So far as possible efforts are made to secure men disinterested in the outcome of the particular contest under consideration, but interested in, as well as capable of, selecting the specimens that will promote breed, variety or type advancement. Judges at the larger fairs and shows are commonly brought from other states, and not infrequently from other nations. The agricultural colleges have coöperated with the smaller fairs in supplying trained judges. Not only do they send members of their teaching, research and extension staffs to officiate, but many of them conduct annual judging schools for the intensive training of private individuals likely to be called upon to act as judges. The states, too, have sometimes taken steps to insure the qualifications of those who judge at the smaller fairs. In Wisconsin, for example, only persons approved by the Department of Agriculture and Markets are permitted to serve

[24] Cf. *ibid.*, p. 455; Wisconsin State Agricultural Society, *Transactions*, 1883-84, p. 40; Iowa State Agricultural Society, *Report*, 1881, pp. 203, 222, 224; Wisconsin State Board of Agriculture, *Annual Report*, 1907, Madison, pp. 375-94.

INDIVIDUAL FARM EXHIBIT BOOTH, SOUTH CAROLINA STATE FAIR

as judges at the county and district fairs.[25] Numerous promotive associations maintain an official list of judges licensed
to make the awards at exhibitions where live stock or products of their particular interest are shown.[26] Fair officials
have made frequent efforts to secure the same judge year
after year at particular fairs to the end that standards may
remain consistent and definite rather than respond to more
or less upsetting reversals precipitated by a change in judging personnel. The general standardization attained by the
types of agricultural products has further enabled judges to
make their work purposeful.

At the smaller fairs the work of the judges is usually
given a practical turn. As each class of exhibits is rated, the
judge explains to the exhibitors and spectators the basis
upon which he has made his decision, pointing out to them
with the exhibits before him the points at which they excel
or fall short. Thus for the exhibitor the contest becomes
a stimulus toward the improvement of his future exhibits,
and for the spectator a means of learning at first-hand the
accepted standards of agricultural production. In other
respects, too, the agricultural exhibits at all fairs have been
made to serve educational purposes. Most fairs require that
crop exhibits bear labels including (with variations) the
name of the variety, place grown, its particular value, etc.,
and that live-stock exhibits provide such information as age,
weight, breeding, etc. Whatever benefits derive from discussion concerning the exhibits and the widening of one's
acquaintance among people interested in the same field of
endeavor, are gained at the fair. Just as the industrialist or
the merchant rarely attempts to conduct his business without
comparing himself with his competitors, so the farmer at

[25] Wisconsin Department of Agriculture and Markets, *Bulletin* 131, Madison,
1932, p. 9.
[26] Cf. *Poultry Show Organization*, American Poultry Association, Fort Wayne,
Indiana, n.d., for a case in point.

the fair is given the opportunity to see himself in relation to his industry, to compare his products with those of other farmers, and to acquire by direct contact many lessons in agricultural improvement.

THE FAIR AS A FOCUS OF POPULAR EDUCATION

But the educational functions of the fair are performed through avenues other than the competitive exhibit of agricultural products. Chief among these are the displays and demonstrations conducted by schools, clubs and other organizations in order to bring certain educational processes or information to the attention of the public. In some cases these displays and demonstrations are made in close coöperation with officials of the fair itself, but often the fair merely furnishes the occasion for other groups to carry their work to the public. It would be both an idle and an impossible task to list all the activities of this nature carried on at the fairs; we shall content ourselves, therefore, with the presentation of examples typical of different classes of agricultural exhibitions.

The National Swine Show has recently included in its annual exhibitions a series of programs illustrative of the kinds of educational activity conducted through a specialized show. The National Swine Show began as a competitive display of pure-bred breeding swine, and while this feature continues to play an important part, the show has been broadened to deal also with the production of swine for the commercial market. Since hogs yield a larger gross income to American farmers than any other type of live stock sold directly, the problem facing the swine industry is one of meeting the market demands. The market standards are set largely by the pork-consuming public and the meat packers; the production of market hogs of the correct type, weight, age and finish, with the most economical consumption of feed, is a problem confronting the producers. Packers and producers have evolved in the swine industry a so-called national pork policy — a unity of purpose in producing the type of hogs that the commercial hog market demands. The wide publicity given this policy at recent National Swine Shows constitutes essentially an intensive program of agricultural education.[27]

This program begins with an exhibition of finished market hogs, conducted coöperatively by the Illinois state fair (where the National Swine Show has been held since 1931), the National Swine Growers' Association, the National Live Stock and Meat Board and the National Order Buying Company. The hogs are first exhibited and judged on the hoof. They are shown in classes of different breeds and weights, and usually rated by a committee of three judges representing different interests — one a farmer breeder, one an agricultural college professor, and one a meat packer or commercial buyer. Certain specimens are then slaughtered, their carcasses being returned to the show and displayed in refrigerated cases near the remaining live hogs. Placards indicating the actual value to the butcher, based upon current prices, point out to the farmer the most profitable types of pork producers. Alongside this is another meat exhibit consisting of various cuts of fresh pork and cured-pork products, displayed to please the taste of the city housewife and explained by placards showing their food values, cost to the consumer, etc. Finally, pork-cutting demonstrations instruct the visitors in the best methods of preparing, cooking and serving pork.[28]

Another educational feature of the show is the hog-grading demonstration. Hogs of all the common market types and weights are sorted into different pens, where the

[27] Cf. *Breeder's Gazette*, Oct., 1930, p. 5; *ibid.*, Sept., 1931, p. 12.
[28] Illinois State Fair, *Premium List*, 1932, Springfield, p. 126.

weights and the current market prices are displayed while the demonstration is in progress. The men in charge explain the basis of the market grades and the reasons for price variations. Other educational features include a collegiate students' swine-judging contest, discussions on various problems of swine production and marketing, and an exhibit of the so-called Record of Performance — an attempt to determine the most efficient strains of breeding stock by carefully computing feeding costs, rates of gain and value of pork produced from selected matings.[29]

This extensive educational program gives a new meaning to the show of pure-bred swine. The pure-bred breeder is enabled to see the relationship between his interests and those of the commercial swine industry. He finds here the guide to the production of the kind of breeding stock that produces the desirable market classes, the ultimate basis upon which his business rests. Thus it may be seen how the fair is used for the benefit of one agricultural industry, not alone for the competitive display of its products but also for the conduct of a broad educational program embracing the interests of producer, processor and consumer of such products.

The educational exhibits and demonstrations at general agricultural fairs are of bewildering variety. The agricultural extension services, though they coöperate with the specialized shows, put forth their greatest efforts at the state, county and neighborhood fairs. The general character of these activities is much the same at different classes of fairs, though of course at the larger fairs a far greater variety of exhibits and programs is in evidence, more completely and carefully planned than those of the small fairs. At the state fairs a popular type of exhibit is the so-called county-project booth, portraying in some manner the results

[29] *Ibid.*, pp. 126 *et seq.*

of the year's work in the county along some particular line of agricultural activity or study; at county fairs similar exhibits made by townships or other local rural groups present the same type of display. At the Iowa state fair in 1931 the following characteristic exhibits were included in the county-project department: an exhibit of grasshoppers, accompanied by placards explaining proposed methods of control; a soil-building exhibit, portrayed by means of animated figures, placards, etc.; a corn exhibit showing the results of a test of different strains of corn conducted on a hundred farms in the county in question; still another reporting the success of alfalfa growing in one county; and others suggesting methods of controlling weeds and crop diseases.[30] Farm women, too, make exhibits portraying their county projects. Those at the 1929 Iowa state fair included: a display showing the farm home-maker how to entertain unexpected company — the preparation of an "emergency shelf" of canned goods, the making of menus, the serving of food — all with the slogan "Don't let company surprise, let the company be surprised"; a display of each step in the process of home rug making; a display of clothing, analyzing the criteria of "bargain shopping"; an exhibit of a rural recreation project; and others dealing with various problems of food, clothing, home furnishing, etc.[31]

The boys' and girls' clubs and vocational agriculture schools carry on at the fairs demonstrations depicting the results of their club projects. County groups of club boys at the Iowa state fair in 1932, for example, conducted daily booth demonstrations explaining the value of reforestation and the control of soil erosion, the production of swine and swine sanitation, profitable poultry husbandry, the practical uses of rope, and modern methods of corn cultivation; while

[30] Iowa State Fair and Exposition, *Report*, 1931, pp. 18-19.
[31] *Ibid.*, 1929, pp. 61-63.

4-H club girls tutored visitors in the complexities of modern bread making, canning, clothing and home furnishing.[32] The demonstration teams taking part in these activities are the selected representatives of numerous project groups working during the club year in the different counties, and are sent to the state fair to aid in presenting the educational programs of the extension services. Not only are the accomplishments of the club members thereby rewarded, but the educational work of the agricultural extension system is popularized among the people of the state.

Various educational institutions also utilize the state fair to popularize their work. The agricultural colleges in particular make exhibits and conduct extensive programs serving purposes ranging from the strictly educational to the wholly entertaining. Specialists from the staffs of the colleges give lectures, lead discussion meetings and explain the displays that may be on exhibition. Different departments of the school are responsible for their own exhibits — animal husbandry, agronomy, landscape architecture, home economics, engineering, etc. — all presenting some phase of their teaching, research or extension programs. Likewise, the state universities, the liberal arts colleges and the technical schools seek through various devices to bring to public attention some of the outstanding activities conducted on their respective campuses. The use of educational movies or talking pictures, animated figures, illustrated placards, displays of handicraft, etc., helps to entertain the visitors and to carry some constructive lesson to them. The state welfare schools and institutions constitute another type whose exhibits form part of the fair's educational program. Here the public is appraised of the activities of such groups as the blind, the mentally defective, the deaf or the delinquent, whom the state undertakes to control,

[32] Iowa State Fair, *Official Program*, 1932, Des Moines, *passim*.

support or train. Incidentally these exhibits often are utilized as outlets for the products of such institutions, their
handicraft especially being offered for sale to fair visitors.

Alongside these exhibits and demonstrations are those of
numerous organizations not ordinarily classed as educational, but serving nevertheless certain more or less definite
educational purposes. The Boy Scouts and the Campfire
Girls, the Girl Scouts and the Y. W. C. A., all had places on
the program of the 1932 Iowa state fair. The traveling
library association conducted a series of story hours; the
playground association, a series of interpretative dances. The
Iowa Congress of Parents and Teachers, the Iowa Federation of Music Clubs, the Iowa Federation of Women's Clubs,
and the League of Women Voters contributed features of
educational or cultural interest.[33] The Illinois state fair
holds a State Fair Boys' Agricultural School and a State
Fair School of Domestic Science, each conducted as a
short course of study, class work and laboratory training, for selected groups of young men and women of the
state. The schools are held on the grounds during fair
week and regular curricula are pursued under the direction
of instructors supplied mainly by the state university.[34]
All sorts of private farmers' organizations take advantage
of the fair to hold various kinds of meetings. Nationally
known lecturers, government officials and farm leaders
sponsored by the Grange, the Farmers' Union or the Farm
Bureau are secured to discuss phases of the general agricultural problem or special questions concerning the organization under whose auspices the meeting is held. The most
popular speakers in recent years have been men conversant
with the economic and governmental problems encompassed
in the term "farm relief." Members of the Federal Farm

[33] *Ibid., passim.*
[34] Illinois State Fair, *Premium List,* 1932, pp. 254-58, 317-21.

Board and public and private farm relief exponents are naturally in great demand.[35]

Another type of educational program commonly conducted at fairs has to do with the promotion of good health. Though the "baby contest" is not a new feature of agricultural fairs, the health program has been enormously broadened, especially since the advent of 4-H club work. A typical "better babies conference" is held at the Illinois state fair, under the direction of the State Department of Public Health, where children from six months to ten years of age are examined by a corps of medical specialists to determine the mental and physical status of the children. The examination, competitive or noncompetitive as the parents wish, is conducted free of charge, and affords an opportunity for parents to receive consultation concerning their children and to attend various demonstrations and lectures on child care and child training.[36] Contests and conferences of similar scope and purpose are the rule at other state fairs,[37] and county fairs and even neighborhood fairs often have their baby shows. A champion health boy and a champion health girl are chosen at many fairs as a part of the boys' and girls' club program. State health champions are selected at the state fairs from contestants named at county elimination contests, and national health champions are chosen at the 4-H club congress at the International Live Stock Show.[38]

The enormous variety of quasi-educational features characteristic of a great agricultural fair is further indicated by a running summary of certain other events of the 1932 Iowa

[35] Cf. Iowa State Fair, *Official Programs*, 1929, 1930, 1931, 1932.
[36] Illinois State Fair, *Premium List*, 1932, pp. 305-9.
[37] Cf. Indiana, *Year Book*, 1931, Indianapolis, pp. 292-94.
[38] Cf. Illinois State Fair, *Premium List*, 1932, pp. 296, 302; Iowa State Fair, *Official Program*, 1932, p. 37; International Live Stock Exposition, *Preliminary Classification*, 1932, p. 70.

state fair. Farm women tested their oratorical abilities before an audience in a public-speaking contest. Boys and girls matched wits with one another in live-stock, farm-crop and home-economics judging contests. Political speakers of the major parties addressed the visitors on the issues of the approaching election. Various state agricultural organizations held their annual conventions. The State Fish and Game Department presented a wild life exhibit and stressed in a series of programs the need for conservation. Various cultural interests received attention through Little Theater dramatic productions, demonstrations in community singing and the art exhibit, which comprised not only the works of professional artists in the state but also a special loan collection from the Chicago Galleries Association.[39]

Such features, appearing to a greater or lesser extent at fairs of all types, have come to be an accepted part of the fair system throughout the country. They are phases of a larger educational program carried on by various types of organizations and institutions. A reciprocal relationship arises between the fair and these organizations, the fair being utilized by the organizations as a means of making contacts with a wide public, the programs of the organizations being incorporated by the fair as a means of extending its range of interests and broadening its appeal. Whereas fairs in the golden age and perhaps those of later periods can be regarded as forerunners of popular agricultural education, modern fairs tend more and more to portray the results of agricultural education. Indeed it might almost be said that they are turning more and more to the demonstration of how the results are obtained rather than the exhibition of the results themselves. Such trends are traceable in part, of course, to the extension services of the United States Department of Agriculture, the agricultural colleges

39 Iowa State Fair, *Official Program,* 1932, *passim.*

and the farm improvement associations. Yet the fair has served, and still serves, a purpose in popularizing a great deal of rather technical agricultural information which these agencies have to spread. It was a traditionally accepted institution serving in the first place to give extension agents the chance to meet farmers, to secure their coöperation for demonstration work, short courses and extension schools, conducted apart from the fair, and to coöperate in conducting more effectively a rural social project. The fact that the fair is still a deeply rooted tradition in American agricultural education makes it an efficient servant of great numbers of present-day specialized agencies charged with the stimulation and realization of agricultural improvement.

It does not fall within our present purpose to attempt an evaluation of the effectiveness of the fair as an institution of agricultural education. We have spoken in terms of the organization of the fair in so far as it may be regarded as an educational agency, and in terms of the types of stimulation it presents to its visitors. In the matter of the exhibition of agricultural products, by which it points the direction of improvement as well as the degree of improvement attained within the various branches of the industry, the fair occupies at present a unique place in agricultural organization. In another sense it is merely an intermediary means used by many specialized associations of an educational, semi-educational or promotive nature, to popularize their work. Whether it is the best means for such purposes no one knows with any degree of certainty. A case can be made by its advocates to show that it is. In spite of the relatively wide diffusion of newspapers and periodicals, of agricultural-college and government bulletins and reports, the information contained therein may still be insufficient or unsuited for many persons who should benefit thereby. Especially for those who are not students by training or habit, word of mouth and visual demonstration may well be the most effective method of instruction. Again, the attitude is not wholly extinct that "deep plowin' an' shaller drinkin' is all the book larnin' a farmer needs to know." Consequently, the specialized agricultural agencies often find the traditionally accepted fair institution an avenue of comparatively easy approach to the solution of certain rural problems. It is obvious that the fair no longer serves the educational interest in the same manner that it once did; as a definite agency of agricultural education it may indeed be superseded eventually by other institutions. But it is also obvious that the fair yet remains for numerous specialized associations a focal point for popular expression, and performs at least one educational function that no other institution performs at all: namely, the competitive exhibition of agricultural products under authoritative judges who make the awards, interpret the recognized standards, and instruct exhibitors and spectators in their adoption.

The value of such exhibits is measured for the exhibitor partly by the creative planning and the painstaking effort required to prepare for the show, and for both the exhibitor and the spectator by the amount of information and inspiration derived from them.[40] Rural life permits the free exercise of certain kinds of creative ability which are rewarded at the fairs. The improvement of the farmer's live stock, grain or fruits, or any of his other products, is inherently of the nature of creative art; likewise, with the farm woman's household products and practices. The process may well challenge a wide exercise of initiative, imagination and adaptability. The actual preparation of worth-while fair exhibits necessarily demands the acquiring of certain kinds of information and the development of certain skills and

[40] Cf. Rubinow, S. G., "The Community Fair — A Factor in Rural Education," *School and Society*, July 28, 1917, p. 100.

techniques, as well as constructive planning. To both exhibitor and spectator fair exhibits signify the relationship of individual and collective attainment not only in respect to other attainments but also in respect to the agricultural industry and to society as a whole. Thus the fair, conducive as it is to the development of certain skills and techniques, the acquisition of certain types of information and the realization of the significance of certain social relationships, performs in both organization and operation several well recognized educational functions.

VII

THE RECREATIONAL ASPECT OF THE FAIR

"GOING to the fair" has been a significant recreational event in the social life of many generations of the human family. Whatever may have been the primary purpose served by fairs — religious, commercial, educational — there has been always another, inherent in the very nature of the institution, but usually incidental. No other great interest of human beings is so consistently served in their collective gatherings as is that of social intercourse. It not only brings about, as do other interests, the development of institutions and associations that minister to it in a peculiar sense, but it is satisfied also through a thousand other social phenomena in which it plays a more or less minor rôle.

THE INHERENCY OF A RECREATIONAL ASPECT

Without doubt social intercourse has never been absent from fairs, irrespective of the more serious purposes they may have fulfilled. Religion and pleasure underlay the celebration of primitive festivals; the medieval fairs were curious conglomerations of religion, commerce and pleasure. Education and pleasure vie with each other as the absorbing interests of American agricultural fairs. While the fair has changed in a multitude of ways, a common thread is discernible, in the matter of amusement at least, throughout its long history.

The fairs of different countries or of different regions have become an intimate part of the immediate social scheme; indeed, many of their features have become deeply embedded in folk traditions. The numerous references to markets and fairs in Mother Goose rhymes, for example, bear witness to the permanent enshrinement of the institution in the everyday lives of the English people. Simple Simon, it will be recalled, met a pieman going to the fair; and at the fair, too, Johnny was to have a blue ribbon to tie up his bonny brown hair — to say nothing of the new bonnet. In other instances, too, a simple literature of ballads and songs arose from the activity and excitement occasioned by a visit to the fair, always a seat of the unusual and the enticing. The American agricultural fair has never given rise to such a body of folklore, yet it fits thoroughly into American tradition, representing not only a particular class of the population but an age in the development of a national community.

The agricultural fair, as we have seen, has evolved into numerous types, each following some particular branch of agriculture, and each accumulating incidentally its own characteristic form of entertainment. Except at the most specialized agricultural shows, some definite provision has usually been made for the amusement of visitors. But when one speaks of the recreational aspect of the fair, he should have in mind primarily the general agricultural fair. It, perhaps more than any other type, has provided popular diversion and thereby attained recreational preëminence. The traditional American county fair is a symbol of rural society. The interest in sport and amusement that eventuated in such things as Coney Island and the Kentucky Derby found expression also in the simpler rural festivities of the agricultural fair. The jostling of the motley crowd, the side shows, the races, the music and vaudeville acts, the parades, even the rivalries of the live-stock show or the agricultural exhibit — all, whether instituted for that specific purpose or not, serve in some measure a recreational interest, and some of them boast a long history as purveyors of popular amusement. It is this kaleidoscopic picture of the fair that is most widely encompassed in the experience of the population, calling forth romantic memories and tinging glamorous reminiscences.

The market fairs of colonial America, though never rising to the eminence such institutions attained in Europe, were the occasions of various amusements of the same general character as those that later clustered around the agricultural fair.[1] Apropos of the type of sports current in colonial society, there were some of course, such as cudgeling bouts, bear baiting, bull baiting and gouging, that have since died out, but there were others which have come down to the present day as the pastimes of such periodic outdoor or semi-outdoor concourses of people. There were such simple amusements as foot races, whistling and grinning contests and catching a greased pig; but there were others quite suggestive of the enterprise of the entrepreneur — the commercial entertainer and the vendor of wares. Colonial gatherings of this sort were not without their fortune tellers, peddlers and medicine hawkers, their acrobats, puppet shows and horse racing. All these leading attractions were well organized in the colonies before the Revolution. Many of the sporting customs of the colonists naturally were fashioned more or less directly upon those of England. They represented the implantation of certain elements of the English social heritage upon American soil. An air of crude enthusiasm and rough, elemental enjoyment pervaded many of the sports, some of which assumed the characteristics of a spectacle provided for the pleasure of the onlookers. Cockfighting, racing and animal baiting were not only the interests of fashionable pleasure seekers, but they drew large crowds of ordinary folk who had not yet learned the technique of organized team recreation. Though the increasing humanitarianism of the nineteenth century suppressed

[1] Andrews, Charles M., *Colonial Folkways*, New Haven, 1929, pp. 120 *et seq.*

the more cruel of these amusements, there were survivals of license and chicanery in gambling, cheating, pocket-picking and numerous less condemned infractions of the social pressures which from time immemorial have found their opportunities in the occasions of pleasure-seeking crowds.

Undoubtedly the recreational or amusement aspect of fairs, both English and American, represents traditionally an undisguised attempt to find an outlet for the exuberance characteristic of the rank and file of the population and to indulge the desire for the grotesque, the comic, the skillful and the crafty exhibition. "All's fair at fair time" has a double significance: it denotes the necessity of casting aside the gravity and dignity of one's ordinary demeanor as he mingles with the jostling crowd; it denotes also the harvest season for countless entrepreneurs of almost every degree of fakery, gambling and huckstering, and other artifices within or without the law. While some progress has been made in suppressing such of these activities as have conflicted with moral or legal codes, the social situation created by the general agricultural fair remains even in our own day, conducive to the release of numerous social sanctions. Again tradition undoubtedly plays a part; one expects to find at the fair countless forms of bizarre entertainment, extravagant and impossible exhibitions, and the opportunity to take part in extraordinary, and possibly shocking, pastimes. But quite aside from tradition, the social situation growing out of the fair itself gives rise to attitudes of rough hilarity and reckless behavior, as well as expectant anticipation of illusion and mystery on the part of a more or less unsophisticated gathering. A good deal of human riffraff inevitably follows in the train of circuses, carnivals and fairs. Fly-by-night operators of all sorts of games, vendors of trinkets and refreshments, entertainers who must cater to the lowest common denominator of highly unselected audiences provide the means whereby the tastes of the visitors may be indulged. And the visitors themselves constitute a motley crowd. They represent a wide range of social classes; they are there for a dozen different purposes. In a holiday mood, often (in recent years at least) away from home and therefore freed of many primary-group restraints, many easily succumb to the lure of "trying their luck," testing their strength, treating themselves to the "educational opportunities" offered by two-headed calves, pig-faced boys and Egyptian mummies, or indulging in various intemperances of eating, drinking and spending. And in those entertainment attractions that supposedly have less sinister implications — the racing, the vaudeville performances, the athletic events, the music and parading — there is something of the freedom of the out-of-doors, the wonder of skillful feats and courageous accomplishments, the thrill of close-fought contests, the expansive communion with a crowd. Clearly the social situation produced by the fair frankly caters to uncritical and unsophisticated tastes; the more critical and sophisticated are obliged to lay aside their ordinary standards for the time being.

The first American agricultural fairs as organized by Elkanah Watson were of course largely neighborhood events. The amusement features seem to have been entirely the product of the coöperative efforts of the members of the community who not only organized but also participated in them. It is easy to understand how, in a society still confronted with the stern necessity of constant labor, the patrons of these fairs linked the pleasure-seeking activities in a rationalized relationship to the more earnest duties of improving their live stock, crops or domestic manufactures. So long as the fairs remained primarily local events, commercialized amusement was not a serious problem, nor is it at the present time at the modern neighborhood fair. The amusement features of the early fairs represented a transference to the fair of the same type of communal recreation that was enjoyed in barn-raisings, logrollings or husking bees. Probably none of these particular work-play events were connected with the fairs, but a similar rudimentary coöperative spirit underlay both these activities and many of the amusement features of the fairs. As the agricultural fair became a more established institution, as individual events in particular counties and states became more or less regularized recurrences, as their area of appeal enlarged with the gradual diffusion of information and the extension of communicative facilities, it was inevitable that outside influences should be reflected in amusements as well as in every other department. Again we witness the process of social interaction; in this case gatherings of people were appealed to through a dominant human interest, that interest in turn being intensified by the means used to satisfy it. So it was that as the agricultural fair crystallized into an institution, it gathered into the design various types of amusement elements which were rising in society quite independently of the fair, for wherever crowds assemble there will be found the people whose business it is to provide amusement. Entrepreneurs without number, promoting horse racing, tent shows, vaudeville and circus performances, baseball and other sports and amusements, played their part in directing this evolutionary process and in shaping its results.

Horse Racing

By far the most characteristic sport of the traditional agricultural fair is horse racing. To millions of fair-goers in the last three-quarters of a century it has been no doubt the chief attraction of the fair. It has, like many another form of popular amusement, gradually assumed commercial aspects which have largely supplanted communal folk participation. Racing is of course a very old sport. Contests between gentlemen who owned a few fast horses and ran them as opportunity offered furnished the principal sport in the American colonies before the Revolution.[2] Such encounters were frequent — sometimes on country roads, sometimes in open fields. Just at the close of the eighteenth century, jockey clubs began to be organized. Racing stables were enlarged, race courses built, racing rules formulated and the breed of race horses improved by importations from England. By 1840 racing had become a primary source of American amusement in many metropolitan centers and its popularity soon spread to the rural districts.

Horse racing, especially the contests between trotters and pacers possessed the peculiar power of providing pleasure which was justified in terms of utility.[3] The improvement of driving horses was clearly a part of the general improvement of all domesticated animals. The development of speed and stamina in light-harness horses was a very real problem in an age of limited transportation facilities; in fact, it was no less a problem than the development of size and strength in draft horses in an age of limited power facilities. It was on such a basis that racing was introduced into the agricultural fair, a hybrid activity on the borderline between pure amusement and educational exhibit.[4] Trials of speed between horses of local reputation exhilarated the crowds at rural fairs long before such races began to assume the characteristics of commercialized sport. Even when it was discovered that the racing program involved almost inevitably the appearance of the suspicion-

[2] Krout, John Allen, *Annals of American Sport*, New Haven, 1929, p. 30.
[3] *Ibid.*, p. 29.
[4] Ross, Earle D., "The Evolution of the Agricultural Fair in the Northwest," *Iowa Journal of History and Politics*, July, 1926, pp. 469 *et seq.*

covered jockey, the bookmaker and the pool seller, the disproportionate increase of speed premiums and the distraction of the fair-goers' attention from the more sober purposes of the exhibition, it could still be justified on the ground that it promoted a legitimate branch of agriculture. Above all it was grand sport. And as such it was soon turned to good account in an attempt to swell the fair's attendance and thereby increase its material success.

Professional racing at the metropolitan centers suffered a partial and a temporary eclipse during the Civil War. The turmoil of the War itself was partly responsible; but a wave of popular disapproval occasioned by the commercialism, gambling and chicanery associated with the race tracks made itself felt. The trials of speed at the agricultural fairs, instituted as one means of determining the general usefulness of the horses shown, had already aroused the sporting proclivities of rural people and had given rise to questions of their proper emphasis. Such contests caused great excitement among the spectators at the Iowa state fair in 1857, "the vast multitude shouting and re-shouting, as their respective favorites shot ahead . . .,"[5] and the secretary of the Michigan State Agricultural Society, while conceding the propriety of trials of speed as a feature of their fairs, warned the society in 1856 to so arrange the program that they would not detract from other departments.[6] At the close of the War, however, professional racing enjoyed not only a revival but a luxuriant growth: financial and social leaders came to its support, new and elaborate courses were projected and the American Jockey Club was formed.[7] All this took place at the very time when the agricultural fair, nearing the end of its so-called golden age, was beginning to reflect the

[5] Iowa State Agricultural Society, *Annual Report*, 1857, Des Moines, pp. 25-26.
[6] Michigan State Agricultural Society, *Transactions*, 1856, Lansing, p. 24.
[7] Krout, *op. cit.*, pp. 34 *et seq.*

increasing differentiation of agriculture and agricultural organization. In the following period of readjustment racing became thoroughly intrenched as a feature of state and county fairs. Even in 1868 the humorist, Josh Billings, articulated his impressions of an agricultural fair by reporting that

... thare was two yoke ov oxens on the ground, beside sevral yokes ov sheep and a pile ov carrots, and some worsted work, but they didn't seem to attrakt enny simpathy. The people hanker fur pure agrikultural hoss-trots.[8]

But horse racing was apparently not the only equine sport which delighted the hearts of fair visitors and troubled the souls of fair managers in the golden age. The importance of horse breeding in that period is clearly evidenced in the report that "a grand cavalcade" of all horses on exhibition took place in the forenoon of each day of the Michigan state fair in 1856,[9] and in the dispatch of a Cincinnati *Chronicle* correspondent from the Ohio state fair in 1869 that the program included an exhibition of horses in the ring, "not to determine an award, but simply for the gratification of those fond of such sports." [10] Exhibitions of women's horseback riding, often pretentiously referred to as "female equestrianism," rivaled the races as a sporting attraction at the early fairs. Such an event was in fact the chief amusement feature of the first Iowa state fair in 1854, the president of the society offering a "fine gold watch, to the boldest and most graceful female equestrian. . . ." [11] By popular demand the exhibition was extended over two days, and

8 [Shaw, Henry Wheeler], *Josh Billings on Ice, and Other Things*, New York, 1868, p. 45. Josh also remarked satirically that one day, on which "it rained agin like thunder and lightning" and on which therefore no races could be run, "waz spent in betting on the weight ov hosses. Sevral good hoss-swops waz also did" (p. 44).
9 Michigan State Agricultural Society, *Transactions*, 1856, pp. 37-38.
10 Ohio State Board of Agriculture, *Annual Report*, 1869, p. 175.
11 Iowa State Department of Agriculture, *Yearbook*, 1904, p. 648.

so strongly did the crowd feel that the judges had erred in awarding the prize that they immediately made up a purse of $165 and other presents for a more popular entry and provided for her attendance for three terms at the local "female seminary" and one term at a near-by college.[12] Riding saddles were sometimes offered as premiums,[13] though silver tea sets, spoons and cardcases seem to have been the more popular stakes.[14] This sport, like racing and trials of speed, was justified in terms of utility, for "if a lady is expected to ride or drive through the crowded streets of cities, they must become adepts in the art, or they become liable to many accidents." [15] "His Excellency, the Governor," was one of the judges at the 1864 Wisconsin state fair.[16] Nevertheless equestrianism shared in the displeasure of those who questioned the appropriateness of sporting attractions for the fairs. Ladies' riding especially was pronounced to be "in bad taste . . . as a public exhibition, . . . lower[ing] the dignity of a great state agricultural society . . ." [17] and in the seventies it began to give way to other types of amusement.[18] The issues which it raised were forgotten in the much more heated controversy blazing forth from the problems of the race track.

The debate between the supporters and the opponents of the "pure agrikultural hoss-trots" soon waxed violent. It abounded in fine distinctions between racing and trials of speed, in opinionated statements concerning the type of horses the farmer should strive to produce, in earnest discus-

[12] *Ibid.*, p. 653.
[13] Cf. Indiana State Board of Agriculture, *Annual Report*, 1869, Indianapolis, p. 247.
[14] Wisconsin State Agricultural Society, *Transactions*, 1861-68, Madison, pp. 263, 330-31, 496.
[15] Michigan State Agricultural Society, *Transactions*, 1856, pp. 23-24.
[16] Wisconsin State Agricultural Society, *Transactions*, 1861-68, p. 225.
[17] *Ibid.*, 1871, p. 47.
[18] Cf. *ibid.*, 1861-68, p. 240; *ibid.*, 1869, pp. 119-20; *ibid.*, 1871, p. 47.

PITCHING HORSESHOES AT A COUNTY FAIR

sions of both the morality and appropriateness of the sport, and in many a frank concession to its inevitableness. As early as 1858 it had been remarked that complaints against trials of speed were made chiefly by men whose horses were not fast enough to win speed premiums.[19] Some twenty years later it was held that since there was no other way of testing horses than by racing, ". . . a trial of speed without the pool-box, and under proper authority, is as legitimate as an exhibition of draft horses when put to the test of their ability. . . ."[20] The New Jersey state fair "felt compelled" to offer speed premiums because the breeding of gentlemen's road horses was an important branch of the agriculture of a state situated midway between New York and Philadelphia.[21] A Wisconsin enthusiast maintained that a horse weighing more than twelve hundred pounds was "only good in this country to drive *to* funerals, . . . too slow and logy for us fast Americans."[22] From New York it was reported that "although the people may have a great deal of admiration for fine horses, yet it is only the fast horses, or as it is more popularly phrased, 'the trials of style and speed,' that attracts the most attention."[23] It was stated before the meeting of the Iowa State Agricultural Society in 1882 that

. . . the trotting horse pays his way, and is almost the only thing that does. . . . It is a fact [continued the speaker], that thousands come, pay their fee, and go straight to the amphitheater to see the trots, without whose fees premiums could not be paid to other classes. Whether the desire of those visitors to see trotting should be gratified is in dispute, the truth must be told as regards their value as visitors, under the present arrangements.[24]

[19] Ohio State Board of Agriculture, *Annual Report*, 1858, p. 177.
[20] Michigan State Board of Agriculture, *Biennial Report*, 1880-82, Lansing, p. 602.
[21] *Cultivator and Country Gentleman*, Sept. 30, 1880, p. 633.
[22] Wisconsin State Agricultural Society, *Transactions*, 1883-84, pp. 282-83.
[23] *Cultivator and Country Gentleman*, Oct. 25, 1866, p. 266.
[24] Iowa State Agricultural Society, *Report*, 1881, Des Moines, p. 230. The speaker was James Wilson, presumably "Tama Jim," later Secretary of Agriculture.

That horse racing received some clerical support also seems clear from the fact that one of the most popular events of the 1869 Ohio state fair was a race between a horse owned by the president of the State Board of Agriculture and one owned by a local Catholic priest.[25] That racing was supposed to elicit even divine approbation may be inferred from the report of the 1895 Wisconsin state fair that "there was prompt starting and no collisions; Providence favored the entire meeting." [26] By 1905 at least, racing and trials of speed were generally considered legitimate, since "neither the horse nor the breeder of the horse is responsible for the use to which he is put." [27]

Numerous devices designed to eliminate the undesirable features of racing at the fairs were tried. Some societies abolished racing as such, but recognized speed as one characteristic of the driving horses shown.[28] Some attempted more nearly to equalize the prize money given to racing and other departments of the fair.[29] Others frankly did all the horsemen needed and asked, but endeavored at the same time, by building expensive barns and exhibition halls and offering increased prizes, to expand other divisions of the fair to a commensurate status.[30] Many societies offered premiums for fast-walking horses, a policy approved by the *Cultivator and Country Gentleman* as "sensible, [because]

[25] "This event was amazingly enjoyed by the knowing ones who were posted as to the ownership of the horses, they being no less personages than the popular President of the Board, and the jolly, good-hearted Father Hannon, the Catholic priest of Toledo. Our good dominie was heartily congratulated on the result of the race, and no doubt the President was as fully disgusted." Ohio State Board of Agriculture, *Annual Report*, 1869, p. 177. Reported from Cincinnati *Chronicle*.

[26] Wisconsin State Agricultural Society, *Transactions*, 1895, Madison, p. 81.

[27] Iowa State Department of Agriculture, *Yearbook*, 1905, p. 1000.

[28] Cf. Michigan State Board of Agriculture, *Annual Report*, 1876, p. 483; *ibid.*, 1877, p. 686.

[29] Cf. *ibid.*, 1869, pp. 340-41.

[30] Cf. *Cultivator and Country Gentleman*, Oct. 6, 1870, p. 627.

fast walking horses are what the farmer needs." [31] Others
restricted entries to horses owned within a limited area,[32] to
horses "not used for sporting purposes," [33] to horses "owned
and driven by the exhibitor for thirty days previous to the
fair," [34] or to horses "not trained upon a track." [35] "Farmers' trots" were substituted for trials of speed when the
latter were condemned as disguised horse races, and gentlemen's driving horses hitched to road wagons sometimes
replaced the racers with their professional jockeys. Still
other societies shifted the financial responsibility by allowing private individuals to offer so-called "citizen's premiums," [36] and it was claimed for the Wisconsin state fair of
1905 that of the $23,500 paid for racing all but $3,000 to
$4,000 was collected from the racing men themselves in the
form of entrance fees.[37] But in spite of restrictions, alibis
and circumlocutions, as well as honest differences of opinion,
racing became a generally accepted, if not an essential, part
of the fair. A quarter- or half-mile track came to be perhaps
the most characteristic feature of the fair's permanent
equipment. Fair associations increased their speed purses,
adopted the rules of the professional jockey clubs and often
arranged their dates so that the fairs constituted essentially
a racing circuit. Some associations even fell into the hands
of jockey clubs, under whose control they could be little
more than provincial professional racing meets.[38]

[31] Oct. 3, 1872, p. 634.
[32] Iowa State Agricultural Society, *Report*, 1877, p. 423.
[33] Michigan State Board of Agriculture, *Annual Report*, 1875, p. 424.
[34] *Ibid.*, p. 424.   [35] Iowa State Agricultural Society, *Report*, 1877, p. 412.
[36] Cf. Michigan State Board of Agriculture, *Annual Report*, 1869, p. 358;
ibid., 1875, p. 515.
[37] Wisconsin State Board of Agriculture, *Annual Report*, 1906, p. 317.
[38] Cf. Michigan State Board of Agriculture, *Annual Report*, 1870, p. 220;
ibid., 1875, pp. 398-99, 513; *ibid.*, 1877, pp. 521-27; Ohio State Board of
Agriculture, *Annual Report*, 1880, pp. 431-32; Wisconsin State Board of
Agriculture, *Annual Report*, 1906, pp. 317-19; Iowa State Agricultural Society, *Report*, 1881, p. 286.

This prostitution of the agricultural fair was abetted toward the end of the century by the growth of various other commercialized and professionalized amusements. The popular protest against this conspiracy which threatened the complete perversion of the fair arose synchronously with another popular protest against the practices condoned at the metropolitan race tracks. Horse racing did not escape the vigilance of Anthony Comstock,[39] and the protest which his attacks epitomized culminated in 1908 in drastic legislation by the New York State Assembly against bookmaking and pool selling.[40] In the meantime, the Jockey Club had concocted a plan by which it sought to justify the claim that it endeavored to improve the breed of horses. In 1906 the club stationed breeding stallions throughout the state and established prizes to be awarded at county fairs to the offspring of the horses so distributed. In addition the fact was strongly emphasized that 5 percent of the proceeds from racing in New York was donated to the fairs for the augmentation of their premium funds.[41] The reformers gained a triumph, however, which, though temporary, bolstered up the attempts of many other states to control professional racing within their borders. Racing in the dominantly agricultural regions was confined of course largely to the agricultural fairs, but in all the states the policy of granting public aid to the fairs came to be circumscribed with legislation attempting stringent control of racing and other amusement features.

An analysis of the agricultural fair reveals at this point another of the tremendous changes wrought by the automobile since the beginning of the twentieth century. Within

[39] Cf. Comstock, Anthony, *Gambling Outrages; or, Improving the Breed of Horses at the Expense of Public Morals*, New York, 1887; *Race Track Infamy; or, Do Gamblers Own New York State?* New York, 1904.
[40] Krout, *op. cit.*, p. 43.
[41] *Ibid.*, p. 43.

the space of a few years, riding and driving horses in their utility functions all but vanished from the American scene. The amateur matinee driving clubs, popular in the urban centers in the nineties, either ceased to exist or turned into professional racing clubs. The metropolitan horse shows, organized to aid in the development of various types of saddle and harness horses, were largely replaced by exhibition events almost wholly for the pleasure and pastime of wealthy urban society people. So complete was the motorization of the rural districts that only an occasional farmer still retained a riding or driving horse. Horse racing at the agricultural fairs, therefore, became more than ever a sport instead of an educational exhibit, and even as sport it had now to compete with automobile racing. It still retained much of its romantic appeal, however, the thrills and excitement which it provided representing partially at least a kind of traditional survival. While the amount of money offered in speed prizes has, like that for agricultural products,

TABLE X

PRIZE MONEY PAID FOR HORSE RACING

THE AVERAGE ANNUAL PERCENTAGES OF THE TOTAL PRIZE MONEY PAID FOR HORSE RACING AT VARIOUS STATE FAIRS BY DESIGNATED PERIODS OF YEARS, 1901-30

Illinois State Fair [a]		Iowa State Fair [b]		Wisconsin State Fair [c]	
Period of Years	Percentage of Total Prize Money Paid to Racing	Period of Years	Percentage of Total Prize Money Paid to Racing	Period of Years	Percentage of Total Prize Money Paid to Racing
1901-5	27.70	1903-7	23.41		
1913-17	32.20	1913-17	20.45	1916-20	31.35
1926-30	21.32	1926-30	15.43	1926-30	19.55

[a] Compiled from Illinois State Department of Agriculture, *Transactions* and *Annual Reports.*
[b] Compiled from Iowa State Department of Agriculture, *Yearbooks.*
[c] Compiled from Wisconsin State Department of Agriculture, *Biennial Reports.*

shown absolute increases with the twentieth-century expansion of the fair, relatively it has suffered a general decline.
Table X shows the average percentages of the total prize
money paid for horse racing at various state fairs since
1900.

If we are to judge by the downward trend in the percentage of money paid for the sport, racing has apparently become a relatively less important feature of fairs during the
last thirty years.[42] Though fair associations frequently consider their speed purses a part of their general premium fund,
racing at present is much more appropriately classified as an
amusement attraction. It has lost its agricultural value;
more than ever it reflects the infiltration of commercial and
professional amusement to rural districts and rural institutions. By careful arrangement of their speed programs
numerous fairs have been able to build up a consistent
reputation for good racing and to economize in other entertainment attractions. The romantic appeal of the race track
and the admiration of "good horse flesh" have not ceased
entirely to captivate the farmer even though he may drive
an automobile and do most of his farming with a tractor.

In spite of the general and almost complete displacement
of the light or driving horse by the motor car, a new interest
in horses has arisen among certain urban classes. This interest has been particularly manifested in the larger specialized
agricultural shows. Various types of saddle horses still remain in favor on metropolitan bridle paths and country clubs.
Polo ponies and hunters enjoy considerable urban patronage.
A few harness horses are bred for exhibition purposes. The

[42] County and district fairs have as a rule paid a larger proportion of their
prize money for horse racing than have the state fairs, but the same diminishing emphasis is apparent in both cases. For example, the average annual
percentage of the total prizes paid to racing at the county and district fairs
in Iowa by five-year periods was as follows (Compiled from Iowa State
Department of Agriculture, *Yearbooks*): 1901-5, 58.58; 1906-10, 58.35; 1911-
15, 55.35; 1916-20, 50.66; 1921-25, 38.93; 1926-30, 34.51.

so-called society horse shows held in the larger cities are not
only exhibitions of the finest specimens of these types of
horses, but are distinctly important events in the social
calendar of many metropolitan society leaders. Though they
cannot be classified as a type of agricultural fair, they have
exerted some influence upon certain types of such exhibitions.
At many of the state fairs, society horse shows have been
sponsored principally as a part of the amusement program,
as a bid for the attendance of urban dwellers. At the larger
specialized shows, such as the International Live Stock
Exposition, the American Royal Live Stock Show and the
National Dairy Show, held in the large cities, society horse
shows have been introduced as the leading entertainment
feature. By this means the fair management has solicited
urban patronage for its essentially agricultural exhibition;
at the same time it has provided a form of entertainment
conceivably quite compatible with the tastes of the higher
classes of the rural population who attend these shows.

THE MIDWAY AND SPECIAL ATTRACTIONS

The second type of amusement most characteristic of the
traditional agricultural fair is centered in the midway. The
midway is yet another manifestation of the rise of commercialized entertainment, though of course a very old one.
The vendors of trinkets, the dispensers of food, confections
and drinks, the entertainers — all form the eternal appurte-
nances of the fair. Side shows with their menageries, freaks,
magicians, dancers, fortune tellers and other entertainers
are a legacy of the English fair. These "van" shows, as they
were called in England, journeyed from village to village on
market days, giving performances for the assembled crowds.
In America they became carnival companies traveling about
in much the same manner, and often creating the occasion
for an assemblage of people. Constructed on a grander scale

and including a much wider range of attractions, but of the same general character, was the traveling circus. After 1860 the American circus began to change from the small troupe of a half dozen amateur acrobats with a few horses to a great organization of managers, professional performers, canvassmen, publicity agents, etc., presenting a mammoth production under the ballyhoo of spielers and brass bands, ornate luxury and gaudy display.[43] As the circus widened its clientele it grew in popularity. Everywhere people were keen for amusements of this character. During the latter part of the nineteenth and the early twentieth centuries a series of world's fairs with their exhibitions of magnificent splendor further stimulated the public appetite for amusements of a spectacular order. The midway at these fairs provided the opportunity to reproduce in some measure certain phases of the life of strange and far-off countries — Hawaiian villages and the streets of Cairo — as well as for the exhibition of various unusual creatures, or performances indigenous to the side show. Still another factor which has probably contributed to the wide popularity of midway amusements is the growth of commercial amusement parks, usually situated near urban centers, catering with shows, rides and games to thousands of city dwellers who have little or no other opportunity for outdoor recreation and, recently at least, to thousands of rural dwellers who find them an added point of interest when visiting the city.

Undoubtedly all these means of entertainment would have developed quite apart from any connection they may have had with the agricultural fair. Yet the fair as an outdoor gathering of varied classes of people was admirably adapted to the incorporation of just this sort of feature. Thus the midway, thanks to popular demand, and to the

[43] Sherwood, Robert Edmund, *Here We Are Again*, Indianapolis, c. 1926, *passim*.

amusement entrepreneurs' eagerness to expand their business, came to be an almost universal part of the fair. The state fairs emulated what they must have considered worthy exemplars, the world's fairs, in providing for their midways. The county fairs, not to be outdone, imitated the state fairs, the essential tawdriness of the spectacle becoming more evident at every extension. Cheap imitators and gaudy amateurs hastened to capitalize their opportunity. Conjuring up a picture of the rural dweller, which portrayed him, oftentimes with some justification, as an unsophisticated "rube," the concessionaires prepared a welter of fake exhibits, games of chance, vulgar shows and swindling devices, and descended upon the remotest county fair to reap the harvest.

Probably at no time were all the midway attractions considered either immoral or dishonest, but certainly they might still be challenged on the grounds of appropriate emphasis. It is beyond dispute also that the camp followers of cheap shows, refreshment stands and liquor dispensers tremendously complicate the problem of policing the fairs, not only by importing disturbers of the peace from outside the local community but by stimulating the rowdy elements within it. "Pickpockets and blacklegs were in force, and plied their vocation" at the Ohio state fair in 1858.[44] A decade later a large "mob" of thieves and pickpockets was reported to have arrived at the fair on early trains, but so efficient were the police that the intruders were apprehended before they had time to operate to any extent.[45] The president of the Wisconsin State Agricultural Society, in his opening address at the 1865 state fair, officially warned the visitors to "avoid a swell-mob or any unnecessary crowd" because of the unfortunate fact that "a thieving gentry" was

[44] Ohio State Board of Agriculture, *Annual Report*, 1858, p. 137.
[45] *Ibid.*, 1869, p. 202.

present,[46] and an Iowa fair manager gave similar advice by saying, "if there is any excitement keep out of it." [47] Vagabonds, vendors and "*gentlemanly* persons who having nothing in particular to do, live by their wits" [48] were at first kept outside the fair's gates, where they set up their stands on the streets leading to the grounds and plied their trade free from the jurisdiction of fair officials.[49] "On the outside of the grounds [of the Ohio state fair of 1858] there were any number of *outside shows*; learned pigs, fat women, snakes, monkeys, all jumbling together in Babelish confusion, while lager beer saloons and melon stands supplied those in quest of such delicacies." [50]

It is difficult to discover any well defined policy followed by the fairs, as time went on, in regard to the admittance of shows to their premises. Sometimes these excrescences were strictly banned [51] along with liquor vendors and gamblers.[52] Fair officials passed countless resolutions seeking to regulate them,[53] increased fair-grounds police forces,[54] and sought through interminable discussions a solution to the problem.[55] A delegate to the Michigan state agricultural

[46] Wisconsin State Agricultural Society, *Transactions*, 1861-68, p. 240.
[47] Iowa State Agricultural Society, *Report*, 1881, p. 285.
[48] Ohio State Board of Agriculture, *Annual Report*, 1858, p. 137.
[49] Cf. *ibid.*, 1887, p. 21; Iowa State Agricultural Society, *Annual Report*, 1857, pp. 17-18.
[50] Ohio State Board of Agriculture, *Annual Report*, 1858, p. 138. Reported from *Ohio Farmer*.
[51] Cf. *ibid.*, 1882, pp. 14, 30.
[52] Cf. *ibid.*, p. 301; Wisconsin State Agricultural Society, *Transactions*, 1882-83, p. 2; Iowa State Agricultural Society, *Report*, 1879, p. 96.
[53] Cf. *ibid.*, 1877, pp. 530-31; Michigan State Board of Agriculture, *Annual Report*, 1878, p. 492; Wisconsin State Agricultural Society, *Transactions*, 1881-82, p. 26.
[54] The officials of the Iowa state fair were empowered by the agricultural society to "procure sixty men to act as police at the Fair, to be paid two dollars per day, and to be furnished with tents and straw free" (Iowa State Agricultural Society, *Report*, 1879, p. 104).
[55] Cf. Michigan State Board of Agriculture, *Biennial Report*, 1880-82, pp. 605 *et seq.*; Wisconsin State Agricultural Society, *Transactions*, 1883-84, pp. 38 *et seq.*

convention in 1875 moved "that innocent amusements might
properly be encouraged at county fairs," [56] without of course
defining what "innocent amusements" might be. But in 1883
another Michigan observer deplored the fact that

An honest granger, desirous of visiting Art hall, — mistakes the
entrance, and plunges unceremoniously into a bear den; or, into the
dangerous midst of a band of painted, blood-thirsty, scalping savages.
Seeking to escape, he rushes suddenly into the awful presence of the
"Circassian Beauty," that captivating syren, that has infested agricultural fairs, ever since the birth of the oldest inhabitant.[57]

It was suggested that if these side shows had to be tolerated
they should be put away in a corner of the grounds where
they would not take up valuable exhibition space nor distract
the visitors' attention too readily. Civic and religious organizations grew loud in their criticism of the undesirable
features. The W. C. T. U. in various states was especially
active in attempting to secure the prohibition of liquor selling on the grounds.[58] Many agricultural journals joined in
protesting against the underemphasis of agriculture. State
laws directed principally against gambling and the sale of
liquor gradually afforded some measure of government control.[59] Usually state aid was allowed only to those which

56 Michigan State Board of Agriculture, *Annual Report*, 1875, p. 514.
57 Michigan State Board of Agriculture, *Biennial Report*, 1880-82, p. 605.
The same gentleman delivered himself of the opinion that "while we may
properly encourage the growth of sorghum, as a field crop — we may not be
justified in promoting the raising of *Cain* of another species, — either on the
fair grounds, or elsewhere" (*ibid.*, p. 605).
58 Cf. Michigan State Board of Agriculture, *Annual Report*, 1880, p. 356;
Wisconsin State Agricultural Society, *Transactions*, 1880-81, pp. 24-25; *ibid.*,
1881-82, pp. 25-26; and especially *ibid.*, 1883-84, pp. 44-54. Liquor selling
was prohibited at the Wisconsin state fair in 1882, certain persons agreeing
to reimburse the society for the $500 or $600 revenue that was lost thereby.
Ibid., 1881-82, p. 26.
59 The following dispatch from the Kansas state fair at Leavenworth in
1874 indicates, however, some of the effects of such attempts at state control:
"The act of the Legislature last winter forbidding premiums for speed and
prohibiting the sale of liquors on the ground, has arrayed the turf and liquor
interests against the Fair. Agents have been employed by these interests to

certified (apparently sometimes unscrupulously) to their compliance with the law. Gradually, too, fairs came to be more efficiently managed and better policed, and perhaps even the habits and attitudes of the people underwent some change. As early as 1882 the absence of disorder at the Scioto Valley, Ohio, fair was said to be due not only "to the excellent police regulations," but also to a "disposition of the people to behave themselves." [60] And of the forty-six arrests made at the 1907 Wisconsin state fair "the greater number . . . were from jumping and breaking fences." [61] But in spite of perennial haggling, the midway has come to be an accepted, if not an essential, part of the fair, reflecting again a strange modification of the old, time-honored institution, the original purpose of which was the improvement of agricultural products.

Numerous journalistic campaigns against the abuses of the midway have been conducted from time to time. Perhaps the most important of recent years was that carried on by the *Country Gentleman* during the last decade. Beginning in 1922 with the publication of a series of articles, "Confessions of a Fair Faker," [62] it exposed many of the showmen's tricks and frauds. Among other things, it chronicled the work of one of the better known fair managers of the United States, who after collecting with the aid of a clipping bureau, a "Scrapbook of Fakery" filled with newspaper comments on, and reports of, outdoor amusement companies all over the country, appeared before the annual meeting of

---

meet incoming exhibitors at the trains and represent the Fair as a failure, so as to induce the shipment of stock and articles of exhibition on to St. Joseph." *Cultivator and Country Gentleman*, Sept. 17, 1874, p. 596. Quoted from Chicago *Tribune*.

[60] Ohio State Board of Agriculture, *Annual Report*, 1882, p. 296.

[61] Wisconsin State Board of Agriculture, *Annual Report*, 1908, p. 344. Four pickpockets, however, were arrested, "all of which," it is duly reported, "were prosecuted and served time."

[62] "Confessions of a Fair Faker," *Country Gentleman*, April 8, 1922, pp. 4 *et seq.*; April 15, 1922, pp. 7 *et seq.*; April 22, 1922, pp. 9 *et seq.*

the International Association of Fairs and Expositions in 1922 to urge a "clean fairs" campaign upon the fair managers.[63] It also gave ardent support to a movement to organize the carnival showmen under the official supervision of a dictator or censor, much as baseball and the movies have been organized.[64] Such an organization, the Showmen's Legislative Committee, was actually formed in 1923,[65] but three years later it dissolved, admitting failure to interest the showmen in a consistent effort to "clean up" their shows.[66] In the light of the increased number of fairs, particularly boys' and girls' club shows, neighborhood fairs and specialized agricultural shows, which on the whole, are free from such features, the midway attractions are probably on the wane as a part of the fair's recreational program. Yet the problem is still decidedly one of the most knotty faced by the officials of county, district and state fairs.

The lure of the midway still remains. It is in part no doubt a traditional lure, but the gaudy display and noisy excitement stir certain universal human attitudes and the games and shows and rides whet many a subtle desire of the fair-goer. The breath-taking dips of the roller coaster or the weird contrivances of the fun house may furnish one of his rare opportunities for adventure. Throwing balls at the doll rack to win some trifling prize may furnish the test of one's skill; and if he wins he may carry his plaster kewpie

[63] Macdonald, A. B., "The Scrapbook of Fakery," *Country Gentleman*, Feb. 17, 1923, pp. 1 *et seq.* The assembled fair managers contented themselves with passing a resolution condemning fakery at the fairs.
[64] Macdonald, A. B., "Miss Emma and Her Fair," *Country Gentleman*, Aug. 26, 1922, pp. 3 *et seq.*; — "It's Now or Never for the Carnivals," June 2, 1923, pp. 3 *et seq.*; — "Carnivals Must Clean Up or Be Cleaned," Dec. 1, 1923, pp. 8 *et seq.*; — "Hop-Scotch Grifters," May 10, 1924, pp. 15 *et seq.* Cf. also Johnson, Thomas J., "Crooked Carnivals," *Country Gentleman*, April 25, 1925, pp. 7 *et seq.*
[65] Macdonald, A. B., *Country Gentleman*, June 2, 1923, *op. cit.*, pp. 3 *et seq.*
[66] Macdonald, A. B., "The Nickel Nicker, the Gimmick and the Yap," *Country Gentleman*, May, 1926, pp. 9 *et seq.*

doll or his cheap but ornate Indian blanket as an emblem of his conquest, or present them to his best girl as a bid for her favor. On the merry-go-round he may be no mere farmer lad riding his plow horse to the field, but a dazzling knight astride his charger. At the shooting gallery he may for the moment become a big-game hunter in the wilds of Africa. In the giant swing he may identify himself with Lindbergh; in the toy racer he may imagine himself another Malcolm Campbell. In the dancing girls' tent he may, though a trifle shamefacedly, exult in a certain freedom from social sanctions by seeing himself as a naughty little boy. His curiosity is titillated by the palmist's readings, his credulousness challenged by the show of freaks. At the wheel of fortune or the "beano" game or the "hoopla" booth, he may have the double satisfaction of "beating the game" and of getting something for nothing: arranged as most of them are to make the player fall short of winning by a very narrow margin, these devices raise the tempting gods of chance and vanity to lure him on step by step. In countless ways, traditional and functional, the midway still appeals to the human crowd.

The problem therefore is not easily solved. As long as the fair retains any of the elements of commercialism, it will be faced by the same questions as those faced by the movies and the theater and even the newspaper: "What will the people pay for?" "Shall we give them what they want?" Fair managers are far from agreement in the matter. They are confronted by the necessity of making their fairs pay, of complying with the state laws, of determining just what the consensus of the people is and of harmonizing divergent interests and attitudes. Much of the financial support for the educational purposes of the fair comes from concessionaires' license fees and from the gate receipts collected from visitors who attend solely to enjoy the amusement

attractions. Certainly the provision of recreation and amusement is defensible as a worthy objective of the fair. Exhibitors of live stock, agricultural products and merchandise
demand crowds sufficiently large to justify the fair as an
advertising medium, yet not too pleasure-bent to give a
considerable portion of their attention to the exhibits. Under
these conditions the present-day state and county fairs
attempt to present what they construe to be well balanced
programs — frankly making definite provision for commercial and professional amusement and at the same time
attempting to preclude their overshadowing the educational
features.

The problem of general amusements — those arranged
for or hired directly by the fair management itself — has
grown and changed with the expansion and evolution of the
fair. It has reflected in general the changes particularly in
entertainment and invention which society as a whole has
undergone. The plowing matches of the early fairs were
sporting events which rested upon a utilitarian basis, resem-
bling in this respect the trials of speed on the race track.
Both were justified on the ground that they promoted agriculture. But since the plowing match lacked the romantic
appeal of the horse race, it disappeared as a general feature
of the fairs when the perfecting of the plow did away with
its utility aspect. The demonstrations of fire engines and fire
extinguishers were exciting events conducted on this same
utilitarian principle in another sphere. Even as late as 1904
one fair reporter remarked, "Speed is put to good use when
hitched to a fire wagon." [67] The same vindication may have
been made of the popular military drills in the seventies and
eighties.[68] Baseball, becoming a national sport in the sixties,

[67] Iowa State Department of Agriculture, *Yearbook*, 1904, p. 681. Cf. also
Ohio State Board of Agriculture, *Annual Report*, 1863, p. 129; Wisconsin
State Agricultural Society, *Transactions*, 1869, pp. 121-22.
[68] At a Michigan county fair in 1877 the Kalamazoo Light Guard "in full

came to be a widespread fair attraction,[69] and has remained
so at local fairs, at least down to the present time.[70] The
regular horse-racing programs were supplemented at many
state fairs by exhibition races by famous track favorites
hired for the occasion. The Wisconsin state fair paid $3,000
in 1895 for a special race between "the pacing kings" John
R. Gentry and Joe Patchem, and decided it was a good investment.[71] The Iowa state fair in 1904 paid $3,400 for an
exhibition race by Dan Patch, and $1,600 for a night show
— $5,000 more than was spent for special features the year
before — and "to this extra effort in providing star attractions" attributed the success of the fair.[72] Sometimes the
type of general attractions varied with the location of the
fair. When the Ohio state fair was held at Sandusky in 1858,
for instance, one of the chief features was a boat regatta
on Lake Erie.[73] Prizes for "velocipedestrianism" were
awarded before the end of the golden age, the Indiana
state fair having one class for a "mile trial of velocipedes"
and another for the "most artistic management of velocipedes." [74] "A new feature [of the Ohio state fair in 1882]
was the grand tournament of the 'Ohio Wheelmen'." [75]
Bicycle races became general in the nineties, reflecting a
popular fad of the period, but gave way to automobile races

dress uniform, visited the grounds by appointment, . . . gave a grand exhibition of military drill, battle skirmish and movements upon the field, and
added largely to the attractions of the day" (Michigan State Board of
Agriculture, *Annual Report*, 1877, p. 686).

[69] Cf. Wisconsin State Agricultural Society, *Transactions*, 1861-68, p. 496;
ibid., 1869, p. 121.

[70] The deciding of the New England amateur baseball championship was
a leading amusement attraction at the 1932 Eastern States Exposition, the
largest agricultural fair in that region. *New England Homestead*, Sept. 17,
1932, p. 9.

[71] Wisconsin State Agricultural Society, *Transactions*, 1895, p. 81.

[72] Iowa State Department of Agriculture, *Yearbook*, 1904, p. 98.

[73] Ohio State Board of Agriculture, *Annual Report*, 1858, p. 137.

[74] Indiana State Board of Agriculture, *Annual Report*, 1869, pp. 247, 248.

[75] Ohio State Board of Agriculture, *Annual Report*, 1882, p. 29.

as our means of locomotion became motorized. In 1910 the Wisconsin Motor Cycle Club was allowed to give races following the horse races on one afternoon of the Wisconsin state fair.[76] The wonder excited by the balloon ascension was soon forgotten with the advances in aviation, which brought first airplane demonstrations, then airplane rides for the visitors, and finally airplane stunt flying.[77] The Japanese day fireworks, popular before the close of the nineteenth century, yielded to elaborate pyrotechnic exhibitions depicting some historical epic or spectacle — "The Last Days of Pompeii," "The Burning of Chicago," "The Siege of Port Arthur" or "Vesuvius," or, in a later day, "The World on Parade" and "March On America," featuring the Washington Bicentennial. Such displays helped to revive the night programs of the fair, though constituting a far cry from the inspirational addresses and discussion meetings that characterized the night programs in the golden age. Circus and hippodrome acts were introduced to link the various special attractions together. Music came to be an important adjunct of the entertainment program, and musical organizations from countless local fife and drum corps to nationally known bands made their appearance at state and county fairs. Gradually and partially the farmer has been brought into contact with other sources of good popular amusement; but for long years the fair has been the principal means of bringing together many accepted forms of popular entertainment, science and art which the

[76] Wisconsin State Board of Agriculture, *Annual Report*, 1910-11, p. 32.

[77] It became more or less a standing joke, however, that the balloon ascension always failed to take place. The "satisfaction [of the Adair County, Iowa, fair in 1879] was general, except for a failure of the balloon ascension" (Iowa State Agricultural Society, *Report*, 1879, p. 335). And in 1906 the Wisconsin state fair contracted for airplane demonstrations under the following terms: "$1000 guaranteed, and $2750 to be paid for first successful ascension and flight, and $500 each for added ascensions and flights" (Wisconsin State Board of Agriculture, *Annual Report*, 1907, p. 5).

rural dweller has had no other chance to enjoy and even today would not see in several visits to an urban center.

RECENT TRENDS IN RECREATIONAL FEATURES

The trend toward the professionalization and commercialization of amusement has been partially counteracted in recent years by attempts to make the fair a picture of the rural community's recreational activities as well as of its vocational achievements. Just as the educational features of the fair not only recognize the real in agricultural practices but point toward the establishment of the ideal, so a new type of recreational program is with some success being correlated with a widespread rural recreation movement. Again this movement in so far as it concerns the fair is a part of a more general movement within the whole society. The fair has both incorporated the activities that might have gone on independently of it, and reacted upon these activities in performing recreational services for rural people. Its recreational aspect has been modified as a part of the larger recreational aspect of society, which through such evidences as the Little Theater movement, pageantry, the outdoor movement, the athletic movement, etc., has protested against the standardization, professionalism and commercialism of urbanized and industrialized society. Apropos of this protest the fair has made numerous efforts to make all or part of its recreational activities a matter of community participation.

The tendency is most notable of course in the neighborhood fairs and the boys' and girls' club shows. Here the recreational features are in general of two kinds: first, simple games and contests in which all the visitors may participate; and second, pageants, plays and musical programs presented by groups of amateur artists of the neighborhood. Both are representative of the so-called home-talent entertainment; the latter particularly are often expressions of consistently planned and constructive efforts to serve a neighborhood recreational interest. At the larger fairs — county, district and state — these amateur groups often provide a part of the entertainment program and sometimes participate in competitive contests conducted for the purpose of encouraging the improvement of rural recreation on the same principle that competitive displays of live stock and crops are used to encourage the improvement of agricultural products and farm practices.

In the second decade of the present century the Little Theater movement got well under way, as theatrical enthusiasts in small cities and towns throughout the country organized groups to produce amateur theatrical performances in the various communities.[78] The movement soon spread to rural areas, under the stimulation of its promoters often working through the agricultural colleges. While rural Little Theaters are as yet scattered only here and there in the rural districts, they represent a type of recreation which the fair is both utilizing and encouraging. In 1931, for example, fifteen New York fairs and thirty-one Ohio fairs were reported to be developing such groups,[79] and plays produced by Little Theaters are regular features of the Iowa state fairs.[80] Likewise, the pageant as a form of art came into considerable vogue contemporaneously with the Little Theater movement.[81] The pageant portrays by drama, music, dance and pantomime the history of a community or of a social ideal; it is presented by the members of that community and has the recreational virtue of being able

[78] Coad, Oral Sumner, and Edwin Mims, Jr., *The American Stage*, New Haven, 1929, pp. 312 *et seq.*
[79] Stacy, W. H., "Three Guide-Posts for Local Fairs," *Wallaces' Farmer*, Feb. 7, 1931, p. 172.
[80] Iowa State Fair, *Official Program*, 1931, *passim*; *ibid.*, 1932, *passim*.
[81] Coad and Mims, *op. cit.*, p. 317; Wood, Frances Gilchrist, "The Pageant in America," *Country Life*, Nov., 1916, pp. 21 *et seq.*

generally to give large numbers of people the opportunity to participate. Pageantry, too, has been utilized by the fairs, especially the smaller ones, in an effort to make their amusement features a matter of community social participation rather than commercial and professional provision. Some of the larger fairs are also holding music festivals in connection with their exhibitions, and some engage local musical organizations, many of them rural, to furnish a part of the musical program. A few fairs have prepared amateur circuses or amateur carnivals in which the acts are performed and the shows conducted by local individuals or organizations. Often they have been successful for one or two years, but, lacking the continuity of sponsorship enjoyed by the Little Theater, for example, they have not promised so much in the way of popular entertainment.[82]

The outdoor movement, which has recently given rise to summer camps, hiking clubs and all sorts of camping organizations among both young and old, has also been reflected in the fair. The vacation has come into American folkways, and thousands of farmers drive their automobiles to the state fair and camp for several days. Most of the larger fairs have set aside camp sites on their grounds and equipped them with modern camping conveniences. The boys' and girls' clubs are often provided with separate camping facilities during the period of the fair. Whether the farmer takes his vacation by going to the fair or to some other point of recreation depends of course upon the fundamental motivations which underlie his choice of possibilities. But certainly the increase in attendance at the larger fairs has been due partially to the fair's vacation appeal and to the facilities which many fair associations have made for the satisfaction of outdoor interests.

[82] Macdonald, A. B., "The Best Thing at Our Fair," *Country Gentleman*, May 5, 1923, p. 10.

It is in such ways that the fair as an institution is preserving a certain amount of communal participation in its recreational functions. The evolutionary process that has unfolded in America an essentially urban society has scattered urban amusements to the remotest rural districts. Even many of the forms of recreation that recently have made a wider provision for group participation emanate from urban sources, although they involve a reaction to urban phenomena. Yet the satisfaction of primary-group interests and the expression of individual talents cannot be wholly lost in the standardization thus fostered. The variety of amusements provided by any type of fair depends upon the economic resources, the differentiation of recreational interests and the prevailing moral code of the community which the fair serves. Hence the neighborhood fair and the junior-club fair have emphasized the intimate recreational association of small social groups, in which the recreational interest finds direct physical and psychical satisfaction. The larger general fairs have tended strongly to a spectacular type of amusement characterized by temporary contacts and commercial and professional attitudes, though in numerous instances they are making provision for larger numbers of their constituents to participate. The specialized agricultural show, if it makes any specific provision for amusements, usually does so as a part of its ways and means organization. It shares with all fairs, however, the recreational function of providing emotional release through a break in the even tenor of a community's activities through the association, primary or secondary, with other individuals and groups and through the realization of individual and social achievement.

VIII

THE SOCIALIZATIONAL ASPECT OF THE FAIR

IT remains for us to consider the relationship of the fair to the larger communities in which it operates, as well as the relationship of individuals to their communities effected through the medium of this institution. The fair, as we have seen, serves a complex of interests relating primarily to rural people; it is a focus where a multitude of interests — general and specific, primary and mediate — converge periodically and attain some measure of satisfaction. In serving these various interests — economic, technological, educational, recreational or social — the fair has at one time or another ministered, often in the absence of other agencies, to the farmer's specific needs. It has introduced new crops and new methods into his industry. It has shown him how to improve his practices and how to enlarge or meet the demands of his market. It has been one of his traditional sources of information, one of his means of recreation, one of the outlets for his sociability.

In addition to these varied interests the fair has come increasingly to perform a still wider and more differentiated function, namely, it has helped the farmer to see himself in relation to his work, to other farmers and to the agricultural industry as a unit. In a word it has broadened his social and cultural horizon. Whatever success the farmer may attain in essentially economic or technological realms will be short-lived unless the agricultural industry and rural social organization are significantly related to the larger communities of which, in an evolved social system, they form a part. The farmer must realize the possibilities of his personal and social nature and see himself and his society in relation to still larger social wholes. Just as the fair has an educational aspect and a recreational aspect — and to lesser degrees economic, commercial and technological aspects — so it has a socializational aspect as well, through which it aids in bringing the farmer more completely to the realization of, and participation in, greater social spheres.

The Meaning of Rural Socialization

In the past the exhibits at the fairs have been primarily a stimulus to increased quantitative and qualitative agricultural production. Recently, however, the tendency has been to make these exhibits reflect or idealize the relationship which exists between the farmer and his industry and the larger society. In other words, the fairs in recent years have endeavored to emphasize the matter of an attractive, significant and satisfying rural social life. Whatever the farmer's immediate needs and whatever the solution of society's economic problems, they are not concerned with stimulated agricultural production. We witness the perplexing paradox of farmers' inability to sell their live stock and crops for sufficient money to pay their taxes and interest, at the same time that hungry and ill-clothed men walk city streets. Neither the agricultural fair nor those agencies most closely associated with it can solve this fundamental problem. But within certain limits the fair can and does function in marking the relationship of the farmer not only to rural society but to the whole social structure. A rural society is more than fine live stock, paved roads, tractors and red barns. It is a complex relationship of human individuals and groups seeking through their activities, institutions and associations the fulfillment of their desires and purposes. A sociological analysis of rural society, or of any society for that matter, emphasizes the human factor — the socializa-

tion of the individual by which he comes to a fuller realization of his own potentialities in the larger society about
him.[1] The fair functions as an agency of this socialization.
Again, socialization is not its sole function, nor is the fair
by any means the sole agency of rural socialization; it is
merely one of the media in the vast social complex through
which the process is unfolded.

The fair as an institution within the community is based
upon the interests of human beings. Interests are the outgrowth of organic and psychical needs and in turn give rise
to institutions and associations. The fair, as we have noted,
satisfies both directly and indirectly a wide variety of these
interests and coördinates a multitude of activities arising
from them. The first step toward socialization is revealed in
the recognition by human beings of like and common needs
and the realization that by associated effort these needs can
often be more abundantly satisfied. Social cohesion is easily
and more or less unconsciously maintained in the communal
society of primitive family or tribe. But as soon as interests
become differentiated, institutions and associations become
established around them. The individual is no longer im-
mersed in a social group, so to speak, but stands in an
organized relationship to many social groups. He is a participant in social activities that create in him a sense of ultimate
satisfaction and he is related to society by a variety of
interest bonds.

The specialized agricultural fair furnishes a typical case
of the institution created by an interest group. The ultimate
basis of the interest underlying the specialized show is
economic; the live stock or crops shown are representatives
of special types created to serve some purpose in the agri-

---

[1] Cf. Hawthorn, Horace Boies, *The Sociology of Rural Life*, New York,
c. 1926, pp. 3 *et seq.*; MacIver, R. M., *Society: Its Structure and Changes*,
New York, 1931, pp. 24 *et seq.*

cultural industry. But the activities necessitated in creating
and perfecting these types give rise to an entirely new and
different set of factors that intensify enormously the original
economic interest. There is, for example, the factor of
creative art arising from efforts to produce ideal specimens
of live stock or high-yielding strains of grain. There is the
factor of sentiment — the sympathy engendered in the
shepherd by the care of his flock, the solicitation felt by the
gardener for the tender seedling. There are the factors of
prestige and satisfaction arising from the sense of belonging
to an important and significant social class. There is the
factor of communion with individuals who talk in the same
terms, confront the same problems, strive toward the same
ideal. The specialized agricultural show, where the farmer
sees the finest specimens of the particular products in which
he is interested and the methods whereby they have been
produced, constitutes a point where these factors come to
the surface of his consciousness and an occasion when he
experiences most fully the strength of this interest bond.

Many of these factors exist also in certain phases of the
general agricultural fair, though here, by the very nature of
the institution, the interests and interest bonds are more
diverse at the larger fairs and more limited to locality sentiment at the smaller. The interests underlying the primary
purposes of these fairs, when pushed to their ultimate bases,
are again economic — the improvement of agriculture by
educational or technological means. Yet the economic aspects
are almost wholly submerged in the interests of education,
recreation, prestige, pride in achievement, and social intercourse that the general agricultural fair has come to serve.
The large general agricultural fair brings together a multitude of interest groups, and the individual who participates
in it may experience the process of socialization through a
wide variety of interest bonds. The state fair, for example,

where the coöperative effort of a large number of specialized agencies and interest groups is seen to advantage, provides the opportunity for the participant to select the features on the basis of his personal interests. At the small neighborhood fair, on the other hand, the locality interest necessarily assumes a foremost position and the more differentiated interests are subordinated to those of the local neighborhood, thereby limiting the participant in his choice of features. The socializing effect of the neighborhood fair is usually not lost, however, for the strength of the neighborhood interest, the opportunity provided for all individuals to participate in the event, the intimate, primary-group association promoted, all tend to intensify and vitalize the social contacts which the neighborhood fair fosters, in a way quite as significant sociologically as do the extensity of contacts and the selection of interests provided by the larger fair.

The fair of whatever type furnishes the occasion for overcoming isolation. It is customary to think of the scattered rural farmsteads in America as making the isolation of the rural dweller inevitable, and it is undoubtedly true that rural social life in America lacks something of the solidarity of the European village community.[2] The comparative geographic isolation necessitates a compensating social organization. The chief problem of rural socialization at the present time is a matter of counteracting not so much physical isolation as psychosocial isolation. Many of the material means — the automobile, paved roads, the telephone, the radio — are already at hand. And many forms of social organization have already developed which reflect the extent to which differentiation and socialization have progressed in rural society. The increasing specialization of

[2] Cf. Terpenning, Walter A., *Village and Open-Country Neighborhoods*, New York, c. 1931, *passim*.

agriculture has itself tended to advance the socialization of rural life. It has compelled the farmer to study special techniques both of vocation and of social organization; it has enhanced his consciousness of social interdependence; it has brought him into contact with other people, other ways of doing things, other standards. In all this the fair has a part. From it the farmer has received many an incentive to change the products and the techniques of his industry; but far more important for the subject in hand, it has reflected the differentiation of his interests and has served as one of the forms of social organization by providing both more diverse and more intense social contacts. The social contacts which it provides are of both primary- and secondary-group character. To each of the farmer's interest groups which is recognized at the fair he shows a different side of himself, and becomes more fully socialized by the communion of interest so engendered. Not only are the social nature and the ideals of the individual developed, but his interests are given expression through contacts with objects, ideas, individuals and groups that constitute his experience at the fair. That expression may take the form of intensification of interests already definitely formed and recognized in his own consciousness, or of the expansion of his interests through contacts with new social groups and a consequent multiplication of the individual's social selves. The primary-group features of the fair merge imperceptibly into the secondary-group features — the sights, the chance meetings, the casual contacts — which temporarily or superficially enlist the visitor's attention. The stimulating effects of witnessing spectacular entertainment, for example, are to some extent the evidence of socialization. The casual remark passed between strangers at the judging ring or amphitheater are, though usually temporary, both the means to, and the expression of, a wider social consciousness.

The Fair as a Coöperative Enterprise

The socialization of the rural dweller depends upon the multiplication and intensification of human contacts that dissipate psychosocial isolation. It follows that anything is good for the community that brings people together in friendly social intercourse and places them in a significant relationship to a broader community life. A community institution or a community social program affects this socialization in the measure that it provides the incentive and the means for individuals to become active participants in the process of widening and deepening their social contacts. Some institutions are, of course, principally the concern of special-interest groups, and the socialization resulting therefrom is partially limited by the size and number of the groups concerned and by the extent to which the special-interest groups can strike responsive chords in the potentially interested individuals. An obvious case in point is the specialized agricultural show, though the extent of the appeal exercised by any interest group is a matter of degree. The general agricultural fairs by their very nature partake more of the community enterprise. It is not uncommon for a specialized show to be made the basis of — or sometimes only the initial step in — a rural neighborhood's community program. But more often it is the general neighborhood fair that performs such functions. As we pass from the small local fair to the large state and national fairs, we find a constantly decreasing proportion of the people of the communities served vitally interested in the institution. Considered from the viewpoint of locality, the general agricultural fair progressively becomes a special-interest institution. Yet with each successively enlarged classification of fairs, we find the appeal broadened in an effort to enlist more and more types and classes of individuals. The difference is essentially that of the different functions of socialization capable of being performed by each type of fair. The neighborhood fair fosters the spirit of neighborliness, the intimate, face-to-face contacts of local groups. The larger fairs allow to a greater degree the diffusion of cultural ideals from the larger distributing centers — the city, the educational, artistic and literary institutions, the centers of cultural services. The visitor to the larger fair has, therefore, the opportunity to participate in a larger social life not only through the multiplication of his contacts, but also through the selection of those activities that most appeal to his personal interests.

Generally speaking, it may be said that fairs function as agencies of socialization because they can include in their programs all or a large proportion of the people in the communities which they serve. Though there are certain limitations imposed by the scope of the specialized fair in regard both to locality and type of product, at most fairs some appeal is made to the personal interests of every age, sex and class of the population. The neighborhood fair particularly is an enterprise in which all the residents of the immediate locality can unite. The local neighborhood itself constitutes a common interest for all whose home it is. The locality interest is inevitably a relatively stronger one for country neighborhoods than for city, because it is the seat of both the work and residence of the rural dweller, as well as a very large area of his social living. It is possible for the neighborhood fair to make of this locality interest, more or less inevitable as it is, the basis of a community of fellowship, a consciousness of social responsibility and a realization of individual and social needs. At the neighborhood fair the potential constituency of the institution participates in larger proportion than in any other type. Its organization necessitates the meeting of the people and the working out of a constructive community project. Here neighbor works with neighbor in planning and conducting the fair; the circumstances and conditions under which products are made or grown are more or less common knowledge to everyone who views them. There is enough similarity, furthermore, in the social life and economic status of the group to make a common interest of the improvement of these products or of the recreational or educational aspects of the fair. The satisfactions of intimate social intercourse are available for those keen enough to grasp them. The relatively small size of the group not only permits, but often demands, the complete utilization of the neighborhood's resources, both material and human. In many rural neighborhoods there is a noticeable lack of leadership and a restriction of progressive social vision, but these requirements of social development increasingly filter into the neighborhoods through the rural schools, the agricultural extension services and similar agencies; and the local fair, as we have observed, is one of the principal means of linking these agencies to the rural community. With the leaven of these outside influences, the fair often welds the small rural neighborhood into a more stable social unit, conscious of its own resources, proud of its own achievements and cognizant of its internal and external social relationships.

If the neighborhood fair is organized around the activities of the rural school, the interests of both parents and children are by this very fact united in its conduct. In spite of a certain amount of political maneuvering and personal antagonism arising in its conduct, the school is an institution supported by the whole community, and it tends to make people think in community terms. The child-welfare interest constitutes a strong common bond, uniting individuals not only to one another but to a common organization and a common program of activities. The neighborhood fair, therefore, makes large use of school exhibits. The children are thereby given a strong incentive to produce work of sufficient quality to be put on display at the fair. They receive their reward in this fact of social recognition, small though it be. And parents and friends often receive from the same sources a vicarious satisfaction from the identification of themselves with the children in whom they have a particular interest. The agricultural projects conducted by the school or by the extension services possess the same basis of appeal; but more than that, they usually interact in close association with the actual operations of the farms and homes in the neighborhood. The feeding of a calf or a pig, the raising of a plot of corn or cotton, the canning of fruits and vegetables and the making of wearing apparel for exhibition or project purposes are dependent upon, or readily linked to, similar activities by older members of the immediate community. It is relatively easy, therefore, to draw into the neighborhood fair organization the interest if not the active coöperation of the entire neighborhood.

When the fair is sponsored on some local neighborhood basis other than that of the school — by farmers' club, coöperative association, grange, or the like — or when it is promoted as an end in itself by a simple and temporary organization, it is still inclusive of most of the members of the neighborhood. The strong locality interest, again playing its inevitable part, is supplemented by the strong sense of familism also inherent in rural society. The rural family is much more a social unit than the city family. In its work, its recreation, its possessions, its internal and external social relationships, it functions much more unitedly than does its urban counterpart. As the neighborhood fair reflects the interests of all the individuals in its area — which because of its limited scope it must do — it necessarily reveals itself as an institution of families more than of individuals; the interests of all members of the family are enlisted, the talent of all members given an opportunity to express itself. In the recreational program of the neighborhood fair there is a large place for the recognition and development of amateur theatricals, music and speaking, as well as athletic contests and games that release pent-up physical and psychic energy. In each case there is the possibility of developing human personality by means of giving expression to latent talent and to personal interests. The fair is the great annual marshaling of the neighborhood's resources — not its agricultural products alone, but its ideals, its talents, its cultural attributes as well.

The fairs of larger scope than the neighborhood fair, or the very limited local specialized shows, enlarge their activities to include a wide variety of interests. They do not give rise to the intimate interaction of so large a proportion of the individuals in their constituent areas as do the neighborhood fairs; but the features of the county, district or state fairs and of the larger specialized shows are designed to serve or appeal to the interests of many types of people and groups within the larger community. The neighborhood fairs are founded largely on the coöperation of persons in the neighborhood, aided usually by one or two outside agencies, while the larger fairs are founded upon the coöperation of the countless individuals, classes and organizations that constitute the larger constituent area which these fairs serve. The neighborhood fair is largely the project of a more or less unified group, held together by the bond of locality interest. The larger fairs are institutions of interacting and coöperating interest groups and organizations. As such, they are virtually compelled to provide some sort of satisfaction for almost everyone in the community. Nor should we forget that the agricultural fair that attempts to serve the industry in any generalized sense must necessarily include both rural and urban interests. In a differentiating social organization rural and urban interests are usually closely interrelated; consequently, the fair becomes the concern of a larger community — the county, the state, or sometimes the nation — in which the different social elements, large or small, may reach a better adjustment.

The fair is one of the many projects in which city and country unite. In the rural areas the country towns and villages are important principally as the centers of trade and services for the surrounding country. In such cases there is no sharp demarcation between rural and urban; the town is essentially a part of the rural rather than of the urban social organization. In such districts there is usually a reasonably complete recognition on the part of each group of their mutual interests. Certain antagonisms between town and open country do arise, but in thoughtful moments their mutual interdependence is taken for granted. Consequently, county and district fairs particularly are the results of coöperative efforts on the part of townsmen and farmers. Agricultural interests are assigned the place of importance — but agricultural interests reach much further than the confines of an occupational class. Some share of financial backing is usually provided by business men. As a broad social enterprise, the fair seeks the attendance of townspeople quite as much as that of country people. Even strictly agricultural activities, such as stock raising or fruit growing, have a notable significance for the dweller in town and city; and the fair is seized upon as an opportune means of impressing him with this fact. Moreover, the merchants of a town are expected to support the fair by donation of prizes, purchase of stock in the fair association, advertising and commercial displays. The assistance thus given is of course often regarded by the merchant as a commercial activity — a part of the general conduct of his business. He may look upon it as a means of advertising, an item to be appraised in dollars-and-cents return on his investment. More probably he looks upon it as a contribution to community good will, an investment no doubt commercially important, but socially significant also. Where the town and country economic and social interdependence is pronounced, neither merchant nor farmer can ignore those coöperative projects that promise some measure of community welfare and social good feeling.

Various miscellaneous examples witness to the coöperation of town and country in regard to the fair. Schools are usually closed for certain days or half days so that the children may attend. Local courts often adjourn during the period of the fair. Public and private business is arranged so as not to interfere with the fair's program.[3] The designation of certain days of the fair as "Children's Day" or "Veterans' Day" or "Political Rally Day" suggests the cutting across of various class, occupational and residential lines that places the conduct of the fair on a basis of community interest, rather than upon that of special class interests. Business and professional men sometimes donate their services as ticket sellers, ticket takers or marshals. The city sometimes details members of its police force to the fair's department of public safety, though the fair may be outside the city's jurisdiction. Boy Scouts are enlisted to direct the automobile parking or to aid in some similar capacity; service clubs may be put in charge of some concession. Local chambers of commerce or other business men's associations coöperate in various ways; they often assume charge of the advertising of the fair, sometimes organizing "booster tours" to adjoining counties or outlying regions. Whether the traditional county fair survives in essentially its present form or is supplanted by larger district fairs and smaller neighborhood fairs and club

[3] It is common, for example, for the merchants of the towns in the fair's immediate territory to close their stores during certain hours on fair days.

achievement days, the need for rural-urban coöperation will undoubtedly remain, if not appreciably increase. In any event, the impact of the city, its culture, its standard of living, its techniques, upon the country can take place partly through the medium of some kind of agricultural fair at the same time that that impact is tempered by rural evaluations and interpretations.

The Fair as an Expression of Achievement

In no respect does the fair function as an agency of socialization to a greater extent than in the matter of expressing achievement. First of all it expresses individual achievement. This is especially true of the rural dweller who displays his products at the fair or participates in some other of its activities. But opportunity is given also for many persons whose interests are essentially urban to share in the fair's program and consequently to experience the satisfactions of individual achievement. Next, the fair is an expression of group and community achievement — that of the fair's particular constituency, neighborhood, county, state, or interest group. The smaller fairs bring glimpses of the outside world to the smaller and more remote rural areas; the state fairs are pageants of the world's scientific, industrial, and cultural advances, especially as these relate to agriculture.

It is as an expression of achievement that the fair aids most fully in making the rural dweller conscious of his relationship to a larger social world, and the urban dweller conscious of the rôle played by rural industry. The fair is not so much an agency of popular education nor an occasion for recreation and amusement, important though it is in these respects, as it is the annual gathering together of the resources of a community or of a special-interest agricultural group into a grand display. Such a display not only records the accomplishments, but it signifies the social and

economic importance and expresses the hopes, of the particular segment of society which it represents. What individuals
are accomplishing alone or what small communities or
organizations serving agricultural interests are accomplishing within the bounds of their own areas can be seen in
numerous isolated and unconnected instances. But it is only
at the fair that collective achievement, relatively speaking,
is made the subject of popular interest and vivid demonstration. What the individual live-stock breeder is accomplishing can be seen from a visit to his farm, a drive along the
adjoining highway, or an inspection of his animals as they
are sent to market. But the progress toward an ideal in
live-stock production, or the advances made by a branch of
the industry as a whole is best revealed at an agricultural
fair which assembles the best specimens produced. What the
individual rural homemaker is accomplishing can be seen
from a visit to her home or garden or perhaps to her club.
But what marks the achievements of rural homemakers as a
class is best recognized both by these individuals themselves
and by other groups when the choicest representatives of
their products and activities are displayed at the fair. The
accomplishments of the individual junior club member can
be seen when he markets his calf or harvests his crop of
corn or beans, but the significance of club work as a collective phenomenon is disclosed only in some grand final exhibit
such as a 4-H club achievement day or a state or national
club congress. The projects of Farm Bureau or other farm
improvement association carried on in local neighborhoods
or counties take on new meaning when their results are
displayed or demonstrated, alongside those from other
communities, at the county or state fair. A fair that is
representative of the entire social and economic life of a
rural community — its products, its social organization, its
recreation, its cultural attainments — is the most graphic

presentation of the collective achievement of the community.

Time was when the outstanding agricultural achievements were almost wholly matters of individual effort. The improvements made in live-stock or crop production were largely the results of the individual breeder's or farmer's efforts, without the aid of agricultural college, breeders' association or farmers' club, and without much coöperation from his neighbors. Rural community life was a matter of simple and spasmodic social organization; social and economic life was largely a matter of what the individual farm family could do for itself. Naturally, therefore, fairs until the last twenty years recognized little more than the products of individual enterprise. True, a fair that brings together a grand display of individual achievements expresses community and social achievement of a certain kind. But only in comparatively recent years have fairs come to recognize the accomplishments of groups and communities *as* groups and communities. Prizes were formerly awarded almost exclusively to the individual exhibitors of the best specimens of live stock or crops or handicraft, and while such exhibits still claim by far the largest proportion of the fair's prize money, the policy is becoming increasingly general to award prizes to organized clubs or groups that present a coöperative display. In such cases the prize money is usually not distributed to the individuals participating in the preparation or presentation of the exhibit, but is turned over to the club treasury to reimburse or finance the coöperative effort of the group taking part. The recent accomplishments of agriculture and rural life are as notable as those of former days; they are slightly different in character and perhaps more socially significant, since they reflect a new stage of socialization on the part of the rural population.

The recognition of group achievements extends not only to the awarding of prizes for certain coöperative exhibits and displays, but also to the use of local rural groups to furnish certain features of the educational and recreational programs.[4] The educational demonstrations of club boys and girls, of farm bureaus and rural women's clubs sponsored by the extension services, as well as those of the vocational agriculture schools, are largely representative of coöperating rural groups, under a certain amount of urban stimulation and leadership. Many of these groups also carry on projects essentially recreational in nature that are incorporated in the fair's recreational program. Home-talent plays under the direction of some local Little Theater, pageants in which each neighborhood in a community may be held responsible for a certain scene or act, music by local musical organizations, art exhibits by local art groups, and a wide variety of features conducted by local schools and clubs have become increasingly important recreational attractions.[5]

This does not mean that the sense of individual achievement is in any degree lessened at the modern fair; it merely means that the sense of group achievement has been heightened. The individual who makes an exhibit or otherwise participates in the fair still is recognized sufficiently to give him a sense of pride in his personal accomplishments. In fact, efforts have been made to shift the emphasis from the perfection of the live stock or the crops or the machinery on display at the fair to the human individuals who are responsible for them or who use them. The awarding of herdsmen's prizes, not to the owner of an exhibit of animals, but to the caretaker who looks after it and makes it attractive, is a case in point.[6] Another is the awarding of showmanship prizes to boys and girls or other amateur exhibitors on the

[4] Cf. Stacy, W. H., "Three Guide-Posts for Local Fairs," *Wallaces' Farmer*, Feb. 7, 1931, pp. 163, 172.

[5] *Ibid.*, p. 172.

[6] Cf. International Live Stock Exposition, *Preliminary Classification*, 1932, p. 23; *ibid.*, pp. 72, 74, 122.

A FIDDLERS' CONTEST AT THE POCAHONTAS COUNTY FAIR
WEST VIRGINIA

basis of their exhibition technique, regardless of the quality of the exhibit itself.[7] In many branches of agriculture the products have reached such a high degree of excellence that the contests staged at the fairs are no longer determined merely by the quality of the specimens exhibited, but also by the skill in fitting, handling, arranging and decorating. Thus a new factor is introduced into the fair, furnishing another outlet for individual accomplishment.[8] The sense of individual accomplishment is also made a reality for many more people than formerly through the increased number and variety of contests in which fair visitors may take part — athletic contests, stock- or crop-judging contests, musical and oratorical contests, etc. The use of group demonstrations, displays and contests on the educational and recreational programs has provided an opportunity for the participation of thousands of individuals who would not otherwise have any direct part in the conduct of the fair. The boys' and girls' club exhibits have not only enormously increased the actual number of exhibitors of agricultural products at the fairs, but they have helped to break the magic circle of professional exhibitors whose capturing of the bulk of the prizes year after year has sometimes killed the incentive of the amateur breeder or farmer to show his products. The junior-club exhibitors represent a multitude of rural families who usually have no other direct part in the making of the fair.

In every exhibit displayed at the fair there lies the basis for pride in the personal accomplishment of some person.

[7] Cf. *ibid.*, p. 122.
[8] Unfortunately the same fact may give rise to various deceptive devices and infractions of the rules to make exhibits appear to their best advantage. Cases in point are the practice of "plugging" beef cattle, *i.e.*, injecting paraffin under the skin to give the impression of perfect regularity in the outline of the animal, and the practice of using arsenic in the forced feeding of horses to attain rapid gains in weight.

Though pride and ambition are sometimes anti-social factors, they are also capable of being made the foundation of constructive individual and social achievement. The fair makes large use of them as such. It is in an exceptional position to throw the individual against the background of the group. Traditionally the fair has awarded prizes to the best specimens of agricultural exhibits on the theory that such procedure stimulates ambition and rewards accomplishment. The blue and purple ribbons, the medals, cups and trophies won at the fair are marks of personal distinction. They assume their place in that long list of means by which certain members of society are set off from the rest, and human egos are gratified by the approval or envy excited in the surrounding group. The desire for social recognition is an almost universal characteristic of human nature, and the rewards of the fair, quite aside from any money prizes involved, are the tribute of that institution to personal vanity. There is possibly an element of defense involved therein. The farmer's desire for social recognition has often been left largely unsatisfied; life's greatest social rewards have usually gone to other classes. The importance placed upon the prizes won at the fair may be augmented by this scant recognition that has come to the class as a whole. It is conceivably one of the reasons why the fair in America has become a competitive display of agricultural products instead of a commercial market. At any rate, care is taken to post or announce the names of the winners on the grounds, to stage a parade of the best exhibits, to publish the list of awards in the paper, or otherwise to recognize publicly the winners of the various competitions.

But it is not only the exhibitor or participant who receives from the fair the sense of achievement. The visitors who are spectators only also share in the sense of social achievement that is generated by the fair. Fairs are commonly referred to as "show windows" of a county, state or industry. It is an appropriate appellation. But they are show windows in more than a commercial sense; they are show windows also in a social sense. They do more than advertise the products of a community, an industry or an individual. They concentrate in one place the choicest products of many different kinds of labor and many different people — a miniature picture of the progress made toward some ideal. The contemplation of the picture in its totality generates in both participant and spectator a new appreciation of the agricultural industry, gives a new significance to the meaning of social advancement.

As one views the products of farm and home and factory, the accomplishments of college, training school and agricultural association, he can scarcely avoid having borne in upon his consciousness a sense of the significance of human endeavor, human enterprise, skills, genius and ideals. As he inspects the herds of sleek and well-bred live stock or the bountiful displays of grain and fruit and vegetables, as he watches the demonstration of a coöperative agricultural project by the representatives of a county or of a farmers' club, as he views the historical pageant delineating the social, economic or cultural path that civilized man has trod, as he examines the new scientific inventions and ponders the new ways in which science has been applied to the agricultural industry, he must perceive something of the meaning of the age in which he lives; he must come to a realization again that he is a part of a great society. It must occur to him how small is man, yet how great! He must have a sense of personal and social fulfillment — of his individual satisfactions being realized in a society constantly enlarging its concepts, its functions and its products.

This is essentially what we may call a sense of social significance. It is a kind of ego expansion in which emotional reactions are stimulated by and linked to external objects of admiration and interest. Too often the attitudes and activities, especially perhaps those of rural dwellers, are "culturally inbred." The fair, in so far as it sets standards of live stock or crop production and forces a conscious realization of social relationships and social achievements, is a cultural agency — not always, to be sure, completely practicable — that bears in upon the individual's consciousness with new stimulations, new ideas, new appeals. There he sees what can be done; he is given an opportunity in the grand manner to become cognizant of other people and of out-of-the-ordinary things in the world. Not only is there the element of interaction with other human beings; there is also an element of identification. The participant in the fair comes to a new realization of his own dignity and importance, for here are the fruits of his labors, here are the results of his intelligence, his dexterity, his ideals; and he may look upon his achievement with the satisfaction of a skilled artisan. The spectator at the fair, whether he be a member of the industry which it represents or of some other walk of life, may assume the attitudes and feelings of those who are concerned, may assume a rôle in this drama, the climax of which is the fair. He may thus indulge merely in greater or lesser degrees of sentiment and romanticism; or he may come to a more rational realization of the interdependence of different sections of society, to a fuller appreciation of the contributions of certain classes, to a more definite comprehension of the meaning of society itself. In any case, both participant and spectator advance apace in their sense of social significance.

The growing tendency to emphasize and reward group achievement at the fair contributes to this sense of social significance, as does every effort to make the fair representative not so much of agricultural products as such, as of the activities of the human individuals participating. Exponents of rural improvement programs have suggested repeatedly that the test of every exhibit should be its contribution to rural life. Long ago one such leader, Liberty Hyde Bailey, suggested a type of local fair to which every person and every organized group, as well as newspapers, manufacturers and merchants, would bring what they considered their best contribution to the development of a good community.[9] The opportunities which the fair furnishes for persons with varying personal interests to enlarge and intensify their social contacts, mark it as an important means to social achievement, for every outlet through which the individual becomes a more complete personality makes him at the same time more dependent upon society. The realization of the efforts of men to improve their social living is quite as important in the social sense as the appreciation of ideal products. The fair is increasingly functioning in this sphere.

The fair functions as an agency of socialization in its recreational aspects also. Play is a great medium of socialization. "Association," says Franklin H. Giddings, "is not perfect . . . until it is pleasurable and sympathetic." [10] In almost all agricultural fairs the spirit of the festival remains in some degree. It is still a holiday. It still retains elements of pageantry and ritual. It still calls forth the expression of certain collective emotions and loyalties. It is one of the shrines where the modern American pays homage to the harvest of the earth. There is still the influence of common pleasure: the almost universal appeal of music, the exotic excitement of the midway, the dramatic sweep of pageant or parade, the opportunities for the convivial man to drink

9 "A New Kind of County Fair," *Playground*, Feb., 1912, pp. 380 *et seq.*
10 *The Principles of Sociology*, New York, 1896, p. 116.

and gamble, eat and play, sport and gossip. There is still the sociability of the festive crowd dissipating the humdrum of everyday existence. In athletic contest, in family picnic, in games and friendly visiting, the sense of social cohesion becomes vitalized and enlarged. Never more than in the whole-hearted social expression of the play impulse does the individual know himself to *belong* to society.

One final respect may be noted in which the fair functions as a means of linking individuals and groups to a larger community. The international influence of the American agricultural fair has been little noticed, yet therein lies a significant aspect of the institution. The world's fair, or exposition, of course crosses international lines, and the visitors consequently are brought into contact with the achievements of other nations. Except for those from Canada, however, few foreign exhibits have been presented at the agricultural fairs in the United States. But in other ways the fairs have provided many international contacts, and among certain groups have contributed notably to the development of international good will and appreciation. This is especially true of certain live-stock groups. Many of the larger fairs secure judges from foreign nations to officiate at their annual exhibitions.[11] Numerous Canadian judges are secured for American fairs every year, and men from England, Scotland, the Channel Islands, France, Belgium and Argentina have from time to time been called upon to make the awards. Interested individuals and societies in foreign countries frequently offer special prizes at American shows. At the International Live Stock Exposition a gold medal given by the Shorthorn Society of Great Britain and

[11] It is a rule, for example, for a foreign judge to be selected to award the championships among the fat bullocks at the International Live Stock Exposition at Chicago. In 1932, for the eighth time in recent years, the same man, Walter Biggar of Dalbeattie, Scotland, officiated in this capacity. Cf. *Wallaces' Farmer*, Dec. 10, 1932, p. 639.

Ireland is awarded annually for the best Shorthorn bull. Similar special prizes are provided for animals of their respective breeds by the Southdown Sheep Society of England, the Clydesdale Horse Society of the United Kingdom of Great Britain and Ireland, the Shire Horse Society of England and the Société Royale le Cheval de Trait Belge.[12] The King Albert trophy, so-called by special permission from the late King of the Belgians and offered by the Société Royale for the Belgian horse most representative of the breed, was, at the 1927 International, presented in person by Prince Albert de Ligne, Belgian ambassador to the United States, in what was described as "a social event of brilliance and beauty."[13] Furthermore, the fact that many of our breeds of live stock originated in foreign countries and are still bred there serves as a bond of mutual interest between certain groups here and abroad. Shorthorn, Hereford and Angus cattle, for example, and many of our breeds of horses and sheep originated in Great Britain; Percheron horses, in France; Belgian horses, in Belgium; Jersey and Guernsey cattle, in the Channel Islands, etc. The great fairs and live-stock shows where the winnings of certain strains of breeding enhance the value of lineage and where men gather together, fraternize and romance in interest groups with a strong international flavor, are undoubtedly capable of generating some degree of international good will. Many an American live-stock breeder and exhibitor feels, through his connection with a live-stock interest group, a personal attachment to a like interest group in a foreign land and sometimes to a foreign land itself. Thus do agricultural fairs contribute their mite to the formation of the international mind.

[12] International Live Stock Exposition, *Preliminary Classification,* 1932, *passim.*
[13] *Breeder's Gazette,* Jan., 1928, p. 49.

"Expositions are the timekeepers of progress," said William McKinley the day before he was assassinated at the Pan-American Exposition at Buffalo in 1901.[14] The same may be said of agricultural fairs; they mark year after year the accomplishments of agricultural communities or branches of the agricultural industry. In their educational and recreational aspects, they share their functions with a multitude of other agencies that have come definitely to serve specialized human interests. As expressions of achievement, however, the fairs still retain a unique place in agricultural life. They are still the grand marshaling of agricultural resources — the representation of the best a rural community has to offer from its economic and social life. Individual achievements are reflected against the background of group endeavor and appreciation; community achievements are seen in comparison with one another; and both are linked in significant relationships to still greater individual and social activities and broader groups and communities. Thus does the fair function in aiding the rural dweller to make new social contacts and to intensify his interest bonds, to become conscious of his relationships to other individuals and groups, and to lend the strength of his own class to the stability of the larger community. The fair acts as an agency of socialization in that, under the periodically renewed spirit of festivity which it fosters, all the participants and spectators may sink certain of their personal interests deeper into the roots of sociality and may perceive more clearly the meaning of society itself.

[14] Richardson, James D., *A Compilation of the Messages and Papers of the Presidents, 1789-1908*, 1909, X, 393.

PART IV
CONCLUSION

IX

THE FAIR IN A CHANGING SOCIETY

In the foregoing chapters the fair has been viewed always against the background of a changing society. Only incidentally has reference been made to the process of social evolution as it is revealed in the development of the agricultural fair. Before bringing this study to a close it seems advisable that we address ourselves briefly to a consideration of this process.

The Fair as a Social Institution

The preliminary steps in such a task are the definition of the fair as a social institution and an analysis of the forms it assumes with reference to present agricultural associations and communities. In places where it flourishes, the fair is a customary mode of expression and conduct for large numbers of rural as well as urban people. It is a socially established means of group activity, definitely created or incidentally utilized by an agricultural association or a community to carry out certain purposes and to serve certain interests. The fair as an institution consists, to echo William Graham Sumner's analysis of all institutions, of a concept and a structure.[1] The concept is an ideational formulation of what it is desirable or necessary to do, an underlying idea, notion, doctrine or interest constituting a conceptual basis for certain organized social activity; and the structure is the complex of officials, instrumentalities, rules, procedures and sanctions by which desirable or necessary social action is carried on. In evolving to the status of social establishment, that is, in becoming an institution, the fair

[1] *Folkways*, Boston, c. 1906, p. 53.

has incorporated both communal and associational activities. Numerous elements have been recognized and drawn from the whole community into the conformation of the fair, permitting such things as communal festivity and communal recreation to grow into more specific forms of social establishment. At the same time definitely organized associations have seized upon the fair as a means of promoting their own or the community's interests, and have therefore contributed to it elements of a distinctly associational nature. The association, in other words, has created its own institution, or has given recognition and direction to the elements that constitute the institution.[2]

The agricultural fair is conducted by an association — the agricultural society or the fair association, a purposefully organized group of officials and members forming sometimes a public and sometimes a private body, through which the various aspects of the institution come to expression.[3] Usually the fair is conducted by a private corporation or a temporary group made up of interested individuals, but sometimes, particularly in the case of state fairs, by an appointive or elective group having the status of government officials responsible to the state. The active members of the fair association are usually not numerous; sometimes the officials constitute almost the sole membership, sometimes they are merely the spokesmen for a more or less well organized group of members. Membership is attained by a variety of methods: sometimes any individual becomes a member of the fair association by paying a membership fee or annual dues; sometimes shares of stock in the association are sold, every purchaser automatically becoming a member; sometimes tickets are sold which confer member-

[2] Cf. MacIver, R. M., *Society: Its Structure and Changes*, New York, 1931, pp. 15 *et seq.*
[3] Cf. *ibid.*, pp. 15 *et seq.*, for a fuller discussion of the distinction between institution and association.

ship upon the purchasers, as well as extend the privilege of attending the fair or making exhibits without any further expense. The membership of the association is important therefore, as a source of financial support and as a radiator of interest in the fair throughout the community which the institution serves.

In every case the officials form a closely knit center and the members a more or less extensive fringe giving various degrees of support to the particular social program which the fair association carries on. Together, they may well be thought of as constituting a kind of latent membership, even though they may have already made a partial investment of money, time and effort toward the realization of certain of their interests through the fair.[4] In addition to these individuals that have attained definite membership in the association, the fair depends in part for its support upon many other members of the community. Relatively few inhabitants of the community are members, in the strict sense, of the organization, yet they bear a relationship to the organized group almost as close as that arising out of active membership. Their participation in the fair can be counted upon, either to extend the range of exhibits or to enlarge the crowd of visitors.

The fair association itself furnishes the continuity; the officers carry the organization through the inactive period from one annual exhibition to the next, taking care of the grounds, supervising construction work, booking attractions, arranging for exhibits, making contacts and maintaining relationships with coöperating organizations, preparing classifications, collecting premium funds, and carrying on publicity work in behalf of the fair.[5] In the case of the

[4] Cf. Coyle, Grace Longwell, *Social Process in Organized Groups*, New York, 1930, pp. 95 *et seq.*
[5] The Iowa State Fair Board of the Iowa Department of Agriculture, for example, publishes in May, July, August and October of each year, a magazine, *Greater Iowa*, devoted to publicity for the Iowa state fair.

larger fairs such activities constitute a year-round job; even for the smaller fairs they require a goodly portion of someone's time and energy for several weeks or months of the year. Under such circumstances we find in the fair, as in other associations, the appearance of paid leadership. The officials of the fair association, especially the secretary, tend to become professional fair managers. They devote all or a considerable part of their time to the conduct of the fair, become more or less "expert" in matters of fair finance, publicity and management, and measure their tenure of office, their personal prestige and often their income by the success of the fair.[6] This policy of employing leadership brings to the management of fairs the means of increased efficiency, expert knowledge and the instruments for articulating existing or potential interests of rural people. But it also tends to turn the conduct of fairs into a business in which lie certain vested interests and institutional values. In addition to the secretary or manager, the closely knit nucleus of the organization consists of a president, a treasurer, and a corps of assistants, usually called superintendents, heading various departments of the fair, such as live stock, farm products, horticulture, poultry, home economics, etc. — the division of labor and its correspondingly differentiated organization being carried as far as the size of the fair necessitates.

Most of the more permanently organized associations, as we have noted already, own land, buildings and equipment. The ownership of these physical assets is often vested, in the case of the state fairs, in the state itself; in the case of other fairs, in the legally established and controlled association, or corporation. Ordinarily the smaller fairs — the neighborhood fairs, most of the boys' and girls' local club shows, and the local specialized shows — have little or no

[6] Cf. Coyle, op. cit., pp. 121 et seq.

permanent property of their own, since they are sponsored by a loose temporary organization or by some rural association devoted to numerous purposes other than the conduct of the fair.

The core of the agricultural fair is the exhibition of agricultural products for prizes. These products are avowedly displayed for the purpose of promoting the agricultural interests of a local, state or national community. Whatever may be said to the contrary, this is the essential feature of the fair. Yet, as we have noted, the agricultural interest served by the fair is in reality a complex of interests — some, educational, technological and economic, being primarily agricultural; others, such as power, prestige and social intercourse, pervade all associations of whatever kind. Hence it is that the fair appeals to one person in a way that fails utterly to attract another, or appeals to a number of interests of varying intensity in the same individual. For this reason, too, fairs of the same general type present a varied program. They provide certain attractions, cater to certain classes of visitors, or apportion the prize money in certain ways. Thus they function in response to the demands of those who maintain them, whether these be members of the community who attend the exhibition, the state, associations, or individuals who render financial assistance.

Often these demands are determined by the coterie of more or less professionalized officials who manage them. The avowed interest of the fair is not always the real one; it may be conducted to serve the interests of prestige, financial gain or political preferment of the individuals who exercise the power of the organization. Sometimes the entertainment or amusement features, for example, may be stressed to the virtual exclusion of others, as has frequently happened in the matter of horse racing, side-show attractions or bizarre stunts, notwithstanding the fact that the fairs are boldly proclaimed to be educational agencies devoted to the improvement of agriculture. It is possible also, by manipulating the distribution of prize money, to over-stimulate the exhibition of products not common or sometimes actually unsuited to the region which the fair serves.[7] But interesting as this topic is, it must be obvious that any attempt to classify fairs on the basis of the motivations that govern those who are responsible for their establishment and maintenance is practically impossible.

The Outstanding Features of the Agricultural Fair

The visitor to the agricultural fair, as he surveys the event in full swing, will ordinarily distinguish four main elements. The first and essential feature is, of course, the display of agricultural products exhibited before judges who pass on their merits. Judging day is the occasion of great activity in the barns where the live stock is quartered. Herdsman, shepherd and groom are up early. The cattle must be washed and curried, their horns and hoofs polished. The horses must have their flowing manes braided with bright-colored bunting and decked with artificial roses. The sheep must be given a final touch with the blocking shears. And in the swine pavilion fate plays favorites across the color line, for the Chester White gets his sifting of talcum powder while the Poland China has his ebony bristles shined with lampblack. By the middle of the forenoon these animals in their tonsorial elegance, so to speak, are being led class by class to the judging rings, where an appointed individual or committee, supposedly learned in the qualities they should

[7] A case in point is the offering of prize money at county fairs to a large number of breeds of poultry, many of which are neither grown in nor practically suited to the county in which the fair is held, a policy that often turns the poultry display into a professional poultry fanciers' holiday at the expense of local exhibitors and farmers.

possess, examines them and makes the awards. In various agricultural exhibit halls are displayed fruit, grain, vegetables, flowers, culinary articles and handwork. Through aisles and booths the judges pass, inspecting the wheat, potatoes or gladioli and sampling the cakes and pickles. After the judging has been completed, usually during the early part of the fair, ribbons or tickets are displayed to indicate the prizes won and the exhibits are left till the close of the fair to be viewed by the visitors.

The second most common feature of the fair is the entertainment program; only the very narrowly exhibitive shows fail to provide it. The larger fairs tend toward commercialized types of amusement — music and performances by professional entertainers, horse races, automobile races, fireworks spectacles, airplane stunt flying and an extended midway, with its side shows, games and rides — all designed for financial gain. Such features are less prevalent at, or often entirely absent from, the smaller fairs, where the amusements are furnished by the members of the community. Among these forms of entertainment are foot races, horseshoe pitching, baseball games and community singing.

The third general feature usually characterizing the agricultural fair consists of the exhibits of educational institutions, government agencies, propagandist organizations or civic groups. Such displays are usually made in booths where placards, pictures, models and mechanical devices have been arranged to attract the visitors' attention. In connection with the displays, demonstrations are conducted, lectures and entertainments given, and pamphlets and trinkets distributed. The extent of these exhibits varies with the scope of the fair. The small neighborhood fair may have no feature of this type other than the exhibit or demonstration furnished by the local school or the county agricultural or home economics extension agent. The great state fair, on the other hand, providing as it does the opportunity for reaching great numbers of people, will have the exhibits of agricultural colleges and other educational institutions, state and national departments of agriculture, livestock breeders' associations, farm bureaus, clubs, etc., and of a conglomerate variety of propagandist organizations ranging perhaps from the Anti-Saloon League or the National Association for the Advancement of Colored People to the National Meat Producers' Association or the Horse Association of America.

Finally, the visitor will ordinarily find in the agricultural fair what, for want of a better term, may be called the commercial feature. It consists of the exhibits of manufacturers and merchants who use the fairs as a medium of advertising. Probably the most impressive display of this sort is that of farm machinery — tractors and engines; farm lighting, heating and water systems; plows, threshers and corn binders; fences, gates and mechanical barn doors; milking machines and cow stanchions; garden tools and hay forks; individual hog houses and automatic grain feeders — an endless array of machines, tools and appliances that suggest to the observer something of the extent to which the mechanization of agriculture has gone. At the early fairs, farm machinery was often awarded prizes, as were agricultural products, in order to stimulate mechanical invention and improvement. Later, when the manufacture of machinery became a factory industry, the machinery exhibits came to be regarded as commercial and fairs ceased to offer prizes for such displays. Finally there was a noticeable tendency, about the beginning of the present century, for the manufacturers not to display their articles but simply to make of their booths a sort of convention headquarters where dealers and distributors might gather and place their orders. Recently, however, the farmer, the ultimate consumer of these articles, has come in for an increased share of attention, and not only are the articles themselves on display, but they are operated and demonstrated, not for prizes, but with an eye to sales. The commercial and industrial exhibits cover a wide range of articles interesting to rural dwellers. At the booths of local department stores, of grocers, furniture, hardware or automobile dealers and many others, small samples are given away, demonstrations made and orders solicited. Thus survives a suggestion of the old medieval commercial fairs or their modern successors, the sample fairs.

The essential feature is, of course, the competitive display of agricultural products; it is that which distinguishes the agricultural fair. The other features may be present in greater or lesser degree and number, depending upon the scope of the fair and the particular interests both of the people to whom the fair is made to appeal and of the officials who manage it. The entertainment and amusements, the educational and propagandist exhibits, the commercial and industrial displays, constitute accretions around the central core of the institution, accretions that obtain in response to the desires and needs of those who are connected with or who frequent the fair.

The Principle of Social Evolution Revealed in the Fair

Even a hasty glance at the contrast between the agricultural fairs of the early nineteenth century and those of the present time invites consideration of the process of social evolution as it is revealed in this institution. No fact is more fundamental regarding human society than that it changes. In all its aspects, in all its structures and functions, it undergoes a process of continuous modification, molded now by the physical environment, now by the social heritage, now by some outstanding leader, now by the surge of certain needs and desires of the people whose life it encompasses. The whole of society in its time process manifests a continuous and directional change in which social structures and social functions have arisen from potentialities in a sort of communal social solution into more or less definite and purposeful realities. Human society is, therefore, but a manifestation of the ageless process of social evolution. Likewise, specific structures and specific functions within society illustrate this basic social fact. Our present interest lies in only one of society's countless institutions, the agricultural fair, and in its evolution from an indistinct and general status to a more differentiated one.

The concept of social evolution implies merely an increasing specialization of structure and function within a social system, the nature of the system being thereby more completely revealed and the purposes of society more fully served.[8] It deals with the attainment of a more definite form or variety of forms of the social entities through the operation of the process of differentiation. By means of the evolutionary clue we orient ourselves to the study of society or of particular social institutions in a number of significant respects. First, it minimizes the importance of the essentially fruitless search for specific social origins. Again, it enables us to perceive the emergence of distinct types or type stages. It helps us, furthermore, to safeguard ourselves against a too segmentary view of society and to place the object of our interest in its proper relationship to other social facts. We have therefore sought the origins of the fair only in so far as they depict its emergence from an undifferentiated milieu, and have attempted in portraying its historical development to indicate how it has attained more definite forms and functions.

The evolution of society itself is clearly perceivable in a

[8] Cf. MacIver, *op. cit.*, p. 405 and *passim*.

brief analysis of the changes which have taken place in the character of the institution called the fair. The concourses of primitive people who are known to have gathered together for various purposes became, as the means of communication and transportation developed, more and more common. Even in primitive times the curiously mixed religious and commercial purposes served by the great assemblages began to differentiate in favor of the secular emphasis. At no time probably did they serve exclusive ends; in primitive society the religious, economic, commercial, recreational and social interests and the institutions supporting them were relatively not differentiated, and in medieval society they were only partially so. As definite religious institutions and associations emerged, the old religious concourses lost much of their significance; religious interests began to be served more fully elsewhere. Concurrently the commercial interests, by no means absent in the religious gatherings, came to be emphasized more and more consistently. By the Middle Ages the commercial aspect of the fair had become dominant; and the institution, since it served an undeveloped medieval commerce, existed on an essentially commercial or economic basis. But it was commercial only by virtue of its emphasis; it still possessed religious aspects and social and recreational aspects as well. The fair could not remain a commercial institution, however; as a new type of economic life emerged, with its new means of communication and transportation, its new instruments of commerce, its new methods of manufacture, its new economic institutions and associations, the fair was transformed again by the process of differentiation. The primarily commercial type of the institution made usually one of two adjustments: either it changed its general emphasis, allowing the formerly latent or subsidiary pleasure aspect to become dominant, or it retained its commercial characteristics, but redefined its purposes to serve new commercial ends. In the first instance, there emerged the pleasure fair, which, however, ultimately offended public sanction or felt the pressure of competing institutions to such an extent that it was largely abolished or abandoned; in the second, the commercial fair survived not as a place of exchange but as an exhibit of samples. Meanwhile, the so-called exposition was arising with its commercial, educational, recreational and exhibitive aspects; this fair attempted to portray on a grand scale the whole of the society which it represented. Thus did differentiating human society necessitate also the evolution of types and functions within the fair.

If it were necessary to list the agricultural fair in one of the foregoing categories, it might well be considered to partake most of the nature of the exposition. It has always made an appeal primarily agricultural, serving an interest relatively narrow in comparison with the earlier types of fairs; nor should we overlook the fact that the earlier fairs incorporated forms and functions which later developed within the exposition itself. For the agricultural fair, too, is subject to the inexorable law of social evolution. As an institution it has drawn many of its characteristics, many of its concepts and instrumentalities, from the types of fairs that preceded it; many elements present in those fairs have again sprung from the social amorphousness, as it were, to take form in this particular institution. It is impossible, by the very nature of the case, to trace in detail all these formations; exactly when or where or how social particulars first begin to take form it is not often given us to know. Historical events, significant as they are, are yet for the sociologist but clues to trends. They facilitate his interpretation of social evolution by clarifying or marking the type facts with which he deals.

The genius of Elkanah Watson was, in the first place, a

precipitating factor in the development of agricultural fairs in America. We cannot say just where or how he came by the ideas which he incorporated into his Berkshire societies and fairs; all we know is that possessed of a particular social heritage, and grasping a situation that reflected a dominant national spirit, he pursued certain of his own personal interests in a way that happened, both fortuitously and purposefully, to serve certain of the interests of the rural people of his time. Attitudes and interests always underlie the formation of institutions and associations. In the establishment and conduct of his fairs, Watson selected those interests that not only enhanced his own satisfactions but made articulate for his neighbors many of their underlying desires. He helped them to create and participate in an institution in which those desires could be satisfied. He coöperated with them in effecting the organization of associations designed to attain the interests of prestige, patriotism, social intercourse, economic gain and perhaps even a faint trace of religion. The practical agricultural societies and the fairs were the means of achieving these ends. Watson's activities constitute the historical events which, considered sociologically, mark the emergence of a new type form of social institution. They show, as has already been intimated, the conspicuous crystallization in a single unity of many elements from the old types of fair at the same time that the introduction of the competitive exhibition of agricultural products gave the institution a new turn that has remained its distinguishing characteristic.

The comparatively homogeneous and unspecialized character of rural society in the early nineteenth century was obviously not conducive to the development of highly specialized agricultural institutions and associations. The early fair was therefore general in character, serving the interests of the general farmer, the live-stock breeder, the women in the rural household. As a means of entertainment and social intercourse it served farmers particularly, but townsmen also, and its variety of diversions was sufficiently wide to attract young and old, gay and sober, sportive and devout.[9] In the simpler social organization then prevailing, rural educational, economic, technological and recreational associations were either very crude or totally unthought of; they waited upon the evolution of the whole society — upon the advancement of invention and experimentation, the accumulation of wealth, the attainment of leisure, and particularly upon the emergence of specialized agricultural interests. The differentiation that took place later in the century in agricultural social organization was fundamentally related to the economic and technological changes in agriculture itself. The agricultural societies, which reached their efflorescence in the golden age, were relatively undifferentiated associations, and they made their principal enterprises, the fairs, serve a pretty inclusive agricultural interest.

The rapid differentiation which economic, political, social and technological interests underwent in the last half of the nineteenth century gave rise to more clearly defined associations to serve them. This process placed in the hands of new and more specialized organizations many tasks which had formerly been performed principally, if they had need to be performed at all, by the old agricultural societies. The accumulation and diffusion of agricultural information, the testing and spread of agricultural machinery and technical processes, the improvement of live stock, the creation of a rural social consciousness, the formulation of agricultural political programs, the promotion of agricultural economic

[9] The same may be said, of course, of most of the general fairs of the present day, though the process of social evolution, in addition to calling forth specialized types of the institution, has effected changes in the relative importance of fairs to rural society.

A DAIRY CALF CLUB DEMONSTRATION TEAM AT A WISCONSIN FAIR

and commercial agencies, all began to come within the province of more specialized groups. The fair thereupon came to be not the predominant rural institution, but one agency through which the specialized associations functioned.

The Grange, the various farmers' alliances, the coöperative buying and marketing associations and the live-stock registry associations were among the private groups whose inception bore witness to the differentiation which agriculture was undergoing. An enormous increase in the number and variety of government agencies — schools, experiment stations, departments, bureaus, extension services, etc. — directed the concern for agricultural interests into public channels. Since the primary purpose of the fair was considered in a general way to be the promotion of agriculture, the assumption of so many functions by other agencies necessitated a redefinition of the purposes of the old societies. Fairs continued to multiply with the westward expansion of the people, but gradually as many new associations found a place in rural society and as the agricultural riches especially of the Middle West began to be uncovered, the fair became more and more a specialized means for displaying the resources of the land.[10] Hence it grew particularly in its exhibitive features and most of the old agricultural societies ceased to function except for purposes of conducting the annual exhibition.

These trends affecting the fair's primary function of agricultural promotion were closely related to others influencing its secondary function of recreation and social intercourse. Pioneer society was distinctly leavened by the

[10] The Minnesota state fair in fact followed closely upon a Minnesota display at the exposition in New York City in 1853, exhibiting the resources of the territory and advertising it to potential settlers. Cf. Hall, Darwin S., and R. I. Holcombe, *History of the Minnesota State Agricultural Society from Its Organization in 1854 to the Annual Meeting of 1910*, St. Paul, 1910, *passim*.

fair, which broke the monotony of isolation and afforded the year's greatest opportunity for increasing social contacts. But the progress of social evolution brought tremendous changes in this realm too. The new agricultural associations created of themselves a new area of social intercourse for their members. Many of them, like the Grange and other benevolent associations, fostered literary interests through pamphlets, newspapers, magazines and farm periodicals, which led eventually to wider personal contacts. Enlarged educational facilities, from the one-room country school to the extension services of the agricultural colleges, aided in making rural children and usually rural adults better acquainted with one another. Such aspects of social evolution were accelerated, especially after the beginning of the twentieth century, by the mechanization of our entire social structure. Rural social needs have attained a certain satisfaction in the variety of social contacts created as a byproduct of the commercial activities made possible by the new means of transportation and communication. Thanks particularly to the automobile, farmers' holidays come more frequently. The Sunday picnic and the week-end fishing trip, for example, and even the vacation tour have become common modes of rural recreation, and the Saturday-night visit to town a highly significant folkway of rural America.

The rôle of the automobile, moving pictures, the radio and other mechanized means of amusement as social forces is pertinent here, as it is in a hundred other aspects of our social life. The automobile proved a boon particularly to the state fairs. By reducing the time-space element it stimulated both an increase in attendance and an increase in exhibits. No longer were state-fair visitors dependent upon the railroad for transportation and upon hotels and private homes in the city for lodging; now they could drive to the fair in their own automobile and camp a few days on the

grounds, or more often return home after the evening performance. Formerly it was usually the farmer himself, in
need of a new bull or ram or desirous of investigating a new
plow or binder, who, after outlining to his wife and the boys
the week's work to be done at home, took the train to the
state fair. It was, in numerous respects, an expensive trip,
not often to be undertaken except in case of necessity and
then commonly by only one member of the family. But the
automobile has revolutionized the customs of fair-going.
Now the farm family is likely to rise before dawn, do the
morning milking and hustle the cows off to pasture, snatch
a hurried breakfast and, locking the house and leaving the
collie on guard for the day, set out in their automobile for
the fair. Early in the forenoon the entire family is on the
state fair grounds at Des Moines or Columbus, Hamline or
Sedalia, Springfield, Milwaukee or Syracuse. The comparatively cheap transportation furnished by the automobile
changed the fair crowd from one consisting largely of individual farmers to one of farm families. A consequent change
took place in the character of the fair. When the agriculturally interested farmers comprised the bulk of the fair
crowd they thronged to the live-stock barns, the implement
trials and the evening discussion meetings. But when the
farmers' wives and children, as well as types of rural people
not seriously interested in agricultural improvement itself,
began to attend in great numbers, the state fair program
became impressively broader. The educational features
— lectures, demonstrations, discussions, etc. — were made
to include the interests of farm women and farm young
people. And a vast expansion of the entertainment program
witnessed to a growing popularization of the fair. Typically
the farm family that pointed homeward in their automobile
after the evening performance or retired to spend the night
in their tent on the camping ground had enjoyed not a staid

agricultural discussion but a fireworks pageant, a society horse show or a popular vaudeville entertainment.[11]

But the automobile affected the fair indirectly too, and with perhaps less happy results. It made possible a much wider area of social intercourse, in which the fair did not figure but which tended nevertheless to compete with the satisfactions it once had brought. In this, all sorts of commercialized entertainment conspired; the movies particularly came to serve the amusement interest steadily and consistently, whereas the fairs served it only periodically. Amusement is no longer something to be taken in large amounts from whatever source may be available; the general supply is a relatively steady one from which people can make a number of choices. The influence of the automobile has been reflected, furthermore, in the incipient movement toward centralization among some of the older agricultural fairs. The area of fair attendance is no longer limited to the few miles that can be traversed in a day by horse-drawn vehicles or to the radii served by a railroad line. The state and district fairs have benefited accordingly. Their spectacular amusement programs have come to satisfy the desire for this type of enjoyment in a way and to an extent that the smaller fairs cannot match; the automobile and good roads furnish the means whereby people have been able to patronize them. The area of fair administration and appeal has for these fairs been enlarged; never before have individuals whose desires lean toward the spectacular type of satisfaction derived from the fair been so abundantly able to gratify them. Without the crowds furnished by the automobile, the state fairs could never have grown to their present size. Only the larger and richer fair associations, however, able to afford greater expenditures of money and to provide more

[11] Cf. Stong, Phil, *State Fair*, New York, c. 1932, for a fictional account of a farm family's week at the state fair.

efficient organization and management, have succeeded in meeting the increasingly heavy demands of their patrons for commercialized entertainment. Held usually in the larger towns or cities, they have combined, sometimes purposively, sometimes incidentally, the "city pull" with the attractions of the fair, the attendance usually mounting accordingly. Thus have the processes of urbanization and commercialization affected the social evolution of the fair in so far as it can be, or has been, considered an institution of rural recreation or amusement.

What of the future, so far as the fair is concerned? The development of rural associations serving new or more completely differentiated agricultural interests and the development of the various means of enlarging the area of social contacts for rural people — both aspects of the process of social evolution — have been paralleled by a process of adjustment on the part of the fair itself. It, too, has necessarily responded to social evolution. It has come to perform more specialized functions. It has branched into more differentiated forms. Its area of administration has become significantly enlarged. Not only have technological changes in transportation and communication created the media of new and wider contacts but the types of services which the fair renders have expanded at a hundred different points, necessitating a broader area of organization in order that such services may be efficiently utilized. The emergence of a class of fair managers actuated by a professional attitude has also contributed to the continuous redirection of the institution, both as regards the functions it performs and the constituency it serves. This adjustment is, by the very nature of the case, never complete. From the attempts to deal with these changes arise many of the most perplexing problems of fair associations — problems of finance, organization, amusement — all encompassed in the redefinition of the fair's purpose and a differentiation of its forms and functions. To see the trends in this adjustment, we have only to hark back briefly to generalizations of the four important developments that have taken place in American agricultural fairs since they turned to a refining and perfecting of their organization about the beginning of the twentieth century.[12]

The extent to which specialized agricultural shows have become established, with their emphasis clearly upon the exhibition of particular types of agricultural products, with their purpose of serving primarily particular branches of the industry, with their support from particular groups pursuing relatively specialized interests, illustrates most advantageously perhaps the processes of differentiation that have been transforming the institution. The recent growth of the neighborhood fairs and of local boys' and girls' club achievement days has to some extent counteracted the centralizing tendency noted among the county fairs. These types are adjustments of the institution which mark a return to neighborhood participation serving the interests of neighborhood social intercourse, recreation, and agricultural education. The emphasis upon boys' and girls' club work in particular denotes a modern refinement of the original purpose of agricultural fairs; namely, the improvement of agricultural products.

The larger general fairs have expanded both in size and in the variety of the attractions they present. By increasing the prize money and distributing it to larger numbers of people, they have consistently encouraged the competitive display of agricultural products, fulfilling thereby the particular function for which the fair as an institution is best suited. In addition, they have enlarged their attractions in a hundred ways — furnishing demonstrations of the latest

[12] Cf. *supra*, Chap. V.

agricultural advances and incorporating programs for the creative participation of their visitors, as well as utilizing the latest devices of mechanized entertainment. The establishment of interfair relationships, such as those achieved by the International Association of Fairs and Expositions and by the state associations of fair managers; the permanent location of, and the construction of well equipped physical plants by, most of the larger fairs, both general and specialized; the increasing complexity of the organization of larger fairs under the management of a more or less professionalized personnel; the conduct of judging schools by agricultural colleges in an effort to aid in the standardization of methods of rating agricultural products — all these are indicative of the way in which fairs have become more definitive units within the social system.

The fair as an economic and educational agency has undoubtedly played a part in augmenting agricultural efficiency. It performed a certain type of function when one of agriculture's ideals was "making two blades of grass grow where but one had grown before." It aided in meeting a contemporary "farm problem." But in the eternal process of social change farm problems change also; and the fair as it makes adjustments to new conditions comes *ipso facto* to perform new kinds of functions. The possible future function of the fair in the light of the present economic crisis is difficult to predict. We can only note in passing that these functions — if not the very existence of certain types of the institution — will depend in large measure upon the economic and social readjustments which our society, especially our rural society, may undergo. The fair in its present organization and functioning is markedly dependent upon an economic base presupposed by a commercial agricultural industry. It has evolved correlatively with the differentiation of agriculture, its specialized forms developing to serve the purposes of specialized branches. Its future will be affected largely by the direction which the course of social evolution takes: whether our agriculture continues on these commercial lines or returns to a more self-contained organization than now exists.

In any event, it must be clear that the historical development of the agricultural fair not only illustrates the course of social evolution but points the way for the future. Gradually the fair has made adjustments to the differentiating interests of the entire society, and especially to those of the agricultural industry. Specialized forms and functions have emerged out of the processes of change — not freed entirely, to be sure, from traditions that have invested such institutions from medieval and even primitive times — and have come to play a comparatively definite rôle in present-day rural organization. What the future of the fair will be no one can predict in detail. As a social institution, however, responding to a myriad of forces conditioning and stimulating the process of differentiation, the fair will continue to be subject to social change. Certain of its forms may cease to exist; certain of its present functions may be dropped and others assumed. Surely the evolutionary clue will help us to follow whatever changes may occur, just as it has aided us to understand the long course of social evolution through which the fair has come.

BIBLIOGRAPHY

BIBLIOGRAPHY

Bibliographical Note

The following bibliography contains not only all the references cited in the text, but also a long list of other materials consulted during the course of the research. The most valuable primary sources are the *Reports, Transactions* and *Proceedings* of the various state boards and departments of agriculture and of the state agricultural societies. Many of these publications contain not only summary accounts of state and local fairs but statistical information of varying degrees of completeness. Good collections of such volumes are available at the New York Public Library and at the libraries of Columbia University, Iowa State College and the McCormick Historical Association in Chicago. Other valuable source material may be found in the *Premium Lists* and *Official Programs* prepared by all the larger state and national fairs and shows and by many of those purely local in scope. Such publications are usually to be had for the asking from the secretaries or managers of the various fairs. The files of numerous farm journals are also indispensable for research in this field. In the present work the files of the *Cultivator and Country Gentleman* were relied upon heavily for information regarding the Golden Age period. For the period since 1900 the files of the *Breeder's Gazette* are unsurpassed, though much valuable material is obtainable from those of numerous other periodicals including the *Field Illustrated*, the *Wallaces' Farmer*, the *Iowa Homestead*, the *New England Homestead* and the *California Cultivator*. It has been the custom for these magazines to print, during the autumn when the fair season is in full swing, more or less extended reports and news items which are invaluable for the study of our subject but which it would be impracticable to list in a bibliography such as this. Materials available from the agricultural colleges are somewhat limited in scope; they consist principally of bulletins and circulars designed to aid in the organization of local fairs and shows. No attempt has been made to list in the bibliography original editions of those items that have passed through more than one edition. The reference given is, in every case, that of the edition available to the author at the time of writing.

PRIMARY SOURCES

I. REPORTS, TRANSACTIONS, PROCEEDINGS, ETC.

American Poultry Association, *Poultry Show Organization*, Fort Wayne, Indiana.

California State Agricultural Society: *Transactions, Reports*, Sacramento.

Carman, Ezra A., H. A. Heath and John Minto, *Special Report on the History and Present Condition of the Sheep Industry of the United States*, United States Department of Agriculture, Bureau of Animal Industry, Washington, 1892.

Commissioner of Agriculture, *Report*, 1867, pp. 364-403, "Agricultural and Horticultural Societies and Clubs," Washington.

Commissioner of Agriculture, *Report*, 1875, pp. 437-68, "History of Our Rural Organizations," Washington.

Commissioner of Patents: *Reports*, 1857, 1858, *Agriculture*, Washington.

Communications to the Board of Agriculture, Vols. I, II, London, 1797, 1800.

Corey, A. R., "History of State Fairs and Methods of Financing," Minnesota State Agricultural Society, *Annual Report*, 1916, pp. 327-31, Minneapolis.

Dodge, Allen W., "A Prize Essay on Fairs," Massachusetts Society for Promoting Agriculture, *Transactions*, n.s., Vol. I, No. 3, Boston, 1858.

Illinois Department of Agriculture, "Reports of the Agricultural Fairs Receiving Aid from the State of Illinois," 1928, 1929, 1930, Springfield.

Illinois Department of Agriculture, "Reports of the 4-H Club Exhibits," Springfield, 1930, 1931.

Illinois State Board for Vocational Education, *Bulletin* No. 54, "Report of the Vocational Agriculture Section Fairs, 1931-1932," Springfield.

Illinois State Department of Agriculture, *Transactions*, especially 1853-54, 1871, 1896, 1901 to 1917 inclusive; *Annual Reports*, 1917-18 to 1930-31 inclusive, Springfield.

Illinois State Fair, *Official Program and Entry List*, 1932, Springfield.

Illinois State Fair, *Premium List*, 1932, Springfield.

Indiana State Board of Agriculture, *Annual Reports*, especially 1869, Indianapolis.

Indiana, *Year Book*, 1931, Indianapolis.

International Association of Fairs and Expositions, "Address by President E. L. Richardson," Thirty-seventh Annual Meeting, 1927, Oklahoma City.

International Association of Fairs and Expositions, "Budgeting and Accounting," 1927, Oklahoma City.

International Association of Fairs and Expositions, *Proceedings of the First Annual School in Fair Management*, 1924, Oklahoma City.

International Association of Fairs and Expositions, *Report of Thirty-ninth Annual Meeting*, 1929, Oklahoma City; *Report of Forty-first Annual Meeting*, 1932, Oklahoma City.

International Association of Fairs and Expositions, "The Advertising of State Fairs and Expositions," 1926, Oklahoma City.

International Live Stock Exposition, *Official Catalog*, 1932, Chicago.

International Live Stock Exposition, *Preliminary Classification*, 1932, Chicago.

Iowa County and District Fair Managers' Association, *Proceedings*, 1931, Des Moines.

Iowa State Agricultural Convention, *Proceedings*, 1931, Des Moines.

Iowa State Agricultural Society, *Annual Reports*, especially 1857; *Reports*, especially 1877, 1879, 1881, Des Moines.

Iowa State Department of Agriculture, *Yearbooks*, 1900 to 1931 inclusive, Des Moines.

Iowa State Fair, *Official Programs*, especially 1929, 1930, 1931, 1932, Des Moines.

Iowa State Fair, *Reports*, especially 1929, 1931, Des Moines.

Lowell, John, "On the Utility of Cattle Shows," New York Board of Agriculture, *Memoirs,* III, 139-45, Albany, 1826.

Massachusetts Department of Agriculture, *Monthly Fairs Letter*, Boston, Feb., 1932.

Massachusetts Department of Agriculture, Statistical Reports of Massachusetts Fairs, 1929, 1930, 1931, mimeographed material, Boston.

Massachusetts Society for Promoting Agriculture, *Papers*, Boston, 1806.

Massachusetts State Board of Agriculture, *Annual Reports*, Boston.

Michigan State Agricultural Society, *Transactions,* especially 1856, Lansing.

Michigan State Board of Agriculture, *Annual Reports*, especially 1869, 1870, 1875 to 1880 inclusive; *Biennial Report*, 1880-82, Lansing.

Michigan State Department of Agriculture, "Report to Michigan Association of Fairs," 1932, mimeographed material, Lansing.

Minnesota State Agricultural Society, *Annual Reports*, especially 1901 to 1931 inclusive, Minneapolis.

New York State Department of Agriculture, *Annual Reports*, Albany.

New York State Department of Agriculture and Markets, *Annual Reports*, especially 1927 to 1931 inclusive, Albany.

New York State Department of Farms and Markets, "The New York State Agricultural Society," *Bulletin 161*, Albany, 1924.

New York State Horticultural Society, *Proceedings of the Seventy-seventh Annual Meeting*, 1932, Le Roy, New York.

Ohio State Board of Agriculture, *Annual Reports*, especially 1858, 1863, 1869, 1880, 1882, 1887, Columbus.

Oregon State Department of Education, Annual State, County and School Fair Conference, *Report*, 1916, Salem.

Pennsylvania Department of Agriculture, *Annual Reports*, Harrisburg.

Pennsylvania State Board of Agriculture, *Reports*, Harrisburg.

Pennsylvania State Farm Products Show Commission, *Premium List*, 1932, Harrisburg.

Philadelphia Society for Promoting Agriculture, *Memoirs*, Vol. I, Philadelphia, 1808.

Poore, Benjamin Perley, "History of the Agriculture of the United States," Commissioner of Agriculture, *Report*, 1866, pp. 498-527, Washington.

United States Agricultural Society, Seventh National Exhibition, *Premium List and Regulations*, 2d ed., Chicago, 1859.

United States *Census*, Washington.

United States Department of Agriculture, *Yearbook*, Washington, 1932.

Wisconsin Department of Agriculture and Markets, *Bulletin* No. 131, Madison, 1932.

Wisconsin State Agricultural Society, *Transactions*, especially 1861-68, 1869, 1871, 1880-81 to 1883-84 inclusive, 1895, Madison.

Wisconsin State Board of Agriculture, *Annual Reports*, especially 1906, 1907, 1908, 1910-11, Madison.

Wisconsin State Department of Agriculture, *Biennial Reports*, 1915-16 to 1929-30 inclusive, Madison.

Wisconsin State Department of Agriculture, *County and District Fair Reports*, 1926 to 1931 inclusive, Madison.

II. NEWSPAPERS AND MAGAZINES

American Farmer, II, 217-20, Oct. 6, 1820.

Breeder's Gazette, files in Iowa State College Library; Vols. cited XCIII, XCIV, XCV, XCVI.

Cultivator and Country Gentleman, files in New York Public Library; Vols. cited, XXVII, XXVIII, XXX, XXXV, XXXVII, XXXIX, XL, XLV, LIII.

Des Moines, Iowa, *Tribune*, June 18, 1932.

Fair News, files in New York Public Library.

Farmer's Magazine, Edinburgh, I, 328-34, July, 1800; VII, 346-52, Aug., 1806.

Field Illustrated, files in New York Public Library; Vol. cited, XXVII.

Gentleman's Magazine, LXIX, 329-36, April, 1799; LXIX, 703, Aug., 1799.

Greater Iowa, scattered issues.

New England Homestead, scattered issues; Vol. cited, CV.

Wallaces' Farmer, files in New York Public Library and Columbia University Library; Vol. cited, LVII.

III. BULLETINS, CIRCULARS, ETC.

Agricultural Fairs, Mississippi Agricultural and Mechanical College, Extension Bulletin 14, Agricultural and Mechanical College, 1919.

Brehm, C. E., *Agricultural Exhibits and Fairs*, Tennessee Agricultural Extension Publication 127, Knoxville, 1924.

Dean, J. M., *Fairs and Their Educational Value*, Mississippi Agricultural and Mechanical College, Extension Bulletin 37, Agricultural and Mechanical College, 1926.

—— *Selecting and Preparing Exhibits for Fairs*, Mississippi Agricultural and Mechanical College, Extension Bulletin 29, Agricultural and Mechanical College, 1924.

Fairs, Alabama Polytechnic Institute, Extension Circular 90, Auburn, 1926.

Farrell, George E., *Boys' and Girls' 4-H Club Work under the Smith-Lever Act, 1914-1924*, United States Department of Agriculture, Miscellaneous Circular No. 85, Washington, 1926.

Galpin, C. J., and Emily F. Hoag, *The Rural Community Fair*, University of Wisconsin Agricultural Experiment Station, Bulletin 307, Madison, 1919.

Goddard, L. H., and W. A. Lloyd, *Illustrative Exhibits at State and County Fairs*, Ohio Agricultural Experiment Station, Circular 101, Wooster, 1910.

Hamilton, John, *Agricultural Fair Associations and Their Utilization in Agricultural Education and Improvement*, United States Department of Agriculture, Experiment Station Circular 109, Washington, 1911.

Holmes, George K., *List of Agricultural Fairs and Exhibitions in the United States*, United States Department of Agriculture, Bureau of Statistics, Bulletin 102, Washington, 1913.

Jordan, Samuel M., "Entertainment for Farm Fairs," Missouri State Board of Agriculture, *Monthly Bulletin*, Vol. XXI, No. 3, Jefferson City, 1923.

Junkin, Kathryne, *International Fairs and Expositions*, United States Department of Commerce Trade Promotion Series, No. 75, Washington, 1929.

Lancaster, Robert R., *A Standard Premium List for Fairs*, Colorado Agricultural College, *Extension Bulletin*, Series 1, No. 167-A, Fort Collins, 1920.

Lowrey, M. W., *Planning Educational Exhibits*, Georgia State College of Agriculture, Extension Bulletin 392, Athens, 1930.

Moran, J. Sterling, *The Community Fair*, United States Department of Agriculture, Farmers' Bulletin 870, Washington, 1917.

Nelson, W. L., "The County Fair in Missouri," Missouri State Board of Agriculture, *Monthly Bulletin*, Vol. XIV, No. 7, Jefferson City, 1916.

Ray, S. H., *Live-Stock Classifications at County Fairs*, United States Department of Agriculture, Farmers' Bulletin 822, Washington, 1917.

Reichsbahnzentrale für den deutschen Reiseverkehr, Berlin, "Germany's Great Agricultural Fair" and "German Agricultural Society 50 Years Old," mimeographed material released in 1931 and 1932 respectively.

Remey, Oliver E., *The Small Agricultural Fair*, Massachusetts Department of Agriculture, Circular No. 17, Boston, 1920.

Rubinow, S. G., *Fairs and Their Educational Value*, North Carolina Agricultural Extension Service, Circular No. 69, Raleigh and West Raleigh, 1918.

—— *Some Results of Fair Work in North Carolina*, North Carolina Agricultural Extension Service, Circular No. 94, Raleigh and West Raleigh, 1919.

—— *The Organization and Management of Fairs*, North Carolina Agricultural Extension Service, Circular No. 68, Raleigh and West Raleigh, 1918.

Score Cards for Fairs, State College of Washington Extension Service, Bulletin 107, Pullman, 1923.

Smith, C. B., *Boys' and Girls' 4-H Club Work*, United States Department of Agriculture, Miscellaneous Circular No. 77, Washington, 1926.

The Agricultural Fair, University of Arizona Agricultural Extension, Circular 71, Tucson, 1931.

True, Alfred Charles, *A History of Agricultural Education in the United States, 1785-1925*, United States Department of Agriculture, Miscellaneous Publication No. 36, Washington, 1929.

—— *A History of Agricultural Extension Work in the United States, 1785-1923*, United States Department of Agriculture, Miscellaneous Publication No. 15, Washington, 1928.

SECONDARY SOURCES

I. GENERAL WORKS

Andrews, Charles M., *Colonial Folkways*, "Chronicles of America" Series, Vol. IX, New Haven, 1919.

Ashley, W. J., *An Introduction to English Economic History and Theory*, 2 vols., 4th ed., London, 1909.

Bidwell, Percy Wells, and John I. Falconer, *History of Agriculture in the Northern United States, 1620-1860,* Carnegie Institution Publication No. 358, Washington, 1925.

Carrier, Lyman, *The Beginnings of Agriculture in America,* New York, 1923.

Carver, Thomas Nixon, *Principles of Rural Economics,* Boston, c. 1911.

Coad, Oral Sumner, and Edwin Mims, Jr., *The American Stage,* "The Pageant of America," 15 vols., Vol. XIV, New Haven, 1929.

Cole, Arthur Harrison, *The American Wool Manufacture,* 2 vols., Cambridge, 1926.

Comstock, Anthony, *Gambling Outrages; or, Improving the Breed of Horses at the Expense of Public Morals,* New York, 1887.

—— *Race Track Infamy; or, Do Gamblers Own New York State?* New York, 1904.

Coyle, Grace Longwell, *Social Process in Organized Groups,* New York, 1930.

Defoe, Daniel, *A Tour Thro' the Whole Island of Great Britain,* 4 vols., 5th ed., London, 1753.

Encyclopaedia Britannica, 24 vols., 14th ed., London, 1929.

Encyclopedia Americana, 30 vols., New York, 1918.

Ernle, Lord, *English Farming Past and Present,* 2d ed., London, 1919.

Fippin, Elmer O., *Rural New York,* New York, 1921.

Flint, Charles L. [*et al*], *Eighty Years' Progress of the United States,* Hartford, 1869.

Galpin, Charles Josiah, *Rural Life,* New York, 1918.

Garnier, Russell M., *History of the English Landed Interest,* 2 vols., London, 1892, 1893.

Giddings, Franklin Henry, *The Principles of Sociology,* New York, 1896.

Gras, Norman Scott Brien, *A History of Agriculture in Europe and America,* New York, 1925.

Gray, Lewis Cecil, *History of Agriculture in the Southern United States to 1860,* 2 vols., Carnegie Institution Publication No. 430, Washington, 1933.

Gross, Charles, ed., *Select Cases Concerning the Law Merchant, A.D.*

1270-1638, 3 vols. Vol. I, *Local Courts*, Selden Society Publication, Vol. XXIII, London, 1908.

Haas, J. Anton de, *Foreign Trade Organization*, New York, 1923.

Hawthorn, Horace Boies, *The Sociology of Rural Life*, New York, c. 1926.

Hoffer, Charles Russell, *Introduction to Rural Sociology*, New York, 1930.

Hutchinson, William T., *Cyrus Hall McCormick*, New York, c. 1930.

Johnson, Clifton, *New England and Its Neighbors*, New York, 1902.

Jull, Morley A., *Poultry Husbandry*, New York, 1930.

Krout, John Allen, *Annals of American Sport*, "The Pageant of America," 15 vols., Vol. XV, New Haven, 1929.

Lang, Andrew, ed., *The Nursery Rhyme Book*, New York, 1897.

Lipson, E., *An Introduction to the Economic History of England*, 3 vols., 4th ed., Vol. I, London, 1926.

MacIver, R. M., *Society: Its Structure and Changes*, New York, 1931.

Mavor, William, *General View of the Agriculture of Berkshire*, London, 1809.

Philp, Robert Kemp, *The History of Progress in Great Britain*, London, 1859.

Plumb, Charles S., *Types and Breeds of Farm Animals*, Boston, c. 1906.

Pound, Arthur, *Native Stock*, New York, 1931.

Rew, R. H., *An Agricultural Faggot*, Westminster, 1913.

Richardson, James D., *A Compilation of the Messages and Papers of the Presidents, 1789-1908*, 11 vols., Vols. I and X, Bureau of National Literature and Art, 1909.

Rogers, James E. Thorold, *A History of Agriculture and Prices in England*, 7 vols., Vol. I, Oxford, 1866.

Sanford, Albert H., *The Story of Agriculture in the United States*, Boston, c. 1916.

Schevill, Ferdinand, *Siena*, New York, 1909.

[Shaw, Henry Wheeler], *Josh Billings on Ice, and Other Things*, New York, 1868.

Shepardson, Whitney H., *Agricultural Education in the United States*, New York, 1929.

Sherwood, Robert Edmund, *Here We Are Again*, Indianapolis, c. 1926.

Smith, Clarence Beaman, and Meredith Chester Wilson, *The Agricultural Extension System of the United States*, New York, 1930.

Steinel, Alvin T., *History of Agriculture in Colorado*, Fort Collins, 1926.

Stephenson, George M., *A History of American Immigration, 1820-1924*, Boston, c. 1926.

Sumner, William Graham, *Folkways*, Boston, c. 1906.

Terpenning, Walter A., *Village and Open-Country Neighborhoods*, New York, c. 1931.

The Farmers' Centennial History of Ohio, 1803-1903, Ohio State Department of Agriculture, Springfield, 1904.

Thompson, James Westfall, *An Economic and Social History of the Middle Ages (300-1300)*, New York, c. 1928.

Toynbee, Arnold, *Lectures on the Industrial Revolution of the Eighteenth Century in England*, 3d ed., 9th impression, London, 1927.

Vogt, Paul L., *Introduction to Rural Sociology*, New York, 1917.

Watson, Elkanah, *Men and Times of the Revolution, or Memoirs of Elkanah Watson*, 2d ed., Winslow C. Watson, ed., New York, 1857.

Whitehead, William A., *Contributions to the Early History of Perth Amboy and Adjoining Country*, New York, 1856.

Wickson, E. J., *Rural California*, New York, 1923.

Wiest, Edward, *Agricultural Organization in the United States*, University of Kentucky Studies in Economics and Sociology, Vol. II, Lexington, 1923.

Woodward, Carl Raymond, *The Development of Agriculture in New Jersey, 1640-1880*, New Brunswick, 1927.

Wright, Chester Whitney, *Wool-Growing and the Tariff*, Harvard Economic Studies, Vol. V, Boston, 1910.

II. WORKS WITH SPECIAL REFERENCE TO FAIRS

Bourquelot, Félix, *Études sur les foires de Champagne*, In "Mémoires présentés par divers savants a l'académie des inscriptions et belles-lettres de l'institut impérial de France," 2. ser., t. V, Paris, 1865.

Dexter, T. F. G., *The Pagan Origin of Fairs*, Perranporth, Cornwall, n.d.

Dillon, R. C., *A Sermon on the Evils of Fairs in General and of Bartholomew Fair in Particular*, London, 1830.

Frost, Thomas, *The Old Showmen and the Old London Fairs*, London, 1874.

Hall, Darwin S., and R. I. Holcombe, *History of the Minnesota State Agricultural Society from Its Organization in 1854 to the Annual Meeting of 1910*, St. Paul, 1910.

Huvelin, P., *Essai historique sur le droit des marchés et des foires*, Paris, 1897.

Morley, Henry, *Memoirs of Bartholomew Fair*, London, n.d.

Morrish, R. W., *A History of Fairs*, International Association of Fairs and Expositions, 1929, Oklahoma City, Chicago, n.d.

Norton, C. B., *World's Fairs from London, 1851, to Chicago, 1893*, Chicago, 1890.

Plowman, Thomas F., *Fifty Years of a Showman's Life*, London, 1919.

Stong, Phil, *State Fair*, New York, c. 1932.

Walford, Cornelius, *Fairs Past and Present*, London, 1883.

Watson, Elkanah, *History of Agricultural Societies on the Modern Berkshire System*, Albany, 1820.

Zetter, C., *Évolution des foires et marchés travers les siècles*, Paris, 1923.

III. ARTICLES

Adkins, Charles, "Possibilities of the County Fair," *Orange Judd Farmer*, LXV, 85, Aug. 3, 1918.

"Agricultural Shows or Fun Festivals," *Live Stock Journal*, CXIV, 227, Sept. 4, 1931.

"Agriculture at 'Agricultural Fairs,'" *Orange Judd Farmer*, LXIII, 1, 6, Sept. 15, 1917.

Alcott, Carroll D., "How a County Fair was Developed," *Dakota Farmer*, XLIII, 689, Aug. 1, 1923.

"All the Fun of the Fair," *New Statesman*, IX, 441-43, Aug. 11, 1917.

Allix, André, "The Geography of Fairs: Illustrated by Old-World Examples," *Geographical Review*, XII, 532-69, Oct., 1922.

"A New Kind of County Fair," *Playground*, V, 380-82, Feb., 1912.

"An Old-Established Fair in Modern France," *Geographical Review*, II, 153-54, Aug., 1916.

"A Novelty at a State Fair," *Home Progress*, VI, 170-71, Dec., 1916.

Archer, H. G., "Country Fairs," *Good Words*, XL, 301-7, 1899.

"Are All Fairs Educational?" *Dakota Farmer*, XLIV, 550, June 1, 1924.

"A Rejuvenated County Fair," *Ohio Farmer*, CXLVI, 255, 288-89, Sept. 4, 1920.

"Are Our Fairs Keeping Up with the Times?" *Farmer's Advocate and Home Magazine*, LX, 1225, 1245, Sept. 3, 1925.

"A Successful Community Fair," *Rural New Yorker*, LXXV, 1045-46, Aug. 5, 1916.

Austin, William, "The Origin of Markets and Fairs, and the Early History of Those at Luton," *Home Counties Magazine*, XIV, 38-48, 104-11, 1912.

Barrett, Michael, "Ancient Scottish Fairs," *American Catholic Quarterly Review*, XXXVI, 209-22, April, 1911.

Beeson, Sterling, "The County Fair," *World To-Day*, XVII, 859-65, Aug., 1909.

Bemis, M. E., "Agricultural Fairs in Arizona," *California Cultivator*, LXXI, 277, 291, Sept. 22, 1928.

Black, George D., "Need of a New County Fair," *Ohio Farmer*, CXL, 238, Sept. 22, 1917.

Bonham, L. N., "Live-Stock Expositions as Educators," *Breeder's Gazette*, XL, 822-23, Nov. 13, 1901.

"Boost Your State Fairs," *American Thresherman*, XXVII, 8, July, 1924.

Boothe, Stella, "Let's Go to the County Fair," *Public Health Nurse*, XV, 387-92, Aug., 1923.

Bradford, Margaret, "Now Then, a 4-H Fair!" *Breeder's Gazette*, XCV, 26, Sept., 1930.

Briffault, Robert, "Festivals," *Encyclopaedia of the Social Sciences,* Edwin R. A. Seligman, ed., Vol. VI, New York, 1931.

Briggs, John Ely, "The Sioux City Corn Palaces," *Palimpsest,* III, 313-26, Oct., 1922.

Bunner, Rudolph F., "A Coöperative Fair," *Country Life,* XXI, 50-51, April 1, 1912.

Butler, Tait, "Advantages of the Fairs," *Progressive Farmer,* XXXVI, 787, Sept. 10, 1921.

—— "Agricultural Fairs in Europe," *Progressive Farmer,* XXXIX, 898, Sept. 20, 1924.

Butterfield, Kenyon L., "Farmers' Social Organizations," *Cyclopedia of American Agriculture,* 4 vols., L. H. Bailey, ed., Vol. IV, *Farm and Community,* pp. 289-97, New York, 1909.

Castaigne, André, "Strolling Mountebanks," *Harper's,* CIII, 841-51, Nov., 1901.

Chapman, Ethel M., "Women's Interests at the Fair," *Farmer's Advocate and Home Magazine,* LXI, 226, Feb. 18, 1926.

Chapman, Lyman T., "Exhibitions — Whither and How," *Nor'-West Farmer,* XLIX, 7, 56, 61, June 20, 1930.

Chase, Daniel, "Farm Boys and Girls at a State Fair," *Normal Instructor and Primary Plans,* XXXIII, 89-90, June, 1924.

Chase, Frank M., "When Johnny Saw the Fair; the Early Beginning of Our Modern Fairs," *Successful Farming,* XX, 13, 40-41, Aug., 1923.

Chase, Sidney M., "Asahel and Lavinia at the Fair," *Outlook,* C, 455-64, Feb. 24, 1912.

Christian, C. F., "The Biggest Little Fair in Ohio," *Ohio Farmer,* CLIV, 253, Sept. 27, 1924.

Clarke, Ernest, "Agriculture and the House of Russell," *Journal of the Royal Agricultural Society of England,* 3d series, II, 123-45, London, 1891.

Clifford, Mrs. Perry, "How a Good Community Fair Was Built," *Dakota Farmer,* XLVII, 1013, Dec. 15, 1927.

Coffin, Robert P. Tristram, "Tipsham Fair," *Virginia Quarterly Review,* VII, 241-50, April, 1931.

"Confessions of a Fair Faker," *Country Gentleman,* LXXXVII, 4-5, 37, April 8, 1922; 7, 21, April 15, 1922; 9, 28, April 22, 1922.

Cooper, Courtney Ryley, "The Fixer and the Fake," *Country Gentleman*, LXXXVII, 7, 22, May 6, 1922.

Cox, U. T., "Fall Festivals as Means of Advertising," *Rural New Yorker*, LXXV, 1151, Sept. 2, 1916.

Craven, Ida, "Public Amusements," *Encyclopaedia of the Social Sciences*, Edwin R. A. Seligman, ed., Vol. II, New York, 1930.

Crawford, Nelson Antrim, "Agricultural Societies," *Encyclopaedia of the Social Sciences*, Edwin R. A. Seligman, ed., Vol. I, New York, 1930.

—— "Government Services for Agriculture," *Encyclopaedia of the Social Sciences*, Edwin R. A. Seligman, ed., Vol. I, New York, 1930.

Davis, Charles Belmont, "The Fair and the Farmer," *Collier's*, XLVIII, 22-23, 29, Oct. 14, 1911.

Davis, Clyde, "How to Succeed With Community Fairs," *Progressive Farmer*, XXXII, 901, Aug. 25, 1917.

—— "Making a Go of the Community Fair," *Country Gentleman*, LXXXII, 1409-10, Sept. 15, 1917.

De Jong, J., "Preparing the Vegetable Exhibit," *Nor'-West Farmer*, XLVIII, 34, 39, June 20, 1929.

Drips, W. E., "Do They Gamble at Your Fair?" *Wallaces' Farmer*, LV, 1420, 1445, Sept. 6, 1930.

Eckhardt, Betty, "West Virginia Goes on the Stage," *Country Gentleman*, XCIV, 26, 100, May, 1929.

Eckles, C. H., "National Dairy Show," *Book of Rural Life*, 10 vols., Vol. VI, Chicago, c. 1925.

"Educational Work at Fairs," *American Fertilizer*, LIII, 68, Nov. 20, 1920.

Ellenwood, C. W., "Modernizing Our Fruit Shows," *Ohio Farmer*, CLII, 478-79, Nov. 17, 1923.

Ellis, Carlyle, "A New Sort of Country Fair," *Delineator*, LXXXIX, 15, 46, Oct., 1916.

Ellis, Grace McIlrath, "Styles Should Change in Fair Exhibits," *Successful Farming*, XXX, 10, 17, Aug., 1932.

"Fair and Fair Exhibit Experiences," *Progressive Farmer*, XXXIII, 562-63, May 11, 1918.

"Fair Association Builds Exhibit," *Extension Service Review*, III, 110, July, 1932.

"Fair Experiments," *Nor'-West Farmer*, L, 8, June 20, 1931.

"Fairs, Yesterday and Today," *Nor'-West Farmer*, XLVII, 7, 14, 20, 32, June 20, 1928.

Farmer, Clifford, "Will Your Community Have a Fair?" *Successful Farming*, XXIV, 13, 42-43, June, 1926.

"Farmers' Associations' Competitions at Agricultural Shows," *Farming in South Africa*, IV, 491, Dec., 1929.

Farrell, George E., "Agricultural Fairs," *Book of Rural Life*, 10 vols., Vol. I, Chicago, c. 1925.

"Features for Fairs," *Nor'-West Farmer*, XLVI, 10-12, May 20, 1927.

Ferrin, E. F., "National Swine Show," *Book of Rural Life*, 10 vols., Vol. VI, Chicago, c. 1925.

"Filling the Classes," *Nor'-West Farmer*, XLVIII, 7, 51, June 20, 1929.

Forbes, Rank C., "In Defense of Herefords," *Breeder's Gazette*, XCVI, 4, 17, Nov., 1931.

Ford, Guy Stanton, "International Expositions," *Encyclopaedia of the Social Sciences*, Edwin R. A. Seligman, ed., Vol. VI, New York, 1931.

Forsyth, W. Howard, "As a Judge Sees County Fairs," *Breeder's Gazette*, LXXXIX, 168-69, Feb. 11, 1926.

Fox, Kirk, "Everyone Enjoys Camping; Why Not Go to the Fair?" *Successful Farming*, XXV, 7, 46, Aug., 1927.

Francis, David R., "Southern Agricultural Fairs and Expositions," *The South in the Building of the Nation*, 12 vols., V, 586-92; "The Influence of Agricultural and Industrial Fairs and Expositions on the Economic Development of the South since 1865," VI, 568-73, Richmond, c. 1909.

Gage, Earle W., "The Farmer's Fall Fair," *American Thresherman*, XXII, 9, 74-75, Aug., 1919.

Geissel, H. L., "The Great Fair of Nishny-Novgorod," *Scientific American Supplement*, L, 20837-38, Dec. 1, 1900.

"Going to the County Fair," *Practical Farmer*, CXIV, 295, Sept. 1, 1918.

Gregan, Paul, "Matters of Moment; Goin' to the Fair," *Irish Economist*, VIII, 89-101, April, 1923.

Gross, Charles, "The Court of Piepowder," *Quarterly Journal of Economics*, XX, 231-49, Feb., 1906.

Hamilton, John, "Influences Exerted by Agricultural Fairs," *Annals of the American Academy of Political and Social Science*, XL, 200-10, March, 1912.

"Hardin Tries a New Kind of Fair," *Wallaces' Farmer*, LI, 1385, 1390, Oct. 22, 1926.

Hartman, S. C., "The Spirit of the Fair," *National Stockman and Farmer*, XLIV, 550, Aug. 7, 1920.

Hitchcock, A. P., "The County Fair," *Country Life*, XVI, 196, June, 1909.

Horne, R. H., "The Great Fairs and Markets of Europe," *Harper's*, XLVI, 376-85, Feb., 1873.

Howells, William Dean, ["Fairs in America"] "Editor's Easy Chair," *Harper's*, CVI, 163-67, Dec., 1902.

Howes, E. A., "The Cattle Show," *Nor'-West Farmer*, XLVIII, 8, 16, 55-57, June 20, 1929.

"How Farmers Run a Fair," *Orange Judd Farmer*, LXIII, 3, 18, Oct. 6, 1917.

Hutt, W. N., "Make Plans Now for a 'Community Fair,'" *Progressive Farmer*, XXXII, 469, April 14, 1917.

Huxley, Julian, "Before the Fair," *Spectator*, CXXXI, 733-34, Nov. 17, 1923.

"Improving the Country Fair," *Nation*, XCVII, 160-61, Aug. 21, 1913.

Jack, Walter, "How They Make a Successful County Fair," *Rural New Yorker*, LXXXI, 1061-62, Sept. 2, 1922.

Jaenicke, F. E., "The Midway Problem," *Nor'-West Farmer*, XLVI, 10-11, March 21, 1927.

Jenny, Gerald, "Our Fairs and Expositions Mirror Progress," *Banker-Farmer*, XI, 10, Aug., 1924.

J. E. P., "The International Anniversary Show," *Breeder's Gazette*, LXXVI, 1147-48, Nov. 27, 1919.

Johnson, George F., "The First State Fair," *Pennsylvania Farmer*, CI, 547, Nov. 30, 1929.

Johnson, Thomas J., "Crooked Carnivals," *Country Gentleman*, XC, 7, 41, April 25, 1925.

Jones, Richard Lloyd, "The Significance of State Fairs," *Collier's*, XLVI, 16-17, 41, 44, Oct. 1, 1910.

Kelsey, Ray T., "Boys' Club Clean Up the County Fair," *Ohio Farmer*, CLII, 374, 395, Oct. 20, 1923.

Kennedy, Carl N., "Will Our Local Fairs Survive?" *Wallaces' Farmer*, LV, 1917, 1935, Dec. 13, 1930.

"Kick the Crooks out of Midway," *Wallaces' Farmer*, LV, 1631, Oct. 11, 1930.

Klein, Jack, "County Fairs," *California Cultivator*, LXIX, 235, Sept. 3, 1927.

—— "Fairs Improve Livestock Types," *California Cultivator*, LXVII, 203, Aug. 28, 1926.

Kulischer, Joseph, "Fairs," *Encyclopaedia of the Social Sciences*, Edwin R. A. Seligman, ed., Vol. VI, New York, 1931.

Lampson, Godfrey Locker, "The Agricultural Show," *Contemporary Review*, CXXXVIII, 480-85, Oct., 1930.

Lansing, David, "The Country Fair," *Outing*, LI, 3-15, Oct., 1907.

Lantis, L. O., "Local Fairs," *Ohio Farmer*, CXLI, 790, June 22, 1918.

Lavery, Urban, "The Romance of the Country Fair," *Independent*, LXI, 552-56, Sept. 6, 1906.

Lawrence, Jay, "The Why of the Fairs and Shows," *Breeder's Gazette*, XCI, 17-18, Jan. 6, 1927.

Levine, C. O., "An Agricultural Exhibit in China," *Breeder's Gazette*, LXXXIII, 543, April 19, 1923.

Lewis, H. R., "Poultry Shows," *Book of Rural Life*, 10 vols., Vol. VIII, Chicago, c. 1925.

Lloyd, Nelson, "The County Fair," *Scribner's*, XXXIV, 129-47, Aug., 1903.

Lovejoy, P. S., "Fair and Very Much Warmer," *Country Gentleman*, LXXXVIII, 9, 28, Feb. 24, 1923.

McClymonds, A. E., " 'Crops as a Community's Clothes,' " *Breeder's Gazette*, LXXXII, 229-30, Aug. 31, 1922.

Macdonald, A. B., "A Fair for Farmers, Not Fakers," *Country Gentleman*, LXXXVIII, 11, 40, March 3, 1923.

—— "Carnivals Must Clean Up or Be Cleaned," *Country Gentleman*, LXXXVIII, 8, 26, Dec. 1, 1923.

—— "Hop-Scotch Grifters," *Country Gentleman*, LXXXIX, 15, 31, May 10, 1924.

—— "It's Now or Never for the Carnivals," *Country Gentleman*, LXXXVIII, 3-4, 22, June 2, 1923.

—— "Miss Emma and Her Fair," *Country Gentleman*, LXXXVII, 3, 28-29, Aug. 26, 1922.

—— "The Best Thing at Our Fair," *Country Gentleman*, LXXXVIII, 10, May 5, 1923.

—— " 'The Friendliest Fair,' " *Country Gentleman*, LXXXVII, 7, 18, Aug. 19, 1922.

—— "The Nickel Nicker, the Gimmick and the Yap," *Country Gentleman*, XCI, 9, 92, May, 1926.

—— "The Scrapbook of Fakery," *Country Gentleman*, LXXXVIII, 1-2, 36, Feb. 17, 1923.

Macleod, M. A., "The Agricultural Societies of New Brunswick; Their Origin and History," *Agricultural Gazette of Canada*, X, 441-45, Sept.-Oct., 1923.

McMahon, John R., "Making Fairs Fit the War," *Country Gentleman*, LXXXIII, 10-11, 24, July 6, 1918.

—— "The Big Little County Fair," *Country Gentleman*, LXXXIII, 2, 24-25, Aug. 17, 1918.

Magie, J. M., "Paris's 'Ham Fair,' " *Harper's Weekly*, LVII, 21, May 10, 1913.

Mahan, Bruce E., "The Blue Grass Palace," *Palimpsest*, III, 327-35, Oct., 1922.

Mann, A. R., "Agricultural Education," *Encyclopaedia of the Social Sciences*, Edwin R. A. Seligman, ed., Vol. I, New York, 1930.

"Markets and Fairs in England and Wales," *Journal of the Ministry of Agriculture*, XXXIV, 97-99, May, 1927.

Markham, L. A., "Get Up a Community Fair — Do It Now," *Progressive Farmer*, XXXII, 902, Aug. 25, 1917.

Mathewson, Roy, "A Fair With No Admission Fee," *Rural New Yorker*, LXXVI, 1317-18, Nov. 17, 1917.

May, Earl Chapin, "Our County Fair, as It Was and Now Is," *New York Times Magazine*, Aug. 30, 1931, pp. 14, 20.

"Memories of the Fall Fair," *Canadian Magazine*, XXXI, 381-83, Aug., 1908.

Mercier, W. B., "Making Community Fairs Better," *Progressive Farmer*, XXXVIII, 1122, Dec. 1, 1923.

["Middle West County Fair,"] "The Spectator," *Outlook*, LXXXVII, 474-76, Nov. 2, 1907.

Moore, Don V., "Keeping Carnivals Clean," *Country Gentleman*, XC, 17, May 30, 1925.

Moran, J. Sterling, "The Community Fair," *Playground*, XI, 76-79, May, 1917.

Morgan, Tom P., "The Old County Fair," *Country Gentleman*, LXXXIV, 22, 56, Oct. 18, 1919.

Moritzen, Julius, "The Country Fair," *Cosmopolitan*, XXX, 153-61, Dec., 1900.

Murphy, Donald R., "A Fair Where Everybody Helps," *Wallaces' Farmer*, XLIX, 841, June 6, 1924.

Nadal, E. S., "A Horse-Fair Pilgrimage," *Scribner's*, XXX, 387-99, Oct., 1901.

O'Brien, Harry R., "Up-and-Stepping County Fairs," *Country Gentleman*, LXXXVII, 6, 23, July 15, 1922.

—— "What's the Law Between Fairs?" *Country Gentleman*, LXXXVIII, 9, 36, March 17, 1923.

Parson, Timothy, "What the Fairs Mean to Me," *American Thresherman*, XXIV, 9, 17, Aug., 1921.

"Planning the Community Fair Exhibit," *Wallaces' Farmer*, LI, 1065, Aug. 13, 1926.

Platt, Elliott H., "Connecticut Fairs," *Bureau Farmer*, Conn. ed., V, 16, Aug., 1930.

Plumb, C. S., "International Livestock Exposition," *Book of Rural Life*, 10 vols., Vol. V, Chicago, c. 1925.

Randall, E. W., and William P. Kirkwood, "The State Fair," *Delineator*, LXXVI, 250, 311-13, Oct., 1910.

"Rejuvenated County Fair," *Hoard's Dairyman*, LVIII, 665, Oct. 31, 1919.

"Report of the Special Committee on Fairs and Exhibitions," *Agricultural Gazette of Canada*, X, 157-59, March-April, 1923.

Richie, W. H., "A Rural Community Fair," *Rural Manhood*, XI, 390-91, Dec., 1920.

Rist, L. Boyd, "Boost Your County Fair," *Successful Farming*, XXI, 14-15, June, 1922.

Roberts, M. Carter, "The County Nurse and the County Fair," *Public Health Nurse*, XIX, 348-53, July, 1927.

Ross, Earle D., "The Evolution of the Agricultural Fair in the Northwest," *Iowa Journal of History and Politics*, XXIV, 445-80, July, 1926.

—— ["The Iowa State Fair"], *Palimpsest*, X, 269-316, Aug., 1929.

Routzahn, Mary Swain, and E. G. Routzahn, "Health Education at Fairs," *Public Health Nurse*, XX, 220-24, May, 1928.

Rubinow, S. G., "Building a State System of Fairs," *Breeder's Gazette*, LXXIV, 12-13, July 4, 1918.

—— "The Community Fair — A Factor in Rural Education," *School and Society*, VI, 96-101, July 28, 1917.

Ruhl, Arthur, "At the County Fair," *Collier's*, LI, 20-21, 34, Aug. 16, 1913.

Rummell, L. L., "A Few County Fair Lessons," *Ohio Farmer*, CLII, 476-77, Nov. 17, 1923.

—— "An Educational County Fair," *Ohio Farmer*, CLII, 424-25, Nov. 3, 1923.

—— "Are We Race Horse Crazy?" *Ohio Farmer*, CLIII, 581, 585, April 6, 1924.

—— "Lessons of the County Fairs," *Ohio Farmer*, CXLVI, 525, Oct. 30, 1920.

—— "Making a County Fair Worth While," *Ohio Farmer*, CLIV, 333, Oct. 18, 1924.

—— "Some Reflections on the Fairs," *Ohio Farmer*, CL, 525, 549, Nov. 18, 1922.

—— "The County Fair Worth While," *Ohio Farmer*, CLVI, 561, Dec. 5, 1925.

"Russian Fairs," *Geographical Review*, II, 154-55, Aug., 1916.

Sanders, Alvin H., "Calves, Clubs and Cheating," *Breeder's Gazette*, XCVI, 4, 16, Nov., 1931.

—— "Showing and Knowing," *Breeder's Gazette*, XCVI, 10, 21-22, Sept., 1931.

—— "The Boys and Their Baby Beeves," *Breeder's Gazette*, XCVI, 5, 12-14, Oct., 1931.

Secor, Alson, "Our Fairs and Expositions," *Successful Farming*, XX, 14, 30, Dec., 1923; XXI, 16, 107, Jan., 1924; XXI, 17, 67, Feb., 1924.

"Seeking Agriculture at the Fairs," *Orange Judd Farmer*, LXIII, 3, Sept. 22, 1917.

Sewell, Mrs. Charles W., "Community Fairs, Fall Festivals or Harvest Home," *Bureau Farmer*, VIII, 27-28, Sept., 1932.

Sinclair, R. D., "Back on the Trail of Show Ring History," *Nor'-West Farmer*, XLVIII, 27, 29, 61, June 20, 1929.

Singmaster, Elsie, "Big Thursday," *Century*, LXXI, 364-79, Jan., 1906.

"Some New Ideas at Fairs," *Pacific Rural Press*, CII, 117, July 30, 1921.

Speer, Ray P., "Fairs Converted into 'Food Training Camps,'" *Breeder's Gazette*, LXXII, 171-72, Aug. 9, 1917.

Sponsler, A. L., "Why the First Farm Fair Was Founded," *Dairy Farmer*, XX, 354, Aug. 1, 1922.

Stacy, W. H., "Three Guide-Posts for Local Fairs," *Wallaces' Farmer*, LVI, 163, 172, Feb. 7, 1931.

Stanley, Rufus, "A County Fair Uplift," *Country Life*, XXIV, 52, Aug., 1913.

Stewart, P. H., "Prize Money for Junk," *Country Gentleman*, CI, 9, 64, June, 1931.

Stone, A. L., "The What and Why of County Fairs," *Hoard's Dairyman*, LXX, 81, 106, Aug. 7, 1925.

—— "What About Our Fairs?" *Field Illustrated*, XXXV, 11-13, 42, July, 1925.

Stong, Phil, "County Fair," *Cosmopolitan*, XCIII, 52-53, 106, Nov., 1932.

Stuart, E. H., "How the Show Ring Helps the Live Stock Industry," *Hoard's Dairyman*, LXIV, 163, Sept. 1, 1922.

"Successful One-Day Fairs," *Nor'-West Farmer*, XLVII, 30-31, June 20, 1928.

Taylor, E. H., "Country Fairs," *Country Gentleman*, LXXXV, 11,

30, 32, July 17, 1920; 8, 30, July 31, 1920; 22, 44, 46, Aug. 7, 1920; 9, 36, Aug. 21, 1920.

—— "In the Land of Good Fairs," *Country Gentleman*, LXXXVI, 12, 37, Aug. 13, 1921.

Tesche, W. C., "Fair Exhibits — Also, Good and Bad Ones," *Pacific Rural Press*, CXVI, 181, Aug. 25, 1928.

"The Beginnings of Our Agricultural Shows," *Live Stock Journal*, XCI, 345, April 2, 1920.

"The Characteristic County Fair, Model of 1922," *Literary Digest*, LXXIV, 52-53, Sept. 16, 1922.

"The County Fair," *Harper's Weekly*, XLVI, 1420, Oct. 4, 1902.

"The Country Fair as an Exhibition Center: the Story of One Held in a New England Village Street," *Craftsman*, XX, 581-88, Sept., 1911.

"The Ever Popular County Fair," *Country Life*, XXXVIII, 57-59, Sept., 1920.

"The Fair and the Farmer," *Successful Farming*, XIX, 14, Aug., 1920.

"The Farmers' Experience Meeting: Experiences with Community and County Fairs," *Progressive Farmer*, XXXV, 1068, May 29, 1920.

"The Great Fairs of Russia," *Russia*, I, 13-22, June, 1916.

"The New Art of Pageantry in the United States," *Current Opinion*, LVII, 178-79, Sept., 1914.

"The One-Day Fair," *Nor'-West Farmer*, XLVIII, 18, 25, June 20, 1929.

"The Spirit of the Fair," *Scribner's*, LVI, 552-53, Oct., 1914,

"The Straffordville Junior Fair and Field Day," *Playground*, VIII, 393-95, Feb., 1915.

"The Two-Day Fair," *Nor'-West Farmer*, XLVII, 33, June 20, 1928.

"The Uprising Against Fakers," *Country Gentleman*, LXXXVII, 6, 27, June 3, 1922.

"The Value of Farm Festivals," *Craftsman*, XIX, 637-38, March, 1911.

Thomas, Arthur Caton, "Fairs and the Farmer," *Country Gentleman*, LXXXII, 1915, Dec. 8, 1915.

Thomas, Roy, "A Successful Community Fair," *Progressive Farmer*, XXXI, 1465, Dec. 23, 1916.

—— "How to Hold a Community Fair," *Progressive Farmer*, XXXII, 989, Sept. 22, 1917.

Thompson, George L., "Solving the Problem of the Country Fair," *Bureau Farmer*, Mass. ed., VII 11-12, Oct., 1931.

Thompson, Vance, "The Vagabond Showman of France," *Outing*, XLIX, 483-96, Jan., 1907.

Tomson, Frank D., "The Fairs and Shows," *California Cultivator*, LV, 292, Sept. 4, 1920.

—— "The Significance of the Fairs," *Breeder's Gazette*, LXXII, 174-75, Aug. 9, 1917.

True, Rodney H., "The Early Development of Agricultural Societies in the United States," American Historical Association, *Annual Report*, 1920, pp. 293-306, Washington, 1925.

Usher, Abbott Payson, "The Origin of the Bill of Exchange," *Journal of Political Economy*, XXII, 566-76, June, 1914.

Vergeront, Glen W., "County Fairs Made By Coöperation," *Hoard's Dairyman*, LVIII, 275, Sept. 12, 1919.

["Vermont County Fair"], "The Spectator," *Outlook*, LXXV, 349-50, Oct. 10, 1903.

["Visit to a County Fair"], "The Spectator," *Outlook*, XCVI, 578-80, Nov. 12, 1910.

Warren, Maude Radford, "How to Liven Up a Fair," *Country Gentleman*, LXXXIII, 30-31, June 15, 1918.

Weadock, Louis, "The Forty Thieves," *Country Gentleman*, LXXXVIII, 8-9, 36-39, 42, May 19, 1923.

Weed, A. R., "Putting Agriculture into County Fairs," *Orange Judd Farmer*, LXVIII, 1498, 1515, Oct. 16, 1920.

Weldon, George P., "Will Fairs Be Picture Exhibits?" *Pacific Rural Press*, CXX, 277, Sept. 13, 1930.

"What the Fair Meant to One Boy," *Wallaces' Farmer*, LI, 1167, Sept. 10, 1926.

"What to Do With State Fairs," *Independent*, LXV, 389-91, Aug. 13, 1908.

Whedon, Mary A., "State Fairs: Intelligent Promoters of the Various Interests of Rural Women: Outlets for Their Activities and Meeting Grounds for Social Intercourse," *Craftsman*, XXV, 86-91, Oct., 1913.

"When Our Shows Began," *Live Stock Journal*, LXXXIX, 279, April 11, 1919.

Whitson, Jay, "At Iowa's Biggest Local Fair," *Wallaces' Farmer*, LV, 1588, Oct. 4, 1930.

Wiest, Edward, "Agricultural Fairs," *Encyclopaedia of the Social Sciences*, Edwin R. A. Seligman, ed., Vol. I, New York, 1930.

Wiggin, Kate Douglas, "How We Attracted Two Thousand People to a Country Fair," *Ladies' Home Journal*, XXIX, 15, 44, July, 1912.

Wingfield, Sam G., "The Shill Has All the Luck," *Country Gentleman*, XCIII, 20-21, 50, May, 1928.

Wood, Eugene, "The County Fair," *McClure's*, XXV, 595-607, Oct., 1905.

Wood, Frances Gilchrist, "The Pageant in America," *Country Life*, XXXI, 21-25, Nov., 1916.

Wood, W. R., "Good Fairs Stimulate Better Agriculture," *California Cultivator*, LXVII, 203, 207, Aug. 28, 1926.

Woodward, Carl R., "Odd Bits of Agricultural History; Colonial Fairs and Markets," *New Jersey Agriculture*, VIII, 9-10, Feb., 1926.

—— "Odd Bits of Agricultural History; County Fairs in the Nineteenth Century," *New Jersey Agriculture*, XI, 14-15, Dec., 1929.

—— "Odd Bits of Agricultural History; Early Fairs of State Agricultural Society," *New Jersey Agriculture*, XIII, 15, Oct., 1931.

Worthley, Georgiana, "Ancestors of the County Fair," *Baltimore Sun*, Magazine section, Sept. 4, 1932, pp. 4-5.

Wright, W. I., "How a Community Fair Helps," *Progressive Farmer*, XXXI, 1052, Sept. 2, 1916.

Wrigley, G. M., "Fairs of the Central Andes," *Geographical Review*, VII, 65-80, Feb., 1919.

INDEX

INDEX

A

Accomplishment: efforts to reward, 232 f; individual vs. group, 229 f; of institutions, 235; pride in, 232 f. *See also* Achievement

Achievement, 215, 219; attempt to make fair portray, 212 f; fair as expression of, 229-40; formerly result of individual effort, 231; group and community, 229 f, 240; individual, 229 f, 240; visitors share sense of, 234 f. *See also* Accomplishment

Achievement day, 139 f, 151, 230, 262

Adams, John, 41-42; correspondence of with Watson, 66

Adams, Seth, introduction of Merino sheep into Massachusetts by, 56

Address, 139; annual address inaugurated at fairs by Watson, 62, 64; annual address prominent feature in golden age, 91 f, 162, 164, 211; lectures, 179-80, 249

Advertisers, 149

Advertising and publicity, 97; exposition an organ of, 3, 17; fair a medium of, 209, 227-28, 235, 250, 257*n*; machinery exhibit a matter of, 164; main object of sample fairs, 15; of fairs, 115, 228, 245, 245*n*, 246; studied by fair managers, 117

Agricultural ball, entertainment feature inaugurated by Watson, 63, 64, 69

Agricultural colleges, 104, 231; aid in determining and attaining standards, 167 f; aid in revising premium lists, 169-70; aid in supplying judges, 172; conduct judging schools, 263; contribute to extension work, 101, 258; coöperate with neighborhood fairs, 132; displays and exhibits of, 21, 126, 129, 178, 181, 250; growth of, 99; sponsors of junior-club work, 141; sponsors of Little Theater movement, 213

Agricultural convention, national, 78

Agricultural education, 100, 149, 162, 262; contributions of learned agricultural societies to, 45; fairs of golden age forerunners of, 181; initiated and promoted by fair, 156 f; interest of Federal government in, 101, 135; modern fairs interpreters of, 181; multiplying agencies of, 99; program of, at National Swine Show, 175 f; service of fairs in, 163

Agricultural experimentation, 166, 169; becoming scientific, 73; carried on by gentlemen farmers, 31 f; carried on by Jefferson and Adams, 42; farms for, conducted by agricultural societies, 88 f; in England, 30; premiums offered for, 37*n*, 38-39, 44-46; societies responsible for, 165

Agricultural fair: accepted by learned societies, 66; as a coöperative enterprise, 222-29; as an institution, 243-48; as a show window, 234-35; Berkshire cattle show first type of, in America, 61 f; classification of, 145-51; commercial aspects of, 21, 250-51; constituency of, 226, 229, 261; dominant form of association among farmers, 81; educational aspects of, 155-84; elaboration of, under Watson,

COLUMBIA UNIVERSITY PRESS

COLUMBIA UNIVERSITY

NEW YORK

———

FOREIGN AGENT

OXFORD UNIVERSITY PRESS

HUMPHREY MILFORD

AMEN HOUSE, LONDON, E.C. 4